Taiwan

—ilha Formosa

a geography in perspective

Chiao-min Hsieh

M.A., Ph.D.

The Catholic University of America

WASHINGTON

BUTTERWORTHS

1964

U. S. A.:   BUTTERWORTH INC.
                 WASHINGTON, D. C.: 7235 Wisconsin Avenue, 14
ENGLAND: BUTTERWORTH & CO. (PUBLISHERS) LTD.
                 LONDON: 88 Kingsway, W.C.2
AUSTRALIA: BUTTERWORTH & CO. (AUSTRALIA) LTD.
                 SYDNEY: 6/8 O'Connell Street
                 MELBOURNE: 430 Bourke Street
                 BRISBANE: 240 Queen Street
CANADA: BUTTERWORTH & CO. (CANADA) LTD.
                 TORONTO: 1367 Danforth Avenue, 6
NEW ZEALAND: BUTTERWORTH & CO. (NEW ZEALAND) LTD.
                 WELLINGTON: 49/51 Ballance Street
                 AUCKLAND: 35 High Street
SOUTH AFRICA: BUTTERWORTH & CO. (SOUTH AFRICA) LTD.
                 DURBAN: 33/35 Beach Grove

Library of Congress Catalogue Card No. 64-22305

PRINTED IN THE UNITED STATES OF AMERICA
BY WAVERLY PRESS, INC., BALTIMORE, MARYLAND

PREFACE

THIS BOOK concerns itself with the land and people of the island of Taiwan. It aims at filling a gap in the geographical literature by furnishing a regional analysis of the island of Taiwan. Taiwan has been analyzed, mapped and surveyed, and described in various languages, especially in Chinese and Japanese. Statistical data covering a long period of the island's history have been accumulated; such data are very rare in the Orient. Despite this, few accounts of the island have appeared. The present volume is believed to be the first comprehensive study of the island in the English language. Until the Second World War, this subtropical island lying some 100 miles off the coast of China, midway between Shanghai and Hong Kong, interested people chiefly as the source of fine oolong tea and of nearly all of the world's natural camphor. Today *ilha Formosa*, or "beautiful island" as the Portuguese named it, or *Taiwan*, "big bay", as the Chinese call it, is a focal point in world affairs.

The book is divided into three parts. The first part pictures the natural setting and gives a thorough survey of the physical environment; the second—in order to provide the proper perspective—traces the occupance patterns of the different cultural groups which have settled Taiwan; and the third analyzes the present cultural landscape, including demography, settlement, and transportation, with emphasis on the economic development and problems of the island.

The location of the island has shaped its history. It has been settled by aborigines, Dutch, Chinese, and Japanese and has had a long and checkered existence. It is hoped that simply from a knowledge of the past occupance, one may better understand the "whys" behind the present landscape and problems of Taiwan. As a colony, Taiwan has been a laboratory for the Dutch, Chinese, and Japanese. At present it is an independent state, and one of the pivot points in diplomacy and strategy in Eastern Asia.

The manuscript would have been difficult to complete without the generous support of the Evening Star award from The Catholic University of America, and a research grant from the Committee of the University's Research Council. The author is also indebted to The Catholic University of America for the use of its typing service, and for use of the facilities of its cartographic laboratory.

In recent years three public organizations have produced much data on Taiwan, and they have given generous help to me. They are the Chinese-American Joint Commission on Rural Reconstruction, the Economic Research Institute Bank of Taiwan, and the Provincial Historical

Research Commission. I am indebted to the heads of these organizations, Dr. Chiang Mon-lin and formerly with him Dr. H. C. Chang, Mr. H. W. Chow, and formerly Mr. H. C. Lin. I wish to thank Dr. Chang Chi-yun, my former professor and the founder of the College of Chinese Culture, for sending me his valuable *Atlas of Taiwan*.

I wish also to express my thanks to Dr. Edward A. Ackerman of the Carnegie Institute of Washington, and to Dr. Rhoads Murphey of the University of Washington, who read the book in draft and gave me their suggestions. I also wish to thank Dr. Shiu-ying Hu, Arnold Arboretum of Harvard University, for reading the section on natural vegetation and Mrs. Anthony E. Starcevic of the Department of Library Science of the Catholic University for preparing a preliminary index of the book.

I am grateful to several persons who helped in drafting the maps. First, to my wife, Jean Kan Hsieh, Lecturer in Geography at Trinity College in Washington, and also to Miss Jean Tsou of the University of Wisconsin, and to my former graduate student Mr. Van Scott. During my sabbatical leave from The Catholic University of America this year, while serving as Visiting Lecturer in Geography at the University of Leeds, England, I received much assistance from Mr. G. Bryant, the cartographer in that department, who designed the relief map of Taiwan which appears on the dust jacket of this book. Finally, I wish to express my deep indebtedness to Miss Sarah L. Doran, for undertaking the arduous task of editing and reading the proofs.

Leeds, England   CHIAO-MIN-HSIEH
August, 1964

To my late brother
Ssu-yen HSIEH

Former professor in the National Normal University in Peking and one of the founding professors of the Taiwan Normal University in Taipei.

CONTENTS

Place Names in Taiwan

The identification of many place names in Taiwan becomes easier if one knows a few words of Chinese. The following are examples.

Pei . . . North; thus Tai*pei*—North of Taiwan
Nan . . . South; thus Tai*nan*—South of Taiwan
Tung . . . East; thus Tai*tung*—East of Taiwan
Si . . . West; thus *Si*lo Ho—West Lo River
Chung . . . Central; thus Tai*chung*—Central Taiwan

Shan . . . Mountain   *Ho* . . . River
Ling . . . Peak or Range   *Shui* . . . Stream
Chia . . . Strait or Gorge   *Chi* . . . Creek
Tao . . . Island   *Wan* . . . Bay
Hsu . . . Small Island   *Hu* . . . Lake
Kong . . . Port   *Tan* . . . Small lake

PART ONE

THE LAND

ONE | # Location and Size

IN THE PACIFIC OCEAN off the southeastern coast of China, opposite Fukien Province, lies an island. This island is called by the aborigines *Pekan*, by the Portuguese *Formosa*, meaning "beautiful," and by the Chinese *Taiwan* which means "big bay."

Looking at *Figure 1*, the mountainous island arcs of the Pacific are seen, lying off the eastern coast of Asia. These island arcs constitute the longest chain of volcanic archipelagoes in the world, extending from the Kamchatka Peninsula in the north to the Sunda Islands in the south. Taiwan is one of the islands in this chain.

Taiwan lies 100 miles east of the coastal provinces of mainland China. It is some 695 miles south of Japan, and 199 miles north of Luzon, northernmost of the major Philippine Islands (separated from them by the Bashi Channel). Taiwan is thus halfway between Shanghai and Hong Kong, and midway between Japan and the Philippines.

To the south, the Bataan and Babuyan island arcs lead to the Philippines. In earlier centuries the intervening Ryukyu archipelago in the north, forming stepping stones to Japan, made it possible for primitive fishing boats to make the journey from Japan to Taiwan. These three connections: with the Indo-China peninsula and the Philippines to the south, with the coastal provinces of China to the west, and with Japan to the north, have invited to Taiwan many different cultural groups, including Malayan aborigines, Chinese, Japanese, and even Spanish and Dutch. All of these groups have helped to shape the history of Taiwan.

Taiwan is a strategically significant point in the archipelago that borders the Pacific coast of Eurasia. During World War II the island was used by the Japanese as a stepping stone in the conquest of southeast Asia; at present it is the bastion of the Chinese Nationalists in their ideological struggle with the Communist regime on the mainland.

There are two large islands along China's coast, Taiwan and Hainan. Taiwan is much more significant than Hainan, in both position and

3

resources. Mainland China has seven coastal provinces which face in turn, north to south, the Po Hai Gulf, the Yellow Sea, the East China Sea, and the South China Sea. The East China Sea, most important of these waters, is located along the eastern shoreline's central portion, which includes the Yangtze River, one of the richest regions in China. Were a centrally located base along the Chinese coastline to be chosen, the most logical choice would be along the shores of Chekiang and Fukien provinces, where communication is shortest between the northern and southern seas.

Taiwan is favorably located near this central point. It lies across the principal communication routes along the China coast. In this respect, Hainan is far less important than Taiwan. Being a fairly large island,

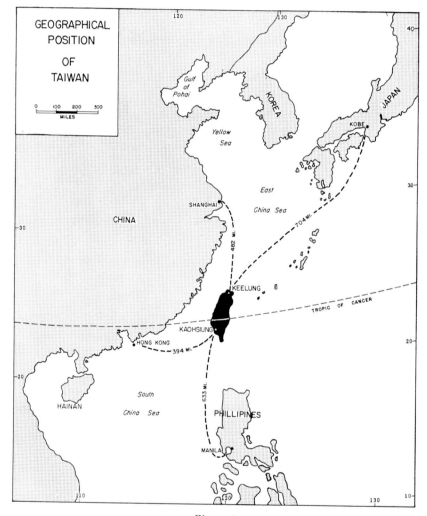

Figure 1

Taiwan has ample space for numerous airfields and military installations, and stands like "an unsinkable aircraft carrier" off the shore of China. Thus Taiwan is not only a salient between the Philippines and Okinawa, but is also an important strategic point in the festoon of islands running from the frozen Arctic along the Asiatic coast to the South China Sea along the western rim of the Pacific Ocean.

Taiwan includes as its administrative areas (*Figure 2*) 16 *hsien*, or counties, and five municipalities—Taipei (the capital), Tainan, Keelung,

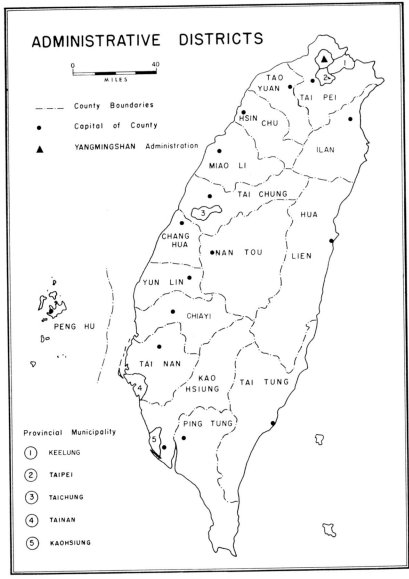

Figure 2

5

Kaohsiung, and Taichung. Politically a part of Taiwan are the 77 surrounding islands, 13 of which are directly adjacent to the main island, plus the 64 islands of the Penghu group in the Taiwan Strait. The total area of the 13 adjacent islands (of which only six are inhabited) is 31 square miles. The Penghu group covers 50 square miles, of which the main island, Penghu, occupies 25 square miles.

The island is important not only for its relative location, but also for the intrinsic value of its land space. Relative location refers to its strategic position; the value of its space indicates the potential energy of the region. Few places rank high by both criteria. For example, the value of Gibraltar's strategic position is very high, but the intrinsic value of its space is very low. Taiwan is one of the few places in which both strategic position and space value rank very high.[1]

The shape of Taiwan is roughly that of a long oval, approximately 240 miles long from north to south, and 98 miles wide from west to east at its broadest point. No place in Taiwan is more than 50 miles from the sea. Its smooth coastline, totaling 708 miles in length, is bathed by the warm waters of the Kuro Siwo current (Japan current). Taiwan covers an area of 13,884 square miles, which is about one-third the size of the American state of Virginia, one-half the size of Ireland, a little larger than the Netherlands, and a trifle smaller than Switzerland. Latitudinally, it lies astride the Tropic of Cancer in a position comparable to that of Cuba.

REFERENCE

[1] CHIAO-MIN HSIEH, "Formosa—A rich island of the Far East," *J. Geogr.*, N. Y., **LI**, 54 (1952).

TWO

Structure

TAIWAN'S ORIGIN

TAIWAN IS AN ISLAND situated off the coast of the Asian continent. To the north it is linked with the Ryukyu Islands, which further connect with the Japan archipelago; to the south it extends to the Philippine archipelago. Thus Taiwan lies at the intersection of these two island arcs, and is part of a festoon of islands running along the Asiatic coast at the western rim of the Pacific Ocean.

These islands are curved so that the concave side faces the Asian continent. The mountain chain of Taiwan also forms an arc; however, its concavity faces not the continent but the Pacific. This striking contrast in curvature between Taiwan and the other islands of the festoon has kindled much interest and curiosity among geologists and geographers.[1-4] Some believe that many years ago Taiwan was part of the continent and that the main mountain chain of Taiwan was virtually a coastal range on the China mainland, with the eastern border of the island being the real continental margin.

The structural alignment of Taiwan with the continent is the result of the thrust faulting which sliced the island into longitudinal belts. These overthrusts came from the southeast over the Pacific, and not from the northwest over the continent as they did both in the Ryukyus and the Philippines. While it is easy to see the disagreement of the structural form between the island of Taiwan and the other islands along the Asian continent, it is not surprising to find that the Neo-Cathaysian trend on the continent also shows a slight curvature facing inland, as manifested by the mountain ranges in the western part of Fukien province. When Taiwan suffered rather severe orogenic movements, during the Tertiary and Quaternary periods, the arc became more pronounced.

The fact that Taiwan cannot be grouped together with the Ryukyus and the Philippines is further illustrated by its rock formations. The oldest rocks in the Ryukyus are of the Paleozoic era; the rock basis of the

7

Philippines consists of diorite (which is not as old as the Paleozoic). In Taiwan the core of the cordillera is composed of schists and granite-gneiss, which can easily be linked with the old land mass of the Archean rocks in Fukien.

Physiographically, Taiwan is not bordered by deep ocean as are the Ryukyus and the Philippines. Taiwan Strait, which separates the island from the mainland, is a rather shallow sea, being from twenty to forty fathoms deep generally, and nowhere exceeding fifty fathoms. The continental coast, though rich in minor indentations that are due to drowned valleys, indicating a relatively recent submergence of land, is generally straight; it apparently follows a dislocation line, as is suggested by its simple, straight, and relatively steep submarine slope. The west coast of Taiwan is occupied by flat alluvial plain and the shoreline is simple and straight. As indicated by the rather close submarine contour lines and their straightness, the west coast is also guided essentially by dislocation. Thus Taiwan Strait is a rift valley or graben intervening between the Asiatic continent and Taiwan. This tectonic depression took place before the submergence of the land. Prior to this submergence the sea floor was probably land surface of low relief, situated between the Taiwan coastal range and the old land of Fukien.

The rift valley of Taiwan Strait evidently resulted from restlessness of the earth's crust, while faulting stretched the surface and created fissures in the crust. There are fissure eruptions in the Strait, issuing large amounts of lava and flooding the surface of the Strait bottom. They are characteristically bedded, so that successive floods have spread over the preceding flows. The flat-lying sheet of lava was solidly cemented and rose only a little above sea level. The Penghu Islands are just such a dissected mesa of basalt.

From these bits of evidence—the contrasting curvature between the Ryukyu arc, the Philippine archipelago, and Taiwan; the structural alignment and rock correlation with the mainland; the character of the Strait's submarine configuration; the simple and smooth coast line of the island, and the existence of extensive basalt mesas formed through fissure eruptions—we may conclude that the island of Taiwan has long been in existence and was actually a part of the China mainland during early geological periods. Not until the Pleistocene epoch, when the Strait sank and formed a rift valley, was Taiwan separated from the continent and isolated as an island.

THE GEOLOGICAL HISTORY

It is difficult to understand Taiwan's present landforms without a knowledge of its geological past. From the evidence recorded in rocks and rock structures, it is clear that the crust of the island has experienced many pressures, foldings, faultings, and other movements. The geological history of Taiwan is a long and complicated one. This book only outlines briefly the main geological events which will help in understanding the present relief of Taiwan (Table 1).

Strong diastrophism took place as early as the pre-Tertiary period, and again near the end of the Eocene epoch. During the late Oligocene compressed folding started and was followed by a large-scale Miocene transgression. Intensive faulting did not appear until the Pliocene, and tilting occurred as late as the Pleistocene. Epeirogenic movement started in the early Pliocene, and spectacular displays of volcanism marked the beginning of the Quaternary period.

Table 1. Earth Movements in the Geological Past in Taiwan*

Period	Epoch	Features
Quaternary	Recent	Faulting, tilting, basalt eruption
	Pleistocene	Upheaval, thrusting, Tatun volcanic activity
Tertiary	Pliocene	Faulting, intrusion of basic and ultra-basic igneous rocks
	Miocene	Miocene transgression
	Oligocene	Folding, extrusion of basic igneous rocks Intrusion of acid and basic igneous rocks, regional metamorphism
	Eocene	Orogenesis, intrusion of acid igneous rocks
Pre-Tertiary		Regional metamorphism

* Simplified from VEI-CHOW JUAN, *Physiography and Geology of Taiwan* (China Cultural Publishing Foundation, Taipei, 1954).

The Chungyang Shan represents the most important mountain building. The close folding of thick sediments in this central mountain system took place before the pre-Tertiary era. After a long period of subaerial denudation and intermittent crustal movements, the original sedimentaries were contorted and regionally metamorphosed into crystalline schists, and the intruded igneous rocks were changed into gneiss and amphibolites.

During the Eocene epoch the sea invaded the geosynclinal depression, which was broadly downwarped on the flanks of a cordillera. This transgression was not very extensive and its deposits occupied only limited areas west of Chungyang Shan. It was then followed by orogenic movement and regional metamorphism at the end of the Eocene period.

In the Miocene epoch the sea invaded the old geosynclinal depression west of the cordillera and also extended an arm to the east. This was perhaps the most extensive transgression, and broad folding was the result. The land was quickly reduced to planation by vigorous erosion, and the eustatic uplifting made possible the local glaciation on top of the mountains which commenced in the Pliocene epoch. Near the end of the Miocene era large-scale faulting occurred in the Chungyang Shan area and continued into the Pliocene. During the late Pliocene the Chungyang Shan system experienced a north–south dislocation, which started from the west with thrust-faulting and migrated toward the east. Since the overthrusting came from the southeast, the eastern part of the island was elevated. The amount of uplifting increased progressively toward

9

the east in a tilting fashion. The Ali Shan thrust was followed by another thrust occurring at the western side of Hsinkao Shan. Thus the eastern block of the island was uplifted once again. The northeast–southwest trending fault of Tzekao Shan, also an overthrusting from the southeast, occurred either simultaneously with the Hsinkao-Shan fault or a little later, and was responsible for the thick accumulations of tableland gravel common in the western part of the island.

The Tatun volcanism that opened up the Pleistocene epoch was followed by a period of relative quiescence, and land surfaces were reduced to low relief. Tableland gravels were deposited with intermittent elevation, interrupted by slight land submergence sufficient for the building of fringe reefs and marine terraces. Then large-scale orogenic faulting again set in, causing dislocation of the Taitung-Hualien thrust faulting, and the formation of a rift valley between the mainland and Taiwan. The Penghu fissure eruption closed the Pleistocene epoch.

The geological history of the island of Taiwan in recent eras is limited to the shifting of strand lines. The land surface has been invaded by the advancing coral sea, building coral reefs and beach deposits around the nearly submerged island. Later, as the sea level shifted downward, the fringe reefs and beach deposits were elevated.

The crustal forces which we have described do not seem to have ceased at the present, as evidenced by the general uprising of the island and the frequent occurrence of earthquakes.

Although large igneous bodies are very rare, small outcrops of various kinds are scattered throughout the island. Some geologists believe that there have been at least five periods of igneous activities in the geological history of Taiwan (*Table 2*):[5]

PERIODS OF IGNEOUS ACTIVITY

PRE-TERTIARY INTRUSION OF ACID IGNEOUS ROCKS.—This is the oldest igneous activity recognized to date and is also the undifferentiated group of igneous rocks closely associated with the Tamanao metamorphic complex.

PRE-OLIGOCENE INTRUSION OF BASIC IGNEOUS ROCKS.—Many small outcrops of these rocks have been found in central Taiwan in the Chungyang Shan range. This period is generally believed to be one of the important epochs of gold mineralization that formed extensive glacier deposits over the island.

LOWER MIOCENE VOLCANISM.—This represents probably the first important volcanic activity, and appeared in northern Taiwan. Mercury ores and zircon minerals were produced in these volcanics.

PRE-PLIOCENE INTRUSION OF ULTRABASIC ROCKS.—The ultrabasic rocks of Taitung, including dolerite, peridotite, crystalline rocks, gabbro, and serpentinite, are products of this period. The intrusion of serpentinite with asbestos and talcs in Chungyang Shan range belongs to the same period. The alkaline basalt, analcite dolerite, and basanite found in the Miocene coal beds of northern Taiwan show obviously close petrologic and stratigraphic affiliation with this period.

PLEISTOCENE VOLCANISM.—This is the most important and most recent volcanic activity in Taiwan. It is found in the Tatun area of northernmost Taiwan, and also in the Penghu Islands in the Strait of Taiwan. In the Tatun Shan area, andesite flows, agglomerate and dacite dikes are country rocks for the well-known sulphur, gold, and copper deposits of the island. The Penghu basalts are fissure eruptions in which the only gem stones have been found.

Table 2. *Igneous Activities and Mineralization Epochs in Taiwan**

Stage	Age	Rock character	Mineral deposit	Region
Tatun	Pleisto-cene	Basalt	Gem stones	Penghu Islands
		Dacite	Gold, copper, alunite	Chinkuashih, Juifeng
		Andesite, agglomer-ate	Sulfur, gold, copper	Tatun Shan
Taitung	Pre-Plio-cene	Basalt, peridotite, gabbro and ser-pentine, and so on		Hengchun
			Asbestos, talc, serpentine	Chungyang Shan
			Nickel, serpen-tine	East Coastal Range
Kungkuan	Lower Miocene	Basalt dikes and sills, agglomerate and tuff	Zircon, mer-cury	Northern part of the island
		Andesitic agglomer-ate and tuff		East Coastal Range
Nengkao	Pre-Oligo-cene	Basaltic agglomerate and tuff, quartz porphyries	Gold quartz veins (?)	Chungyang Shan
Nanao	Pre-Ter-tiary	Granite gneiss, peg-matite, and quartz porphyries	Mica, feldspar	Northeastern part of Chungyang Shan
		Meta-diabase	Manganese, py-rite, and chal-copyrite	Chungyang Shan

* Simplified from VEI-CHOW JUAN, *Physiography and Geology of Taiwan* (China Cultural Publishing Foundation, Taipei, 1954).

11

ROCK DISTRIBUTION

Taiwan's foundation consists primarily of sedimentary rocks of shallow water origin; interbedding of sandstone and shale are most characteristic. With the exception of the scattered outcrops of volcanic rock and small bodies of igneous intrusion, igneous rocks are generally rare. But igneous metamorphisms have transformed some of the sedimentary rocks into metamorphic formations. The rock formation of the island varies in age from very recent alluvial deposits to early sedimentary and crystalline rocks as is shown in *Figure 3*.

The core of the anticline which forms the backbone of the Chungyang Shan is composed of metamorphosed sediments and granite gneiss. On the flanks of the anticline lie Tertiary and Quaternary formations consisting of Eocene slate, Oligocene volcanics, Miocene coal series, Pliocene sandstone and shale with oil possibilities, and Pleistocene lava flows. These formations are arranged in belts which conform to the general NNE–SSW trend of the island. Thus, if one travels from west to east (A to B in *Fig. 3*) crossing the Chungyang Shan, he will witness all of the rock formations described below:

RECENT ALLUVIUM.—The wide western coastal plain is covered with recent alluvial material—sand, clay, and gravel. These materials appear in terrace deposits, alluvial fans, raised coral reefs, and lake deposits, all appearing in horizontal beds. Similar alluvial material fills the basins of Taipei and Ilan on the east coast.

PLEISTOCENE TABLELAND GRAVEL AND CORAL LIMESTONE.—The tableland gravels are scattered along the flat foot hills. The deposits consist of well-rounded sandstone boulders and some andesite pebbles in the lower part, brown sand in the upper, and with lateritic soils on top. They are a collective accumulation of alluvial fans deposited on mountain slopes. The deposits are mostly in tilted positions and lie unconformably on older formations.

PLIO-PLEISTOCENE SANDSTONE AND SHALE.—This formation consists of sandstone with intercalations of mudstone and gravel beds. In the upper part it is composed of a thick formation of conglomerate with occasional beds of sandstone. This conglomerate is most characteristically developed in the Hsinchu and Taichung area where it attains a thickness sometimes exceeding a half mile. As a result of weathering and erosion this formation creates a very rugged, often pinnacle-shaped topography which glows like flame as it reflects the evening sun. Hence the name *Huayen Shan* or "flaming mountains," is used at more than one place in Taiwan to represent the same geological formation.

PLIOCENE FORMATION.—This deposit is well-developed in the Hsinchu area and southward. The lower division is shaly; the upper part consists of alternate beds of sandstone and shale which, in certain regions, form the structural features known as "homoclinal ridges." This bluish-gray sandy shale also makes up the so-called "badland" topography in southern Taiwan.

12

MIOCENE FORMATION.—The Miocene formation is the most widely distributed rock in Taiwan. It covers the area of rolling hills in the western flank of the Chungyang Shan and the entire eastern coastal range. This formation is the most important coal-producing bed in Taiwan.

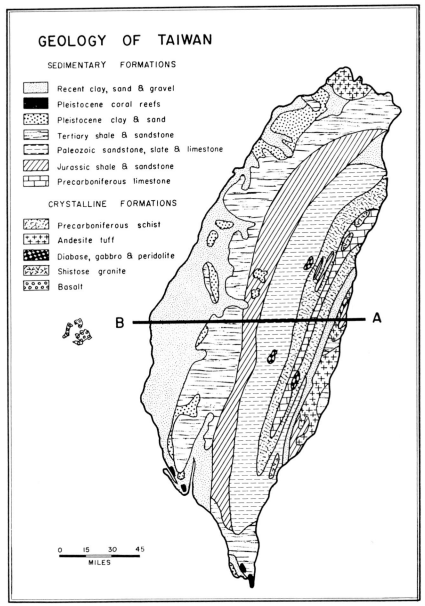

GEOLOGY OF TAIWAN

SEDIMENTARY FORMATIONS

- Recent clay, sand & gravel
- Pleistocene coral reefs
- Pleistocene clay & sand
- Tertiary shale & sandstone
- Paleozoic sandstone, slate & limestone
- Jurassic shale & sandstone
- Precarboniferous limestone

CRYSTALLINE FORMATIONS

- Precarboniferous schist
- Andesite tuff
- Diabase, gabbro & peridolite
- Shistose granite
- Basalt

B ————————————— A

0   15   30   45
MILES

Figure 3

13

OLIGOCENE SANDSTONE AND SHALES.—The Oligocene formation is restricted to the Keelung-Taipei area. Three well-established coal beds, separated by marine shales, limestone, and a few tuff beds, were included in the Oligocene deposition.

EOCENE SLATE FORMATION.—The slate formation covers the greatest area in Taiwan. It occupies the western flank of the Chungyang Shan range and is especially well-developed in the middle of the island, where almost all the high peaks are composed of this formation. The rock as a whole is considered to be of shallow sea origin and is formed chiefly of hard, black slate with well-developed cleavage. The formation lies unconformably upon the metamorphic complex and is intensely folded. It is interesting to note that in the Kaohsiung area pebbles of alkaline granite have been found in the beds. The pebbles are believed to be derived from similar rocks found in Fukien province on the continent.

PRE-TERTIARY METAMORPHIC COMPLEX.—The metamorphic complex is composed of a variety of metamorphic rocks, both sedimentary and igneous in origin. This metamorphic complex occupies the eastern wing of the axial part of the backbone range and is generally closely folded into anticlines and synclines. The rock varies in hardness from the hard crystalline schists in the east, to the softest non-crystalline shales and sandstones in the west.

SUBMARINE RELIEF

Limited to the west by the mountainous province of Fukien and to the east by Taiwan, the Strait of Taiwan runs from northeast to southwest with a width of approximately 90 miles at its narrowest part.

On the western side of the Strait, the continental coast is rich in indentations and drowned valleys, indicating recent submergence of the land.[6] As a whole, it follows the fault line, as is indicated by its simple, straight and steep submarine slope (*Figure 4*). On the eastern side of the Strait Taiwan's western coast is occupied by flat alluvial plains, sometimes as much as twenty miles across. The straight coastline is parallel to the opposite China coast, except for recesses in its northern and southern extremities where it is often cliffed beyond the sandy flat. In the southern part, there is a series of sand spits, lagoons, and a number of drowned valleys of considerable depth. All of these geomorphological features of the western coast suggest recent submergence of land and subsequent deposition of alluvial material carried down from the Chungyang Shan by many transverse rivers. It may also be inferred from the compressed submarine contour that the western coast of Taiwan is essentially guided by pre-existent fault lines.

Limited by fault lines on either side, the Strait of Taiwan is a depressed graben in structure. In the southern part of the Strait there are numerous grooves and submarine embayments, while to the north it dips very gently. Although the sea floor of the tectonic depression is of extremely low relief (20–40 fathoms deep; rarely exceeding 50 fathoms), the submarine topography of the Strait is by no means simple.

14

From isobathic contour lines based on the available sounding data, a detailed relief of the sea floor has been ascertained. The Penghu Islands represent the highest point in the Strait, and are separated into two island groups, the northern and southern, by a narrow channel with a depth of 30 fathoms. These two island groups are circular in outline of their base, as they are constructed of basalt flows and tuffites in alternation of their parts exposed above the sea level.

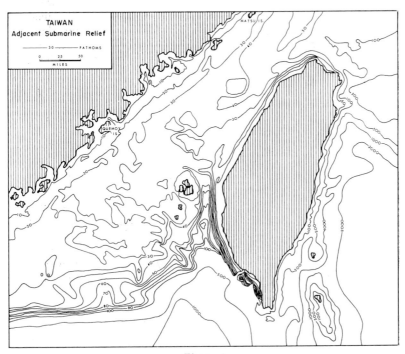

Figure 4

Like the radial valleys in many volcanic fields, several linear submarine furrows appear in the sea floor descending radially from these elevated parts. There are traces of circular furrows around the Penghu Island's elevated parts which are thought to be the result of subsidence of the foundation caused in turn by the weight of effused material.

Not unlike drainage systems on land, the submarine furrows in the northern part of the sea floor—as well as the drowned valleys along China's coast—form an extended system of furrows. That is, all the side-furrows are joined with a main one which lies on the medial line of the Strait. However, such distinct furrows along the middle section of the west coast of Taiwan cannot be found. This may be due to the fact that in that area the littoral sea bottom is thickly carpeted with new deposits.

The southwestern part of the sea floor is composed of two swells. One extends from the Penghu Islands toward the southwest. The two sides of this main swell are quite asymmetrical, the southern one being much steeper than the other. Another swell starts from the middle of the main swell and runs northwestward to the China coast, and also has two side-furrows. While the northern part of the Strait's sea floor dips very gently, the sea floor of the southeastern part has a rather steep descent of a remarkable submarine embayment. The embayment, which is 100–400 fathoms deep and double-terraced on the bottom, is shaped like a broad triangle. The base of the triangle is on the east–west direction, in line with the southern tip of Taiwan, while the apex of the triangle is a narrow furrow extending between the Penghu Islands and the Taiwan coast. This narrow sink groove is the Penghu Channel and is the most conspicuous furrow in the Strait. The origin of this neck furrow is a tectonic depression, as its two sides are limited by two fault lines. The channel, as well as the embayment, has asymmetrical eastern and western walls. The eastern wall on the Taiwan side is much steeper than that on the opposite side, descending from 20 fathoms to 100 fathoms within a distance of about 3½ miles. It seems not quite uniform in slope, being more or less flattened at the three levels of 45–60, 60–80, and 80–100 fathoms. Each of these intrenched on this steep slope. One of them, the river course of Lower Tamshui, reaches a depth of 329 fathoms near its mouth. This river's channels must result from river erosion in the unglaciated lowland of Taiwan, and a submergence of at least 329 fathoms must have occurred there in the recent geological past.

The western wall of the Penghu Channel, including the embayment, is well marked by its terraced descent, the slope being distinctly intervened at the three levels of 45–60, 60–80, and 80–100 fathoms. Each of these terraces has a considerable breadth and extension. These terraces may represent coastal terraces formed in a downward sequence by the intermittent emergence of land, which simultaneously gave rise to the deep river channels which are now drowned.

The submarine configuration of the Strait of Taiwan thus outlined suggests that its origin was due to the depression of land blocks to a depth of not less than 330 fathoms. Prior to this submergence of land the sea floor was an extensive land mass of a very low relief in very late geological history between the axial mountain range of Taiwan on the east and the mountain land of Fukien on the west.

The east coast of Taiwan is quite different physiographically from the west coast. It is straight and its submarine slope is extremely steep, the declivity usually being more than eight degrees. Moreover, a raised wave-cut bench and a higher coastal terrace occur along the shore line.

Submarine topographical features in the southern part of Taiwan are complicated by several furrows and ridges, probably the results of dislocation. Sounding data are insufficient to scrutinize in detail topographical character at each depth, but according to the submarine relief chart constructed by Ting-Ying H. Ma,[7] the following features are the most noteworthy:

(1) There are many submarine plains on the continental slope, and some of them are as deep as to reach the 6560 foot isobathic line.

(2) Some of the submarine valleys are the offshore prolongations of present river valleys, and others have no direct topographical connection with them.

(3) The greater the depth, the more frequent are the submarine plains and the more variable the isobathic lines become. The following series of plains can be grouped, namely (a) 2500–4000 feet, (b) 4000–7500 feet, and (c) deeper than 7500 feet.

It is difficult to explain the origin and process of this complex submarine topography, but many valleys, trenches, and flat plains are shown to be of subaerial or fluvial origin. Especially, each series of submarine plains and those developed on the continental shelf within the isobathic lines from 328 to 656 feet show very similar characteristics, suggesting that these deep-water canyons must have been formed by geological process similar to that which occurred on the land.

As to the relative ages of these submarine plains, the diversity in their height no doubt indicates that these plains were not developed simultaneously. In the eastern part of Taiwan the areas are geotectonically unstable. However, some of the submarine plains look very well preserved, which suggests that the submarine topography should not be regarded as the result of remote geological processes. At the same time, it can be inferred that there were at least three successive crustal movements of considerable magnitude during the late geological times. The periods in which these series of submarine plains were formed are believed to have been in late Pliocene, middle Pleistocene, and late Pleistocene epochs respectively.

REFERENCES

[1] VEI-CHOW JUAN, *Physiography and Geology of Taiwan* (China Cultural Publishing Foundation, Taipei, 1954), p. 34.
[2] Y. ISHII, "General remarks on the geological structure of Japan, including that of Taiwan," *J. geol. Soc. Tokyo* **6**, 99–110, 177–184 (1898).
[3] B. KOTO, "Geological structure of Riukiu Curve," *J. geol. Soc. Tokyo* **5**, 1 (1897).
[4] B. WILLIS, "Geological observations in the Philippine Archipelago," (National Research Council, P. I. Bulletin, **13**, 1937), pp. 1–50.
[5] VEI-CHOW JUAN, *Physiography and Geology of Taiwan* (China Cultural Publishing Foundation, Taipei, 1954), pp. 30–32.
[6] HISAKATSU YABE, and RISAHURO TAYAMA, "A cartographical study of the submarine relief of the Strait of Formosa," *Rec. oceanogr. Wks. Jap.* (1929).
[7] TING-YING H. MA, "Submarine valleys around the southern part of Taiwan and their geological significance," *Bull. oceanogr. Inst. Taiwan* **2**, 1–12 (1947).

THREE

Landforms

THE GEOMORPHOLOGIC HISTORY AND AGENTS

THE LANDFORMS OF TAIWAN have been affected by such factors as the geological basis, climatic environment, and time. Taiwan is composed primarily of metamorphic and sedimentary rocks. The Central Mountain region, in which metamorphic rocks are widely distributed, has been carved into a rugged terrain by the rivers. Sedimentary rocks, located along the flanks of the Central Mountains in inclined beds, have been formed into homoclinal ridges, hogbacks, and cuestas. Structurally, these rock layers have been pushed into folds by horizontal pressures, with pressure from the west making the folds into overthrusts. Since the axis of the Central Mountains is located near their eastern side, that side is much steeper than the western side (*Figure 5*). The eastern sea cliff has an elevation of 2500–4000 feet, making it one of the highest in the world.

Taiwan enjoys a subtropical climate, with characteristically high temperatures, heavy rainfall, and strong winds. If we may assume that the climate in the Tertiary division was not much different from that of the present, then Taiwan has certainly undergone severe erosive activity.

Taiwan's geomorphological development can be traced back to the Miocene epoch, by which period there can be little doubt that the island had been elevated as a land mass. This mass was eroded into tall peaks, and debris filled in the depressions on either side of the Central Mountains. This was the Nengkao Shan period in which the connecting peak lines were as high as 10,000–12,000 feet, establishing the erosional surface of the period. The peaks which exceed the Nengkao Shan erosional surface are monadnocks of the previous erosional surface. After the Nengkao period the island rose, erosion became more active, and the Nengkao erosional surface was destroyed. The forming of a new erosional surface at 7200–7600 feet can be called the Ali Shan period. During this stage local crust disturbances occurred and the Puli Basin depression was formed in the

18

Central Mountains, with deposition more abundant in the western coastal area than in the east. After the Ali Shan period (Mid-Pleistocene) the island rose once again and severe erosion followed immediately. During this period mountain-building was active, and the great fault occurred. After a long period of erosion, an erosional surface at 3300–3900 feet was established. This was the Kuantzu-Ling period, during which depositional material was widely distributed and gravel beds appeared. In the meantime, volcanic lava was erupted from Penghu and Tatun. After the Late

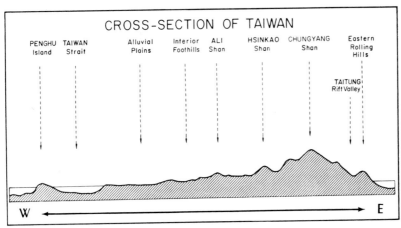

Figure 5

Pleistocene epoch the island experienced intermittent elevation and folding, forming two-layered terraces and the Taipei and Taichung depressed basins. During the same stage the west coast was submerged, and extensive lavation formed the present western coastal plains. The initial surface was still preserved and consequent rivers were developed.

The present landforms of Taiwan are the result of two conflicting forces: tectonic processes from the inside of the earth, and gradation processes from the outside. In Taiwan, tectonic forces include volcanoes, hot springs, faultings, and earthquakes; gradation forces include rivers, glaciers, and sea waves.

TECTONIC PROCESSES

Volcanoes and hot springs

Volcanic rocks in Taiwan are scattered in the Tatun Shan, Keelung Shan, and Taitung coastal ranges, as well as on Penghu and other small islands. In the northeastern part of the island, these volcanic rocks are mainly intrusive in origin; some, however, are effusive. The intrusive rocks were formed earlier than the effusive ones, and their origin is probably Plio-Pleistocene. The volcanic rocks in the northeastern part of the island are hydrothermally altered and have a close genetic relationship with the gold and copper deposits that occur in that region. Volcanic detritus covers the area; it is composed of volcanic ash, boulders, and weathered products of dacite.

There are more than a hundred hot springs in Taiwan. Except for those located along the western plain, most of them have been used for bathing. Some of the springs are not used because of their remote location in mountain gorges. Hot springs in Taiwan can be divided into two groups: one group is located in the volcanic region, the other in the sedimentary and metamorphic rock areas. The former, representing one-fifth of the total number of such springs, is found in northern Taiwan and the volcanic islands around the main island; the remainder are found primarily in the Central Mountain region and the surrounding hilly lands.

In northern Taiwan, the hot springs are called sulfataras and fumaroles. The region is characterized by low hillocks, loose stones, and debris, interspersed at irregular intervals with shallow pits or depressions containing mud, sand, and sometimes foul muddy water. From cracks and fissures in these depressions arise clouds of steam and yellow patches of sulfur which are visible for quite a distance. The muddy water, which bubbles up in a series of explosions, carries the boiling water, sand, and mud, five and six feet up, splashing it all around.

Faults and earthquakes

The most distinct geological fault in Taiwan lies in the Taitung rift valley. The west wall of the valley shows precipitous cliffs of the backbone range, composed of crystalline schists which as fault scarps then continue north to the magnificent sea cliff near Suao, and south to the base of the Hengchun peninsula. The great fault scarp has been cut by consequent rivers into many triangular facets. From these rivers, much debris has been transported to the foothills, and many alluvial fans have been formed at their mouths.

Two other remarkable faults are the west wall of the northern Ilan plain, called the Chiaochi fault scarp, and the east wall of Pintung plain in the south, called the Chaochow fault scarp. Along the foot of both scarps are alluvial fans and fringes. The alternating arrangement of fans suggests the pivotal movement of the faulting. Frequent earthquakes are hazards to both land and man. During the fifty-year period from 1895 to 1945, Taiwan suffered nearly 8,000 shocks, averaging 160 a year. Most of them, however, were small and local.

FEATURES OF GRADATION FORCES

The work of rivers

The mountain peaks in Taiwan are high, and the distance between them and the coast is never more than 50 miles. Consequently, most of the rivers originating in the mountains are short and swift and give the island a radial drainage pattern. The river beds are deeply incised as they descend from the mountains. On reaching the coastal plains, they deposit their debris and build up alluvial fans. Thus, the rivers have two effects in geomorphology: one erosional, the other depositional.

EROSIONAL FEATURES OF THE RIVERS.—The erosive characteristics of the rivers in Taiwan can be represented by incise meander and nick-points, potholes, and river capturing.

Incise meander and nick-points.—One of the most prominent topographical features in Taiwan is the incised meandering of river valleys, which is caused by the recent upheavals and repeated entrenchment and ingrowing of rivers. A recent upheaval is presently causing the rejuvenation of river erosion. The incision terraces are left at various heights on both sides of the valleys. In comparing the river terraces, we discern two distinctive nick-points in the longitudinal profiles of the valleys. One is directly due to the upheaval of land, and consequently, rejuvenation of the valleys; and the other is the result of differential erosion in the various bed-rock strata.

The height of the terraces found along the eastern side of the backbone range greatly exceeds that of the western terraces. This fact seems to suggest either that the upheaval was of a tilting nature, and accompanied by a sinking of land with the lower courses of the eastern river valleys, or that the unwarping of the whole island had its maximum effect along the backbone mountain range which is nearer the east coast.[1]

Potholes in northern Taiwan.—Potholes, scoured out of rock by swiftly flowing streams and plunge pools at the base of waterfalls, are a very characteristic and conspicuous feature in northern Taiwan. Some occur along the coast and are of marine origin, but the majority are of fluviatile origin. Along Keelung River and Chingmei River (tributaries of the Tamshui) the potholes are most highly developed.[2]

Potholes are found along valley sides, on valley bottoms, on rapids, on points of stream confluence, and also on boulders in streams. They range in height to 26 feet above the low stream water level. Most, however, are found within 20 inches of the water's surface.

The form of potholes is highly variable. They may be rounded, ovoid, elliptic, bottle-gourdlike, or other irregular forms. United potholes and potholes at greater heights are usually of elliptic or irregular forms; simple potholes and potholes at lower altitudes are usually round. The potholes vary in diameter from 1 to 173 inches but most are between 4 and 20 inches. The depth of potholes varies from 0.78 to 109 inches but the majority are between 4 and 20 inches, in proportion to their width.

Based on their form and evolution, potholes may be classified as simple, united, and compound.

Simple potholes are generally circular or ovoid. They occur near the water surface and are smaller in diameter, shallower in depth, more rounded in shape, and are sparsely distributed. During erosion, two or more potholes that are near one another may gradually become united, either partially or entirely, with either horizontal or vertical confluence. Compound potholes are a special and very interesting form, usually consisting of two or more sets, occurring on different levels. They are composed either of simple or united potholes. The outer large one may be irregular while the inner ones are smaller and rounded. They may be situated on one, two, or more levels. After the outer pothole has been formed the eddy current attacks certain weak points within it and, perhaps accelerated by the solution function, the new and smaller inner potholes are then carved out. These compound potholes usually occur in rocky channels and rapids where there is a large amount of running water with strong erosive power.

Simple potholes represent the initial stage of their evolution; as the pothole erosion process continues, the united stage appears. Later on, as the pothole-bearing mass becomes lower and lower, the whole mass is then detached by many channels. These channels are usually the result of selective erosion on the weaker zones, that is, joints. This may be called the channel stage, during which the total area of the rock mass is still larger than the water area within it. Later, the water area gradually widens out, and the rocky mass erodes away, leaving only some island-like remnants of pothole-bearing masses scattered here and there above the surface of the water. This is called the island-like remnant stage. Finally, even the remnants are eroded and washed away entirely; this is the ultimate step of erosion. It should be mentioned, however, that not all potholes pass through all the stages mentioned above.

Conditions favoring pothole development in northern Taiwan's streams are polygenetic: abundant rainfall, stream gradation, mass wasting, joints, and rejuvenation all play important roles.

River capture in the Taitung rift valley.—River capture, or river piracy, may arise from either of two causes: one river may have an advantage over another because it is cutting its valley in more easily erodible rocks, or one river may have a much steeper gradient than another. The notable examples of river capture have been reported by Hsu in the Taitung rift valley (*Figure 6*).[3]

River capture occurred in the river Siukuluan Chi, formerly the upper main course of the Hualien Chi. The cause of river capture is that a subsequent river is captured by a consequent one, due to the unbalance erosion between two rivers.

The upper course of the Siukuluan Chi south from Shuishui, was originally extended from the Hualien Chi, but at present the river has been captured by a consequent river which cut through the Taitung coastal range and emptied into the ocean. The evidence of capture can be ascertained by the following facts:

(1) Along the Taitung rift valley, both the valley of the Hualien Chi and the Siukuluan Chi are connected as a through valley without any marked watershed formed by hill or highland. The divide between the Hualien Chi and the Siukuluan Chi is situated near Tafu Village, where the gentle surface is covered with alluvial sediments of sand and gravel. The topographic expression of this lowland indicates clearly that a river was formerly present at the site of this water divide but the river channel was subsequently abandoned. It implies that the water divide is a wind-gap, and it also implies strongly that the upper course of Siukuluan Chi once flowed through the Malantiao Chi to enter into the water course of the Hualien Chi.

(2) The Siukuluan Chi runs from south to north in the rift valley and turns suddenly eastward near Shuishui, cutting across the coastal ranges down to the Pacific Ocean. Such a bending of a river course is immediately recognized to be an elbow of capture.

(3) Gravel beds are extensively distributed in the valleys of both Hualien Chi and the Siukuluan Chi. Although the gravel beds in the two streams are considered to be the same age and contemporaneous deposits in the Pleistocene epoch, they suffer different degrees of dissection along these two valleys. Along the Siukuluan Chi, the gravel beds have been deeply dissected, forming patches of river-terrace 100 or so feet above

the present river bed, especially prominent near Shuishui. In the valley of the Hualien Chi, no such terraces have ever been found as close as these two streams are. It is believed that the development of these terraces is the result of static rejuvenation localized in the capturing river during the process of river capture. In the vicinity of Shuishui, the terraces are very well developed because Shuishui lies just on the point of capture.

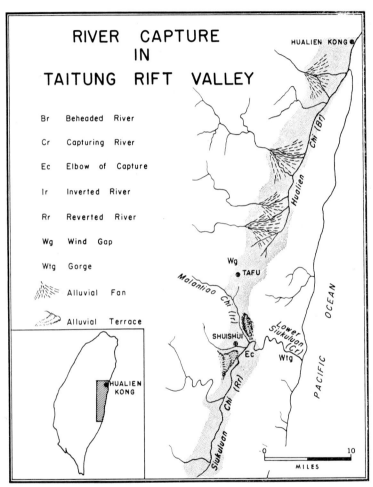

Figure 6. (*After* T. L. Hsu and P. Y. Chen)

(4) The Hualien Chi is an important river emptying near Hualien Kong. It is about 31 miles in length and the stream flows in a broad valley, attaining an average width of 2.5 miles. The volume of water in the river channel of the Hualien Chi is rather small in comparison with the width of the valley, so it appears that the river channel is misfitted to the size of its former valley. Such features are characteristic of a beheaded river which loses its original volume of water in the upper course as a result of river capture but maintains the same broad valley downstream. As the volume of water in the river diminished, its erosional power in the down-

course was naturally decreased. In consequence, the process of deposition rapidly took place, and an alluvial fan was extensively developed at the mouth of Hualien Chi.

DEPOSITIONAL FEATURES OF THE RIVER.—River terraces and alluvial fans are the two most distinctive depositional features of Taiwan's rivers. The terrace has always been considered one of the most important criteria for understanding the natural history of the island. The terraces can be divided into two groups: the lower and the higher. The lower are the terraces 65–131 feet above the present river bed, with exceptional heights up to about 260 feet; the higher are those about 328–984 feet high and, on the eastern slope of the island, even 1300–1640 feet. The terraces of the higher group are characterized by a veneer of red earth.

Alluvial fans vary in size and form. When a swift stream flows down from the high Central Mountain ranges to the western side and nearly level plains, the abrupt change in its gradient causes it to deposit the greater part of its load immediately. In this way a fan is built up, radiating outward from the point at which the tributary emerges. In Taiwan, the fans are especially well developed along the fault line. Some of them are beautifully preserved, though all have been more or less dissected. Most of the fans are of considerable magnitude, measuring in radius from about 140 feet to approximately 350 feet, and in depth to 100 or 130 feet.

The alluvial fans in Taiwan are of several types. According to their developmental history, there are growing fans and graded fans. According to their surface features, there are symmetrical fans and asymmetrical fans. Taking their formation point into account, there are plain fans and valley fans. According to their origin, there are fault fans and discordant fans. Considering their arrangement, there are confluent fans, compound fans, and reconstructed fans.[4]

Despite the alluvial fans, there is a kind of diluvial fan. The diluvial fans are called tableland gravel; they form a very peculiar physiographical feature in the hilly land of the western plains. They are a series of flat-topped tablelands roughly arranged in a north–south direction, all covered with a bed of gravel overlying red soil. They measure several feet in thickness, with the red soil about seven or ten feet in thickness. At places, the boundary between the red soil and the boulders is not very sharp; there is usually a transitional zone of varying thickness consisting of alternating thin layers of gravel and red soil.

The tableland gravel is found at different altitudes. The tilted blocks near the coast are about 984–1300 feet high, the highest area being in the middle part of the island where extended surfaces about 1970, 1640, and 1310 feet above sea level can be found. These three surfaces are divided by very steep cliffs. In the northern part of the island, where the tableland gravel develops close to the slope of the volcanic Tatun mountains, boulders of andesite lavas that came from the volcano are found in the gravel, showing that the tableland gravel is younger than the volcanic eruption.

Glaciation

In Taiwan, the height of most of the mountains that show evidence of glacial action is limited to 13,000 feet, which is below the snow line. How, then, is it possible that the mountains of Taiwan could be glaciated in a tropical location? Study of the submarine topography of the Taiwan Strait shows that the drowned valleys of Taiwan can be traced to a depth of more than 1970 feet, and this suggests that the island was formerly 3300 feet higher than it is now.[5] The former height of the island can be considered to have been about 16,300 feet, which means that it was in the climatic snow line of the tropics. Thus the former existence of the glaciers is probably confirmed. However, it may be difficult to trace them at present because of the remarkable amount of erosion and weathering of the island. Several Japanese geographers have reported the glacial topography of Taiwan's mountains.

The existing evidence of glacial topography in Taiwan includes cirques, moraines, roches moutonées, glacial striae, erratic blocks, and round-headed mountain tops. Also, the plateau gravels that developed extensively on the northwestern part of the island are considered in connection with the problem of the glacial era.

GLACIAL CIRQUES.—On Nanhuta peak of Chungyang Shan, four distinctive cirques and eight obscure ones are found. The latter have been very much worn by water erosion and covered with heavy talus of slate and sandstone.[6]

On Tzekao Shan a remarkable cirque was discovered in the summer of 1931 by T. Kano.[7] The cirque was covered with talus as thick as 330 feet. On Hsinkao Shan there are 21 cirques. The altitude of the cirques ranges from 11,480 feet to nearly 12,130 feet. At their floor, the smaller ones usually stand higher than the larger ones. It is interesting to note that some of the cirques have two floor levels, as is shown by duplicated steps. The cirques are in general semi-circular in outline, although they are highly variable in detail. They are also variable in dimension, being from 230–328 feet in length and commonly very shallow. The smaller ones are only shallow depressions; the larger ones are composed of two or more cirques which have coalesced.[8] In general the preservation of the cirques in Taiwan is rather poor, because of the intense weathering in the tropical climate at so high an altitude. Most of the cirques' walls are broken down to their peripheries, their skirts buried by the debris, and the floors covered with talus. The destruction makes it difficult to trace their original forms. However, the ridges between cirques often still exist as aretes, which can still be discerned.

MORAINES.—On Nanhuta peak of Chungyang Shan some moraines are well preserved at the bottom of the cirques. However, cirques that developed on the outside slope of the mountains have only the slightest trace of moraines. The moraines can be found above an altitude of about 11,150 feet. On Hsinkao Shan, the morainic deposits cannot be found in any large numbers, partly because they are buried under the debris from the surrounding walls and partly because they are deformed by the headward erosion of the incising rivulets. In consequence, the moraines can be seen only as small patches in the shape of mounds, which are made up of sub-angular blocks about 8–20 inches in diameter, with no distinct striations. This well-rounded, smooth, bare rock surface is rare; it shows no trace of fluting, perhaps owing to being worn away by exfoliation.

GLACIAL STRIAE AND GLACIATED SURFACES.—Rocks with smooth, eroded surfaces are found on the walls of the cirques at an elevation of more than 11,480 feet both on Nanhuta peak and on Hsinkao Shan. Ice-eroded surfaces are found also at higher parts of the cirques, being recognized as roches moutonées in Tzekao Shan. The round-headed summits are another common feature of the main summits of Nanhuta Shan, Tzekao Shan, and Hsinkao Shan.

From the above description, glacial topographic features can still be traced in the high mountains of Taiwan. The supply of snow is quite sufficient even at present to yield a firn and is also, under favorable conditions, sufficient for its firnification. The action of water from melting snow is evident as the destroying force on the original features of glacial topography.

The ice-cap theory has been applied to the glaciers in the geological development of Taiwan. The chief reason is that the residual snow is thickest on the top of the heights, forming a sort of snow-cap.[9] In explaining the existence of glaciers in Taiwan, the change of climate has to be considered in addition to the theory of upheaval.

The definite geological age of the glaciation is still not settled. The Pleistocene era has been suggested, as glaciation is to be correlated with the characteristic thick gravel beds which might indicate climatic as well as tectonic events which occurred during that period.

SEA-WAVE EROSION

The characteristics of the coasts of Taiwan are the result of sea-wave erosion. They present a variety of aspects. In some places, many inlets, bays, and islands are to be found; in others, long stretches of unbroken coast are in evidence. Some of these coasts are bordered by stretches of low-lying sand; others are rockbound. Along some coasts deep water is found, and along others very shallow marshes are seen. Variations in type of rock, in geological structure, in quantity of river deposits, and in stability of the earth's crust all act to bring about these different forms of coastline.

The coasts of Taiwan are rather short and monotonous. Penghu Island's coast is much more irregular than that of the main island of Taiwan, where the length of coast line per unit area is only $\frac{1}{80}$ of that of Penghu. The comparatively straight coast of Taiwan is in sharp contrast to the irregular coast of mainland China's Fukien Province, which is just opposite it on the Taiwan Strait.

The coasts of Taiwan are of four types: the eastern coast presents a fault coast line; the western, a raised coast line; the northern, a rias submergent type; and the southern, a coral reef type.

The eastern fault coastline

Starting from Santieulin at the northeastern tip of the island, and ending at the Hengchun peninsula at the south end, the eastern Taiwan coast is rather straight.

With the exception of the coasts along the Ilan delta, which present a concave curve composed of sand and marshes, and at Hualien and Taitung, which are both at the end outlet of the Taitung rift valley, the eastern coast of Taiwan follows a fault line and is thus simple and straight. At the northeastern tip of the island the coast follows the Chiaochi fault scarp, running a sheer 13,120 feet deep to form a continental slope. The rivers in the eastern part of the islands are fierce mountain torrents, more like waterfalls than rivers, so that navigation of any sort is impossible.

The eastern coast is composed of hard rocks, such as sandstone, slate, and limestone. The strike of these rocks is parallel to the coast. Along the coast are found marine terraces and abrasion benches; earthquakes occur frequently; all this indicates that the eastern coast is unstable along a dislocation line.

The western raised coasts

In the western part of Taiwan appears a raised coastline, which is straight, monotonous, and flat; as a result the coast lacks harbors. The shallowness of the water has prevented the sea waves from approaching the coast; thus there is no wave erosion, except where the waves have pushed the sand to build up off-shore bars, spits, lagoons, and marshes. The lagoons of Taiwan are used to raise fish; the marshes are used to raise weeds.

Starting from the south bank of the Tamshui River, and ending at Fong-lien in the south, the western coastal line is 255 miles in length. This coast is composed of gravel, sand, and clay. As a result of the large amount of sand together with strong winds in this rain-shadow dry area, many sand dunes have developed. These are sometimes from 650 to 1000 feet in length and attain a height of several feet. Tidal flats have also developed, some-times 2.5 or 3 miles in length, bounded by offshore bars, spits, and sandbars. Shallow lagoons form, usually less than 3 feet in depth; their water is not brackish, but is sea water, and they are usually used for fishing ponds and as salt fields.

Although most of the western coastline is straight and flat, there is in the southwestern part a drowned valley, at the Lower Tamshui, which pre-sents an important coast landform. This valley was not formed by waves or tidal forces; it can be explained only as the result of drowning.

The northern drowned coasts

The drowned coasts of northern Taiwan extend for 53 miles from Santieulin in the northeastern corner of the island to the mouth of the Tamshui River. The rocks of those coastal areas include slate, sandstone, and shale. The strike of these rocks and the structure alignment is at a right angle with the coast line; therefore the coasts are irregular and are made up of peninsulas and bays, which form rias types of coasts. The port of Keelung is in the rias coast, full of abrasion benches, sea caves, wave-cut arches, notch stacks, and chimneys. Elevated coastal phenomena such as coastal terraces, raised mushroom rocks, and raised wave-cut arches also appear. These features all indicate that the coasts in northern Taiwan have experienced much eustatic change.

On Hoping Island, the rocks are Tertiary soft sandstone and hard limestone, interbedded. They are full of square joints which make them look like "thousands of mats," the name by which they have been known since the Japanese occupation. The limestone contains nodules slightly more than three feet in diameter. Since these limestone nodules are rather harder than the surrounding sandstone, they erode much more slowly than the limestone. As a result, this limestone survived the erosion and the nodules now stand like mushrooms among the sandstone bases. They also resemble many persons standing some fifteen feet above the mats, and so the Japanese called them "a crowd of ten thousand persons."

The south coral reef coasts

The coral reefs appear all around the south coasts of Taiwan. They also appear in the north near Keelung and on the eastern and western coasts. However, conditions such as rocky shores, clear water, and high temperature of the water, all combine to favor the growth of coral reefs along the south coast. These fringing reefs surround the southern tip of the island.

ISLANDS

Around the main island of Taiwan, there are thirteen islands, five of whose physical conditions are presented here.[10]

Peng-chia Hsu

Peng-chia Hsu, or Agincort Island, is the most northern island of Taiwan, lying 34 miles from Keelung. It is 270 acres in area and is 14,100 feet in circumference. It presents a rectangular form, 1.5 miles east to west, 1.4 miles north to south. Its surface is higher in the east than in the west; the highest point, which is 466 feet in elevation, is in the northeast. Steep cliffs on the north, east, and south coasts prevent ships from anchoring. The only place where there is a harbor is on the southwestern coast of the island, where the cliffs curve to the east. Here the abrasion bench is well developed and the rock cliff has been artificially carved out. On the east side of the harbor there is a wave-cut notch with an elevation of a few feet.

Mien-hwa Hsu

Mien-hwa Hsu or Crag Island is about 21 miles northeast of Keelung. It has an oblong form, extending 1640 feet north to south, 1000 feet east to west. Its circumference is 5900 feet. The southeastern part of the island is the highest point. Steep cliffs characterize all its coasts, except the northwest coast, which has a gulf with a radius of 164 feet, and which is connected with a sand bar. It forms a good landing place, even though there are always strong northwest winds.

Kuei Shan Tao

Kuei Shan Tao, or Turtle Island, totals about 3.5 square miles in area. Shaped like a turtle, it is divided into three parts, the "head," the "body," and the "tail." The "head" is elongated in form; its highest point is 833 feet in altitude. Separated from the "head" by a depression is the "body" of the "turtle," which has a rectangular form. Its highest point is 1315 feet in altitude. The main "body" of the "turtle" was originally a conic mountain. The "tail" is a long and narrow spit extending toward the northwest for about half a mile. The island has cliffs on all sides, which make landing difficult. The rocks of the island are andesite, and craters are located on the "head" and on the "body"; this indicates that the present island consists of two volcanic islands which are united.

Huo-shao Tao

Huo-shao Tao, or Green Island, is located 20 miles from Taitung, with an area of 6.5 square miles. The northern part is wider than the southern. The highest point, 92 feet, is in the southwest. The island is of volcanic origin, being composed of andesite lavas and raised reefs. The surface of the island has been dissected by the radiating consequent rivers. The coasts of the island consist of precarious cliffs and there is little level land.

Hung-tun Hsu

Hung-tun Hsu, or Botel Tobago, is an island of 18.5 square miles. The island is characterized by a rugged mountainous terrain of volcanic origin, the highest point of which is 1500 feet. The rivers of the island form a radial pattern and there are incise meanders. The coast line is monotonous, with no good harbors. Raised reefs, a few feet high, are connected with the present reefs, a fact which indicates that the island is still rising.

LANDFORM REGIONS

Taiwan is a mountainous island. About two-thirds of the area consists of rugged mountains (*Figure 7*). A tilted block traverses from northeast to southwest, forming a kind of backbone. The central part of the island is made up of four parallel anticlinal ranges which thrust up 48 peaks of 9850 feet or more in height. Since the mountain chain is nearer to the eastern seaboard (*Figure 7*), the eastern half has many crags and steep slopes. The sea cliffs rise perpendicularly for 295 feet or more and then slope to heights as great as 9850 feet; the western part has gentler slopes and less relief. It is on the western part of the island that many of the rivers cut the land into successive terraces and further build the alluvial plains sloping gently to the sea. Toward the north, the western plains gradually become narrower and higher; in the south, the plains are broader and more level. Because of the heavy rainfall in the subtropical climate, the rivers of Taiwan have been endowed with vigorous erosional power. In the western part of the island, nearly all the rivers have precipitous upper valleys, incised meanders in the middle part, and characteristic terraces along the lower valley. On reaching the coastal area, the streams deposit their debris and build the alluvial plains.

Physiographically, Taiwan has three types of surface configuration, namely: mountains, which occupy about 8886 square miles in area, forming 64 per cent of the whole island; plains and basins, 3332 square miles with 24 per cent of the island; and hills and tablelands, 1666 square miles with 12 per cent of the total area.

Approximately one-third of Taiwan is less than 328 feet in elevation, a little more than one-third is between 328 and 3280 feet, and the rest is more than 3280 feet (*Figure 8*). *Table 3* lists the detailed figures.

The landforms of Taiwan are rather varied. Based on the differences in elevation, in character of rock formation, and in geologic structure, the island can be divided (*Figure 9*) into seven landform regions.

Table 3. Elevation in Taiwan

Elevation in feet	Area in square miles	Per cent of total
Below 328	4304	31
328–1,640	3332	24
1,640–3,280	1805	13
3,280–6,560	2777	20
6,560–9,840	1527	11
Above 9,840	139	1
Total	*13,884*	*100.0*

THE CENTRAL MOUNTAIN RANGES

Nearly half of the island is occupied by the Central Mountain range. It extends 168 miles north to south and 50 miles east to west at the central part. Two steep cliffs form the boundaries of this group of mountains—on the west the Ali Shan fault line and on the east the fault scarp that separates it from the Taitung rift valley.

Old rock schists and gneiss are the foundation of this mountain system. While these are hard and resistant to weathering and erosion, they are complex structures being pushed by horizontal pressure into faulting and folding. After long exposure, the tilted fault block has been eroded into a large number of peaks. Though an individual peak may reach an elevation of more than 12,000 feet, rarely is the relief between two peaks more than 1000 feet. Thus, the area is plateau-like in appearance; however, near the upper level of mountains, heavy rainfall has deeply scored the mountainside with deep gorges and sharp valleys. In addition to this, the remnants of glaciation at the top of some peaks indicate that in the present cycle of erosion, the whole region is still in its young stage.

The Central Mountain system has a complex history. It is evident that the system has experienced intermittent upheavals and local peneplanation, although, with the present knowledge of the island's geology, the exact time of these movements cannot be ascertained definitely. The relative order of succession may be estimated as follows:

The close folding of thick sediments in the Central Mountain system took place long before the Oligocene epoch, and was followed by broad folding in the Miocene era. The land was quickly reduced to planation by vigorous erosion, and the eustatic uplifting that made possible the local glaciation on the top of the mountain commenced in the Pliocene period. In either the late or early stage of this era the Central Mountain system experienced large-scale north–south dislocation. It started from the west with thrust-faulting occurring first in front of Ali Shan and moving eastward. Since the overthrusting came from the southeast, the eastern part of the island was elevated. The lifting increased progressively toward the east, bringing about the tilting. The Ali Shan thrust was followed by another occurring at the western side of the Hsinkao Shan, thus the eastern part of the island was uplifted once again. The northeast–southwest trending fault of Tzekao Shan, also an overthrusting from the southeast, occurred either at the same time as the fault of Hsinkao Shan or a little later, and is responsible for the thick accumulation of tableland gravel in the western part of the island as a consequence of vigorous erosion. The thrust fault that separates the Hsinkao Shan from the eastern flank of the central range may represent dislocation of very recent origin.

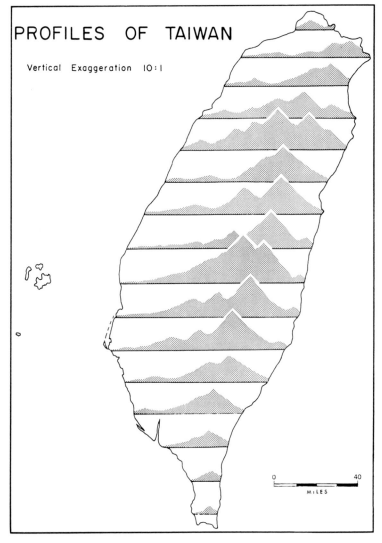

Figure 7. (After WANG)

31

The Central Mountain Range is a collective name for the Chungyang Shan, the Tzekao Shan, the Hsinkao Shan, and the Ali Shan.

Chungyang Shan

The Chungyang Shan (meaning "central mountain") is the easternmost of the system and here the old rock beds are so closely folded that some of them are vertical, thrusting up 32 peaks to an altitude of more than 9840 feet above sea level. The highest peaks are Nanhuta Shan (12,454 feet), the Siukuluan Shan (12,572 feet), Kwan Shan (12,185 feet), and the Chilai Shan (11,624 feet). These peaks are the main water divide of the island, forcing the rivers of the island either toward the east or the west coast.

Tzekao Shan

The Tzekao Shan (meaning the "second highest mountain") is 112 miles long and 17 miles in width. It lies on the northwestern side of the Chungyang Shan, and the two ranges are separated from each other by the fault valley of the Ilan-Choshui River trending north–northwest and south–southwest. Glaciated topography has been reported on the northern part of the Tzekao Shan. The rivers have cut the horizontal beds of slate and sandstone that capped the mountain tops; thus the mountain ranges show a topography of dissected plateaus. In the lower parts of the mountains the river terraces are well developed, and three distinct levels appear (394 feet, 590 feet, and 689 feet, respectively) which obviously represent the successive uplifts of very recent origin.

Hsinkao Shan

Hsinkao Shan (meaning the "new high mountain"; it is also known by the names Yu Shan and Mt. Morrison) lies on the western side in the middle of Chungyang Shan and is a narrow mountain. The mountain represents a horst structure, being blocked out between two fault lines. The mountain is mainly composed of early Tertiary sediments, with the general strike parallel to the Central Mountain range. Except for local foldings, the beds of the mountain dip generally toward the west; thus on the southeastern side of the block, steep cliffs are frequently found. The mountain tops of Hsinkao, with an elevation of 13,064 feet, are the highest points on the island.

An interesting feature of the Central Mountain system is that the highest mountain of the island is not the Chungyang Shan, but the Hsinkao Shan. This may be explained as follows:

First, the Chungyang Shan, situated on the axial part of the closely folded anticline, was more susceptible to vigorous erosion than was the broadly folded Hsinkao Shan.

Second, the number of upliftings experienced by the two mountains differed: the more times a block was uplifted the less elevated it became, owing to repeated erosion. The Chungyang Shan experienced uplifting at least four times, the Tzekao Shan three times, and the Hsinkao Shan only twice.

Third, a fault of large displacement may cause an uplifting in an amount far exceeding the sum of repeated faultings of small displacement. It is known that the displacement of the Hsinkao Shan fault is the greatest.

Last, since it contains in its formation hard and compact quartzitic sandstone, the Hsinkao Shan can resist erosion.

Differences in structure, uplift, and rock character have caused the Hsinkao Shan to stand majestically high above the neighboring mountains.

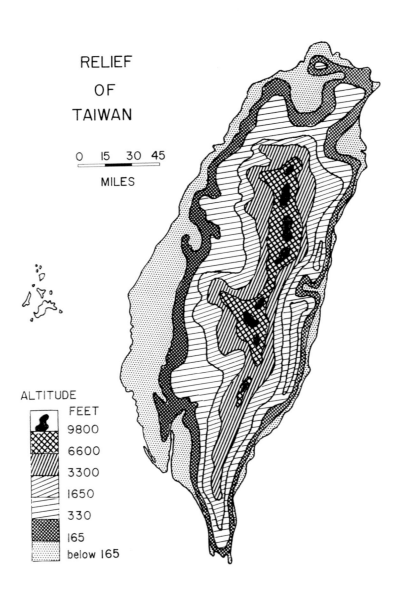

RELIEF

OF

TAIWAN

0   15   30   45
MILES

ALTITUDE

FEET
9800
6600
3300
1650
330
165
below 165

Figure 8

33

Ali Shan

The Ali Shan, standing on the western side of the Hsinkao Shan, is flanked on both the east and west sides by a fault. The mountain is made up of shale and sandstone and has been deeply eroded into a dissected mature land. The Ali Shan is smaller in extent than the mountains to the east and is also much lower in elevation. Its highest peaks rise 8774 feet above sea level, but the average elevation is less than 4920 feet. The beds show a gentle dip toward the southwest and, as a rule, only broad undulating folds are present.

THE TAITUNG RIFT VALLEY

The Taitung rift valley, the most conspicuous geologic feature of the island, is an elongated graben in structure, lying between the eastern coastal rolling hills and the Central Mountains. The trench trends roughly northeast–southwest and meets the sea at both ends. This rift valley is 77 miles long, yet in width averages only from 5 to 10 miles. It appears like a deep slash into the mountainous surface of the island. The great fault scarp of the western edge of the depression, which is 3936–4592 feet in altitude, has been cut by many consequent rivers and has transported much debris to the foothills. Thus, it forms an irregular line at the foothills. Its many triangular facets penetrate the western side of the scarp. These triangular facets may have been caused by their being remnants of the former river valleys that were interrupted by the fault. The famous Tailukuo gorge is the representative feature of the valley. On the eastern edge of the trough, the fault line is not so prominent. The floor of the trough is covered by thick deposits of alluvial material brought down from the mountains by rivers that have cut sharp gorges and have formed alluvial fans.

The configuration of the rift valley is further emphasized by three streams that flow along the valley floor. The Siukuluan River flows 26 miles along the floor and then turns toward the east, cutting through the Taitung Mountains before it pours into the Pacific Ocean. The Hualien River in the north and the Peinanta River in the south, flowing in opposite directions, are 40 and 52 miles long, respectively. The divides between these rivers in the floor are by no means high. The divide between the Hualien and the Siukuluan Rivers is only 580 feet high; the divide between the Siukuluan and the Peinanta Rivers is 886 feet high. The Hualien and Peinanta Rivers have small deltas at their mouths, at the cities of Hualien and Taitung, two seaports located respectively at the northern and southern ends of the trough.

The consequent rivers originating both from the east coastal rolling hills and the Central Mountains descend to the valley floor and flow into the Siukuluan, the Hualien, and the Peinanta Rivers. Since the consequent rivers are parallel with each other, the drainage in the trough forms a trellis pattern. These rivers in the rift valley produce two geomorphic features, alluvial fans and river terraces. When the consequent rivers carry the debris from both sides of the trough and descend to the valley floor, they deposit debris at the foothill, owing to the sudden change in the slope and thus, form alluvial fans.

There are a total of 26 alluvial fans in the trough. There are, however, more consequent rivers flowing from the western edge of the Central Mountains than from the eastern. Only five alluvial fans have been formed in the consequent rivers of the eastern side of the trough, while on the western edge are 21 alluvial fans, seven each formed by the Hualien, Siukuluan, and the Peinanta rivers.

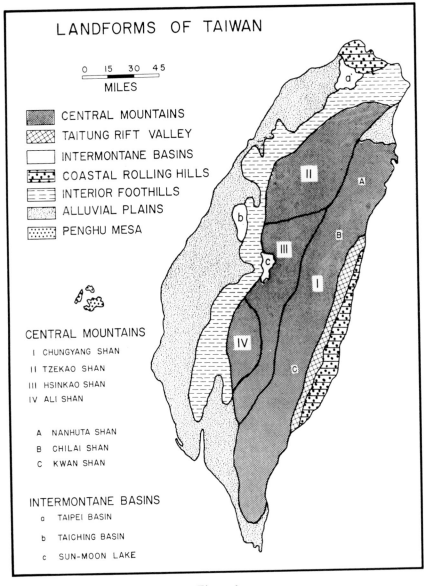

Figure 9

Development of alluvial fans depends upon the amount of water in the river, the gradient of the flow, and the type of parent rock in the upper part of the river, which is the important source of debris carried by the mechanical and disintegration processes of erosion. On the western side of the valley, there is more rainfall than on the eastern, and thus the rivers have more power to carry debris and to form alluvial fans. The most developed of the alluvial fans are those along the Hualien River. There, the floor of the trough is totally covered by thick deposits of alluvial material. This even pushes the Hualien River channel to the eastern side of the valley. Most of the western part of this alluvial plain is formed by the coalescing of several alluvial fans.

Besides the alluvial fans in the Taitung rift valley, there are 18 terraces, covered with laterite. These terraces occur in different layers, varying from several feet to more than 650 feet.

At present, the Taitung rift valley separates the Central Mountains from the eastern coastal hills. In the geological past, before the graben of the Taitung rift valley was formed, the eastern coastal hills were connected with the Central Mountains. Then, all the parallel consequent rivers flowed from west to east and emptied into the ocean. This is evidenced by the fact that on the eastern slope of the eastern coastal hills, gravels appear that originally occurred in the Central Mountains and which were transported here. Also on the eastern coast of the island, gold sand was scattered which had been transported from the Central Mountains. Again on the eastern coast, many drowned valleys have been left by the old parallel consequent rivers; those valleys are many times as large as are the present river valleys. The divides are wind gaps, thus indicating that the parallel consequent rivers once emptied into the Pacific. Later, the faults occurred and formed the graben of the Taitung rift valley. This caused the rivers to divert their flow either to the north or to the south.

INTERMONTANE BASINS

There are three major tectonic basins, the Taipei basin, the Taichung basin, and the Sun-Moon Lake basin, which have the same origin as the rift valley.

Taipei basin

The Taipei basin extends over an area of 155 square miles, with the shape of a triangle. The three sides of the basin are marked by fault lines. The basin is drained by the Tamshui River and its tributaries, the Keelung and the Shintien. The Keelung River flows from the northeast, meets the Shintien River, which comes from the south, at the middle of the basin and is led by the Tamshui which flows out of the basin at the northwest corner, and empties into the ocean.

It is evident that the Taipei basin is a tectonic depression. Also, it was reported that in 1697 A.D. the center of the basin was still waterlogged. Therefore, it is believed that in a former geological period the basin was a lake. Later, as a consequence of the uplifting of this part of the earth's crust, the lake gradually disappeared. The floor of the basin is covered by a thin layer of alluvium, deposited by the Tamshui River and its tributaries.

GEOMORPHIC DEVELOPMENT—The geomorphic development of the Taipei basin can be summarized as follows[11]:

(1) Terraces were formed and gravel was deposited on the terraces.

(2) Under warm climatic conditions, laterization took place and lateritic soils were left on top of the terraces.

(3) Faults occurred and the structural basin was formed through the lowering of the erosion level. The surrounding rivers increased their erosional power and carried their debris into the basin. At that time, the Takokan River, originally flowing from north to south, was captured by the Tamshui River and began to flow from south to north, carrying with it to the basin its deposits and large amounts of water. During that period, a volcanic eruption occurred from Tatun Mountain, and that eruption was probably responsible for the deposition of volcanic ash in the basin.

(4) The sea overflowed and converted the basin into a salt water lake. During that period, marine fossils were deposited. The sea level at that time was higher than the present level of about 200 feet.

(5) The basin experienced a warping movement, tilting from southeast to northwest, and the water in the basin emptied through the water gap at the northwest corner so that the basin floor gradually dried up. The rivers flowed sluggishly on the floor of the basin, and in the northwestern part, marshes and swamps formed in which various kinds of weeds flourished. Wild animals started living in the basin. The basin was lowered again, and again the sea encroached upon it. Part of the basin floor was covered with salt water while some parts of the rivers remained fresh. During that time, early man lived on the high parts of the basin.

(6) The land was then uplifted slightly, the sea retreated, and the rivers in the basin increased their meandering. The early men lived along the banks of the rivers.

(7) The land was lowered again and the sea again overflowed. Again the basin uplifted, the sea retreated, and the land became dry and expanded. In 1697 A.D., a part of the basin faulted and the sea water re-entered.

(8) At last, the land gradually rose, the sea retreated, and the present basin came into existence.

Taichung basin

Taichung basin is also a structural depression, being surrounded by scarps. It has an elongated form, with a length of 25 miles and a width of 8.5 miles. As the Tatu River and its tributaries pour into the basin from the mountain gorges, they deposit their sediments. The surface of the basin is rather flat and is covered by thick deposits of gravels and sands. Drilling records show that gravel beds in the basin extend far below 1000 feet in depth. Undoubtedly, the sinking of the land was the chief cause of that enormous accumulation. After a gravity-meter survey at Taichung in 1947-8 by the Chinese Petroleum Corporation, the origin of the Taichung basin has been more definitely known. The report of this survey reveals that the Taichung basin is not a simple fault angle depression, but a deep, elongated, synclinal basin, bordered on the west by three united anticlinal domes and on the east by an overthrust fault.

Therefore, the Taichung basin is both a downwarping depression and a synclinal basin structure.

In geological history, no marked uplift movement has occurred in the Taichung basin. Thus, the rivers in the basin show only slight erosional power with meander but without any intrenched meandering. The surface of the basin has remained perfect without any disturbance.

Sun-Moon Lake and other basins

In the central part of Taiwan there is a depressed tract of relatively low relief, surrounded by rugged mountains that are about 100 feet high. The depressed tract is occupied by a series of intermontane basins, arranged lineally in a northeastern–southwestern direction. The northern half of the tract is drained by the Peikong River and the southern by the Choshui. Both of these rivers flow to the west.

There are 15 basins in all, and the larger ones include Puli basin and Sun-Moon Lake. Puli basin has the largest area, 46 square miles in size. The smaller basins may not reach even 0.5 square mile in area. Not only do the basins vary in size, but also their floors differ in altitude, ranging from 125 to 2560 feet above sea level. Sun-Moon Lake is located at the highest elevation, 2360–2560 feet above sea level; Puli is at 1246–1640 feet elevation.

These basins owe their existence to crustal movement. The fact that they were occupied by lakes at one time or another is evidenced by the occurrence of peat deposits accompanying heavy white clay. At present, however, all are dried up with the exception of Sun-Moon Lake.

The bedrock beneath the basins consists mainly of clay slates and sandstones belonging to the lower Tertiary age. Recent sedimentary deposits in the basins vary owing to their different physiographic development.

Puli basin is the largest and the most deeply and widely dissected basin among the group. After extinction of the lake, the basin floor was dissected by the rivers. Dissection caused the basin floor to be divided into two plains, the higher and the lower.

Sun-Moon Lake, or Lake Candidius as it is also known, is the largest fresh-water lake in Taiwan and is noted for its beautiful scenery and water-power development. Lavish hotels, restaurants, and souvenir shops flourish along the lake shores.

The lake has an irregular outline, narrow and lozenge-shaped. The inflow from the river is barely sufficient to maintain the water level in the lake, and there was at one time danger of the lake becoming extinct. Recently, however, it has been used as the reservoir for generating electricity. A dam was constructed at the outlet and the water level was raised from 2385 to 2460 feet. This resulted in an expansion of 60 per cent in the size of the lake and is expected to prolong its life.

The many small basins are located mostly southwest of the Puli basin and north of Sun-Moon Lake. All of these basins are extinct lakes. Many have retained their original flat surface, but others have been deeply dissected by streams or have been almost completely obliterated when a broad valley has developed.

PHYSIOGRAPHIC HISTORY—The physiographic history of these small basins presents many interesting problems which can be summarized as follows:[12]

First, the basins were formed by downwarping and faulting. Then water filled in the depressions and formed lakes. Clay was deposited and fine sand then became interbedded with lignite. Later, the region suffered additional crustal disturbances, which made the lake beds incline and caused the streams to be rejuvenated. This resulted in increasing the streams' erosive power and in depositing coarse sand and gravel over the other lake deposits. The basins were filled up and the water was drained away by headward erosion. Thus the basins became dry land. After the deposit of gravels, the region was warped again and the streams were again rejuvenated. The rivers then flowing from high mountains transported boulders and coarse gravels into the basin. Extensive alluvial fans developed on some of the basin plains. The drying up of the lakes took place first in the basins of lower elevation and extended gradually to the higher ones. Sun-Moon Lake, barely saved from extinction, survived because of its higher altitude and its position near the apex of the warping, where it would naturally be the last to be affected by the crustal movement. However, it is destined to be drained away naturally through aggression by ungraded rivers surrounding it.

THE COASTAL ROLLING HILLS

Rolling hills are found in two areas; one, in the extreme north, is called Tatun Mountain; the other, called Taitung Mountain, is on the east coast of the island.

The Tatun Mountain consists of a group of volcanic peaks. The main peak is Tsi Shin Shan, which rises to an elevation of 3903 feet and has a conic form. From that peak, short, swift streams radiate outward. On several peaks are craters, which sometimes store water and form lakes. The limit of the region is marked by the Tamshui and Keelung rivers. At the base of the mountain are six sets of geysers and numerous hot springs containing sulfur, which, coupled with the mountain's charming scenery, attract large numbers of visitors. Tsao Shan and Peitou are resort centers near the capital, Taipei.

The Taitung Mountains on the eastern coast are also of volcanic origin. They extend from north-northeast to south-southwest with an extremely slender outline. The range has a length of 84 miles and is 10 miles wide at its widest point.

The mountains are composed of limestone and sandstone, as well as andesite. They are steeply folded to an elevation of more than 6900 feet in the south, but farther north they are less than 2950 feet high.

The Siukuluan River divides the high part of this area in the south from the lower part in the north. Small streams can be found on the flanks; but only the Shiukuluan River, in its meandering course, is big enough to cut across the central part of the mountain range. This variance between the flow of the river and the mountain structure can be explained by two possibilities. One is that the headwater erosion of the river is so strong that it eventually cuts across the mountain. The other possibility is that the river came into existence long before the folding of the range occurred.

On the western slope of the range, badland topography has developed where the ground water level is lowest and rock formation is least resistant to weathering.

The Pacific coast of this region is rather smooth and without any harbor. Where there is any coastal plain, its width is less than 20 miles at the maximum. On this steeply sloping coast, three distinct geomorphic features have been found. They are marine terraces, the raised coral reef, and the uplifted rock platform.

Marine terraces develop very well in the southern part of the coastal area but are entirely absent in the north. There are two or three wave-cut rock platforms, which clearly indicate that the island has recently been uplifted.

The existence of raised coral reefs along the eastern coast and the frequent earthquakes reveal that this part of the island is still unstable.

According to the geomorphic features in the Taitung coastal range, the physiographic history of the range can be summarized as follows:

Since the Pleistocene epoch, the uplifting movements of approximately 650 feet took place as soon as the new high-leveled terrace gravels were deposited in the coastal range.

This uplifting movement is by no means uniform, but varies in different parts of the range. In the northern part of the coastal range, marked marine terraces are almost entirely absent along the coast.

In the Pleistocene era a temporary subsidence occurred, as is evidenced by the fact that coral-reef limestone occurs on a raised rock platform. It is thought that the rock platform was once submerged, enabling the coral reef to have sufficient depth of sea water to keep it growing. The fact that a recent uplifting has happened is indicated by the occurrence of raised coral reefs and uplifted rock platforms. The evidence of this recent uplifting movement is also supported by the occurrence of the surface fault and the change of sea-level caused by the great earthquakes which took place in eastern Taiwan in 1951.

Although Taiwan is a center of tectonic activity, none of the volcanic peaks of the northern rolling hills or of the eastern coastal rolling hills is active at present.

INTERIOR FOOTHILLS

The interior foothills constitute a narrow belt with an irregular outline, lying between the alluvial plains and the gentle slope of the island's tilted central block. The soft shales and sandstones that underlie the belt have been carved by streams. The belt has an elevation ranging from 820 to 3280 feet, with an average height of 2300 feet. Since all the large rivers of the island traverse this belt, steep gullies and sharp valleys are characteristic of it. At the outer edge of these foothills, the elevation is gradually being reduced to 328–2000 feet; thus, some of the foothills have become tablelands composed entirely of gravel. These thick deposits of gravel have been accumulating rapidly, brought down from the Central Mountains by rivers. In the geological past, this area has been uplifted several times and each uplift of the land rejuvenated the streams. Two or three terraces or erosional surfaces can be identified.

In the foothills of Taiwan, one of the most strikingly characteristic features is the homoclinal ridge (also known as a cuesta or hogback). These are well developed and are widely distributed in the hilly land throughout the island. The forming of these homoclinal ridges is not merely the result of erosion; they also owe their existence to the geological structure and lithical characters.[13] These homoclinal ridges are especially well developed in two types of locality: the dissected flanks of folded mountain ranges, and in a wider zone of hilly land of an isoclinal structure. In both types the homoclinal ridges are composed of thin alternating beds of hard and soft strata that are unequally resistant to erosive agencies. The homoclinal ridges are generally even, so that they have served two purposes: at present, they serve as roadbeds for the main roads; in the past, they were a defence line of strategic importance against attacks by the aborigines who inhabited the Central Mountains.

The most decisive factor in the formation of homoclinal ridges appears to be the torrential streams flowing down the gentle dip slope along the foot of the escarpments. These streams, washing down over the broad, shallow stream beds on the surface of dip slopes, wear away the foot of the escarpments and cause them to recede. This is what is called homoclinal shifting.

Erosion is very slow on the gentle dip slope of resistant rock; but on a steep obsequent slope, or escarpment, it is rapid. The divide formed by the crest-line of the cuesta or homoclinal ridge is thus forced to move toward the dip, and as the general level of the surface is lowered, the subsequent streams and the valley lowlands move also in the same direction. Obviously, the rapidity and extent of shifting are greater on gentle inclines than on steep ones.

ALLUVIAL PLAINS

The western coastal part of Taiwan is in general a flat land consisting of low alluvial plains. It extends from Keelung in the north to Pingtung in the south. This area is about 200 miles long and ranges from 5 to 25 miles in width. When the rivers originate in the Central Mountains and flow out of the interior foothills into the plain, parallel with one another, their debris is deposited and forms a large number of alluvial fans. The plain is thus the coalescence of many alluvial fans and is underlain by recent alluvium. Flowing with a low gradient on the broad alluvial plain, the rivers meander sluggishly across it to the sea.

The coastal plain is monotonously flat and when it reaches the sea, the shore is marked by wide tidal flats. Especially in the south, from Kaohsiung Peninsula to the Choshui River, shore currents have built up spits, off-shore bars, marshes, and many shallow lagoons. The lagoon at Kaohsiung, with its complete shelter and spacious holdground, has been used as an important naval base.

The coastal plain is narrow in the northern part of the island and gradually becomes wide as it extends into the south, especially near Tainan. According to the well-drill record near Hsinchu, the sand deposits extend as deep as 250 feet, without reaching bedrock. The strong winds, the heavy deposits of sand, and the early colonial development of the region, all of which led to the disappearance of the original vegetation, favor the development of sand dunes and barchanes which extend from two to four miles and with an average height of 65 feet. These barchanes are subject to migration. The survey indicates that a barchane migrated 1640 feet in the eight years from 1926 to 1933, averaging 205 feet for every year.

The coastal plain is still rising. The land is being elevated, and the parallel rivers from east to west are becoming extended rivers which produce new alluvial fans. There thus appear some complex fans, combining old alluvial fans with new ones.

The western coastal plain ends at the city of Pingtung, which is located on a plain extending from north to south 31 miles long and 12 miles wide, forming a rectangle. The plain is bordered on the east by the Chaochow fault line. These alluvial fans also pushed the lower Tamshui River to the westward.

While the eastern coast is precipitous cliff, the Ilan plain, which is the delta of the Ilan River, is the most conspicuous alluvial plain in eastern Taiwan. The plain forms an equilateral triangle, each side of which is about 98 feet long. The base of the plain is formed by part of the coast and its apex penetrates the Central Mountains. The Ilan River originates in the Central Mountains and bisects the plain from its apex to the sea. The apex is about 525 feet high, and the Ilan River radiates from it for about 14 miles; the radius of the fan is about 12 miles in length. On this alluvial fan, part of the water seeps underground and reappears at the end of the fan.

Owing to beaches of wave erosion, the coast of the plain bends toward the west and forms a concavity. Along the beaches of the plain, the winds have piled the sands into dunes paralleling the coast; these keep the rivers from emptying into the ocean and lead to the formation of marshes. The sand dunes are prominent features of the landscape, although they rise only 65 feet above their surroundings. The Ilan plain has only one good harbor. This is at Suao, where the plain meets the mountain.

The Pingtung plain and the Ilan plain provide an interesting comparison. The Pingtung plain is located in the southwest part of the island, facing the Taiwan Strait; the Ilan plain is located in the northeastern corner, facing the Pacific Ocean. The origin of these two plains and their geologic structure are rather similar. Both are formed by alluvial fans, both are bordered by great fault lines, the former by the Chaochow fault, the latter by the Chiaochi fault.

PENGHU MESA

The Penghu group of islands in Taiwan Strait (also called the Pescadores, meaning "Fishermen's Islands") consist of 64 islands, with a total area of about 50 square miles. They are politically part of Taiwan, but they are a distinct landform unit west of the main island. The islands are scattered over an area of about 37 miles north–south, across the Tropic of Cancer, and about 25 miles east–west. With the great population density, approximately 276 persons per square mile, and practically without resources, these islands are poor and their people have often lived on relief. The strategic significance of the islands far outweighs their economic importance. They constitute the outpost of Taiwan. Only 11 of the 64 islands have an area of more than 0.4 square mile at high tide; Penghu is the largest, with 25 square miles. Without exception, they are flat and monotonous in outline, averaging in elevation only 98–131 feet above sea level. There are no mountains—the highest point of the largest island is only 157 feet above sea level—nor are there rivers. During the rainy summer, streams and pools are found in the lower parts, but they drain off as soon as the winter comes. A shortage of fresh water is a serious problem, and it is necessary to dig wells. A basalt cliff 65–98 feet high on the shore is the only characteristic feature that strikes visitors approaching from the sea.

The islands are mesa-like remnants of an originally widespread basalt lava flow which is evidently fissure eruption coming up along the channel rift that came into existence in the late Pleistocene epoch. The basalts show columnar structure; they were gradually uncovered by marine erosion and emerged from the sea in their present form.

The water is rather shallow around the islands—131–197 feet in depth—and it is warm. These conditions favor the growth of coral, and around the islands are many fringing coral reefs. The coastline is rocky and irregular. For the 64 islands it totals 199 miles which is about 80 times that of the length of the main island's coastline per unit area. The fringing reefs and irregular coast provide good harbors.

Along the north coast of Penghu, many signs of marine erosion are found in the raised beaches. In many places, the reefs and the broken coral, uncovered here and there at low tide, are used as building material for houses and windbreaks. Earthquakes are not uncommon among these islands. Between 1897 and 1946, about three perceptible shocks per year were recorded, a total of 146. A year may pass without quakes; in another year, there may be as many as 18.

Makun, the largest town on the Penghu Islands, is a great naval base.

REFERENCES

[1] Yashiro Tomita, *Topographical Observations of the River-Valleys of Taiwan, A Preliminary Report* (Geological Institute, Taihoku Imperial University, Taihoku, 1940), p. 892.

[2] Hsi-lin Tschang, "Potholes in the river beds of northern Taiwan," *Erdkunde* **XI**, 296–303 (1957).

[3] T. L. Hsu, and Pei-Yuan Chen, "On the river capture of Hualien Chi," *Bull. geol. Surv. Taiwan* **3**, 35 (1951).

[4] Yoshiro Tomita, "On the geomorphological classification of fans in Taiwan," *J. Geogr., Tokyo* **60**, 2 (1959). [In Japanese].

[5] I. Hayasaka, "The recent physiographic history of Taiwan as observed from geology and geomorphology," *Bull. Ass. Mus. Taiwan* **19**, 116 (1929). [In Japanese].

[6] T. Kano, and K. Tanaka, "The glaciated topography in Nanhutan Mountains of Taiwan," *Geogr. Rev. Jap.* **10**, No. 3, 169–190 (1943). [In Japanese].

[7] —, "The investigation of glacial topography of the Tsugitakayama (Tzekao Shan)," *Geogr. Rev. Jap.* **10**, Nos. 7–11, 606–623, 688–707, 816–835, 990–1017 (1934). [In Japanese].

[8] Y. Sasa, "Glacial topography in the Nutaka Massif (Hsinkao Shan), Taiwan," *Proc. imp. Acad. Japan* **12**, No. 1, 16–18 (1936).

[9] K. Tanaka, *The Mountains and Aborigines of Formosa* (Ganjin Co., Tokyo, 1937), pp. 329–332. [In Japanese].

[10] C. C. Lin, *Landforms of Taiwan* (Provincial Historical Research Commission, Taiwan, 1957), pp. 394–422.

[11] —, *ibid.*, p. 314.

[12] Yoshiro Tomita, "Physiographic development of the Hori (Puli) Basin Group of Central Taiwan (Formosa), *Tohoku geogr. Rep.*, No. 2, 17 (1946).

[13] —, "Physiographical development of homoclinal ridges: an example in Taiwan," *Mem. Fac. Sci. Taihoku* **XIII**, No. 4, 31 (1935).

FOUR

Climate

CLIMATIC FACTORS

TAIWAN'S CLIMATE IS CHARACTERIZED by high temperatures, heavy rainfall, and strong winds. The factors which control the climate are the island's position relative to ocean and the Asian continent, the arrangement of its mountains, and ocean currents.

POSITION

Since Taiwan is an island facing the Pacific Ocean on the east and separated from the Asian continent to the west by a channel only 100 miles wide, its climate is influenced considerably by the seasonal monsoon winds. During the winter, from October to March, the monsoon winds blowing down from the continent strike the northeastern part of the island. These winds contain high moisture after crossing the strait and, as they rise to pass over the high mountains, condensation occurs. Thus, these northeast monsoon winds provide this part of the island with heavy rainfall and cloudy weather. The southwestern part of the island, however, has become a rainshadow area, for the Central Mountain ranges extending from north to south effectively prevent these moisture-bearing winds from bringing their rains as far as the southwestern section. During the summer, from May to September, the island is under the control of southwest monsoons. These winds are light and variable and laden with moisture accumulated during their passage over the Pacific; thus they bring rainfall to the southern part of the island.

Taiwan lies partly in the tropics, extending from 21°45′ to 25°38′ N. latitude, with the Tropic of Cancer passing through the city of Chaiyi in the middle of the island. Thus Taiwan can be compared with the subtropical island of Cuba. Both enjoy an oceanic subtropical climate, but monsoon effects are much more marked in Taiwan.

44

MOUNTAIN ARRANGEMENT

It is this seasonal change of monsoon winds which determines the rainfall regime of the island, but the temperature distribution results primarily from the arrangement of the mountains, which extend from north to south. Not only is there a great deal of difference between the temperatures of the lowland and those of the high mountain areas, but also the temperatures in the east differ from those in the west. The mountains are also responsible for many local winds, such as the mountain and valley winds and foehn winds.

OCEAN CURRENT

The ocean current also plays an important role in the climate of the island. Flowing northward from the Basal Strait, the Kuro Siwo Ocean current is split by the southern tip of Taiwan, forming two currents which ameliorate the climate of the eastern and western coasts respectively. As a result of the presence of these ocean currents and Taiwan's maritime situation, the island has a relatively low seasonal range in temperature. Since the ocean current passing by the east coast is stronger than the one flowing through the shallow Taiwan Strait, in winter the east coast is 0.9°F. colder than the west coast.

TEMPERATURE

Summer in Taiwan is long and hot, but winter is very short and mild. Throughout the island, the annual mean temperature is more than 70°F. The isotherms of mean annual temperature run from west to east, bisecting the island and running parallel to the latitudes. As the latitudes decrease, the annual temperatures increase. Thus, there is little difference in annual temperature between east and west, but there is a great difference between north and south. For example, Keelung, on the northern coast, has an annual average temperature of 71.2°F., while the annual average temperature found in Hengchun at the southern tip of the island, is 75.9°F. As one travels from north to south, with each degree of latitude one finds an increase of 1.5°F. in temperature.

Comparing the average annual temperatures in Taiwan with temperatures of the same latitude on the mainland, the temperature in Taiwan is found to be higher. This relative highness stems from the fact that Taiwan is an island tempered by the influence of the ocean current. For example, the annual average temperature in Swatow, which is in almost the same latitude as the three mainland cities, is 71.1°F.

July is Taiwan's hottest month, and the heat is practically as great in the north as in the south. For that month the average temperature at Keelung is 82.7°F., while at Hengchun it is 81.5°F., showing a difference of less than 1.2°F. Also, the July temperature is not too much different between the east coast and the west coast of the island as shown in *Table 4*. Maximum temperatures in excess of 102.2°F. have been recorded.

In January or February, the coldest months, the temperature differs greatly from north to south, Keelung having a monthly average of 59.3°F.

45

and Hengchun, 68.9°F., showing a difference of 9.6°F. Snow is rarely seen in the lowland although the summits of the lofty mountains are covered with snow for a short time. The maximum temperature in January can reach more than 86°F.

In January and February the temperature varies not only from north to south, but also from east to west, being higher in the east than in the west, as shown in *Table 5*. This is because the ocean current is stronger on the eastern coast than along the western coast.

The extreme minimum temperature of some places in the island is far below 32°F., for instance: Ali Shan, 18.3°F. (February 14, 1935); Taipei, 31.6°F. (February 13, 1922); Taichung, 30.2°F. (February 13, 1922); Tatun Shan, 27.9°F. (January 25, 1940); and Hsinkao Shan, 10.2°F. (March 10, 1944).

Table 4. Comparison of July Temperatures between the Western Coast and the Eastern Coast of Taiwan*

Western Coast	Latitude	Temperature	Eastern Coast	Latitude	Temperature
Taipei	25°02′	82.7°F.	Keelung	25°09′	82.7°F.
Hsinchu	24°48′	82.2°F.	Ilan	24°46′	81.6°F.
Taichung	24°09′	81.8°F.	Hualien	23°58′	80.9°F.
Kaohsiung	22°37′	82.4°F.	Taitung	22°45′	81.5°F.

* Fifty-one Years of Statistical Abstracts in Taiwan, Taiwan Governor's Office, Taipei (1946).

Table 5. Comparison of January Temperatures between the Western Coast and the Eastern Coast of Taiwan*

Western coast	Temperature	Eastern coast	Temperature
Taipei	59.3°F.	Keelung	59.9°F.
Hsinchu	59.0°F.	Ilan	60.4°F.
Taichung	60.4°F.	Hualien	62.9°F.
Tainan	62.5°F.	Taitung	66.0°F.

* Fifty-one Years of Statistical Abstracts in Taiwan, Taiwan Governor's Office, Taipei (1946).

The annual range of temperature in Taiwan varies, being greater in the north than in the south. The annual range at Keelung is 23.4°F., while at Hengchun it is only 12.6°F. The fact that Taiwan has a much smaller temperature range than the eastern coast of China's mainland is also explained by the influence of the ocean surrounding Taiwan. The mean monthly temperature for some representative locations is given in *Table 6*.

The continentality of Taiwan is also less than than of the mainland of China as shown in *Table 7*.

The diurnal variations of temperature in Taiwan range from 41°F. to 50°F. In Taipei the greatest diurnal range is 48°F. in July and the smallest diurnal range is 43.9°F. in February, while in Hengchun the greatest range is 47.7°F. in April and the smallest is 43.3°F. in November.

The relatively small variation of the diurnal temperature is another indication of oceanic influence.

Aside from the latitudinal difference of temperature, the temperature varies also with elevation. As one climbs from the coastal plains to the mountainous regions, the temperature drops. *Table 8* illustrates the vertical distribution of temperature in Taiwan.

Table 6. Mean Monthly Temperature (°F.)*

	Jan.	Feb.	Mar.	Apr.	May	June	July	Aug.	Sept.	Oct.	Nov.	Dec.	Average	Max.	Min.	Years of Record
Keelung	59.9	59.4	62.1	68.4	75.4	79.7	82.8	82.4	79.7	74.1	68.5	63.1	71.2	100.2	41.0	43
Taipei	59.4	58.6	62.6	69.3	75.4	79.9	82.8	82.2	79.3	73.6	68.0	62.2	71.1	101.5	31.6	49
Hsinchu	59.0	58.3	62.6	68.9	75.2	80.1	82.2	81.9	79.7	74.7	70.7	62.2	71.2	99.0	39.2	8
Taichung	60.4	60.3	64.8	71.6	77.4	80.4	81.9	81.5	79.9	74.8	69.1	63.1	71.1	102.7	30.2	49
Tainan	62.6	62.8	69.3	74.1	79.3	81.3	82.0	81.5	80.8	76.6	71.2	65.3	73.8	100.0	36.3	49
Hengchun	68.5	68.9	72.1	76.3	79.7	81.3	81.5	79.2	80.1	77.5	74.1	70.3	75.9	98.8	49.1	49
Taitung	66.0	66.2	69.3	73.6	77.5	80.6	81.5	81.1	79.7	76.1	72.0	68.0	74.3	103.1	45.0	45
Hualien	63.0	63.3	66.2	70.9	75.4	79.3	79.2	80.8	78.8	74.5	70.2	65.7	72.5	96.8	39.9	35
Ilan	60.4	60.8	64.2	69.1	74.3	79.0	79.9	79.2	78.4	73.0	68.4	64.0	71.1	94.8	42.1	10
Penghu	61.2	60.4	65.1	71.8	77.2	79.3	82.4	82.0	80.8	76.5	71.1	64.9	72.9	94.3	45.1	49
Ali Shan	42.4	43.7	47.0	51.1	54.5	56.7	57.4	56.9	55.9	52.5	49.5	45.7	51.1	75.4	18.3	12

* *Fifty-one Years of Statistical Abstracts in Taiwan*, Taiwan Governor's
Office, Taipei (1946).

Table 7. Comparison of Continentality between the
Mainland Eastern Coast and Taiwan

	East coast of mainland				Taiwan		
	Latitude	Annual range	Continentality		Latitude	Annual range	Continentality
Amoy	24°26′	59.1°F.	36	Ilan	24°24′	53.2°F.	28.1
Canton	23°06′	59.9°F.	37	Tainan	23°00′	51.4°F.	27.7

Table 8. Vertical Distribution of Temperature in Taiwan

	Peikang (western coastal plains)	Taipu (foothills)	Ali Shan	Hsinkao Shan
			(Central Mountains)	
Elevation	30 feet	950 feet	7900 feet	12,600 feet
August temperature	81.6°F.	68.7°F.	56.8°F.	44.0°F.
February temperature	61.7°F.	51.8°F.	43.7°F.	17.6°F.
Annual mean temperature	74.3°F.	60.8°F.	51.0°F.	39.2°F.

47

RAINFALL

Taiwan has abundant rainfall throughout the year. Many stations have an average annual rainfall of 98.5 inches. But the rainfall in Taiwan is by no means evenly distributed. In general, the eastern coast has more rainfall than the western coast, and lowlands receive less rain than mountain slopes, where the air masses are forced to ascend and discharge their moistures. The isohyets indicating 78.8 inches coincide with many places on the 1,600 feet contour lines. The east coast has a heavier rainfall (more than 78.8 inches) than the west coast, owing partly to the prolonged winter rains and partly to the rugged terrain. The areas receiving more than 148 inches of annual rainfall are found in the northern and southern extremities and on some of the high mountain peaks of the Central Mountain ranges (*Figure 10*). Houshaoliao, on the northern tip of Taiwan near Keelung, has recorded for the past 38 years an average annual rainfall of 258.9 inches with a recorded maximum of 331.28 inches in 1912, making it one of the wettest spots in East Asia.

The driest part of the island is the west coast with an annual rainfall of only 40–60 inches. The reason for this dryness is two-fold: first, during the winter when the northeastern monsoon blows, the west coast becomes the rain shadow area. Also, in the more northern coastal area the wind blows nearly parallel with the coast and brings hardly any rainfall. Second, during the summer the southwest winds are parallel with the southwestern part of the coast and thus little rainfall is produced. Chutang, in the center of this west coast, for instance, has had for the past 32 years an average annual rainfall of only 47.3 inches with a minimum rainfall of 27.2 inches. Among the peripheral islets, Yuweng-Tao in the Penghus is the least rainy place. It has had for the past 44 years an annual mean rainfall of 36.2 inches with a minimum annual rainfall of 16.3 inches.

Comparing rainfall (*Figure 10*) with the relief (*Figure 8*), the relationship between the two can be immediately noticed. The rainfall increases gradually from the west coast to the Central Mountains as the elevation increases. *Table 9* reveals the vertical distribution of rainfall in Taiwan.

Table 9. Vertical Distribution of Rainfall in Taiwan

Location	Peikang	Chuchi	Yiuyenlin	Ali Shan	Hsinkao Shan
Distance from the sea (miles)	10.5	26.7	34.7	43.4	52.8
Altitude (feet)	30	425	3500	7900	12,600
Rainfall (inches)	58.7	100.3	120.0	171.6	135.0

The most striking feature of Taiwan's rainfall is that the dry and rainy seasons occur in the north and in the south at opposite times. In the north the rainy season is from October to March as in the cities of Keelung, Ilan and Taipei (*Figure 11*). During this period Keelung has a precipitation of 64 inches which is 56 per cent of the total rainfall of 114 inches. On the other hand, during these months the south enjoys continually fine and delightful weather and irrigation is a necessary agricultural practice. In the south the rainy season lasts from April to September as in the cities of Hengchun, Tainan and Taitung (*Figure 12*). During these months, Hengchun has a rainfall of 79 inches which makes up 88 per cent of its total rainfall of 90 inches (*Table 10.*)

This great contrast of rainfall between the north and the south is due to the monsoon winds and the island's mountain arrangement. During the winter period, from October to March, the strong northeast monsoon, carrying a large quantity of moisture from the East China Sea, comes in contact with the mountain ranges which traverse the island from north to

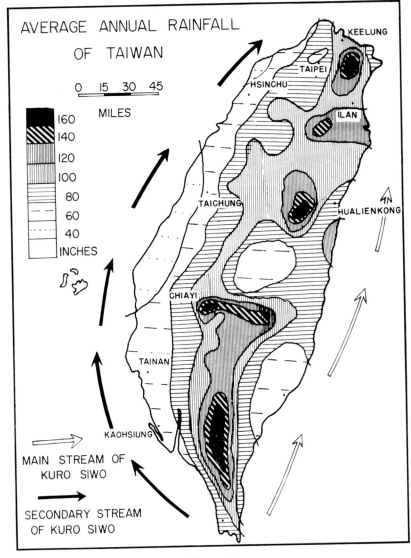

AVERAGE ANNUAL RAINFALL
OF TAIWAN

0 15 30 45
MILES

160
140
120
100
80
60
40
INCHES

KEELUNG
TAIPEI
HSINCHU
ILAN
TAICHUNG
HUALIENKONG
CHIAYI
TAINAN
KAOHSIUNG

MAIN STREAM OF
KURO SIWO

SECONDARY STREAM
OF KURO SIWO

Figure 10

49

south. As the air rises over the mountains, condensation causes clouds and rain. The winds that reach the south during these months have lost the greater portion of their moisture and so bring clear dry weather.

During the summer months, from April to September, the southwest monsoon prevails over southern Taiwan. The southwest monsoon is light and weak. Under the hot sun frequent local thunderstorms occur, bringing abundant rainfall to southern Taiwan. Strong winds occur only during the occasional typhoons. It is during this period that the northern part is rather dry.

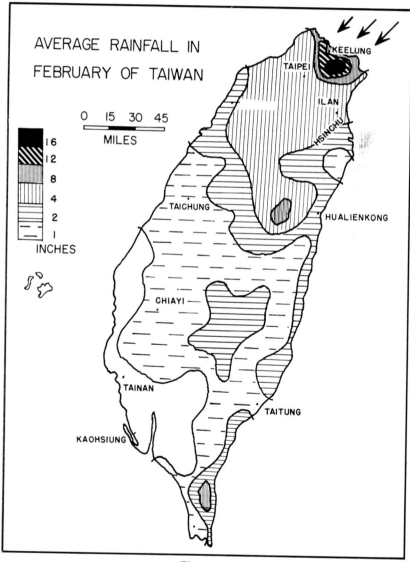

Figure 11

Not only is the rainy season opposite in north and south (*Table 10*), but the character of the rainfall is also different. In the north the rainfall, brought by the northeast monsoon, seldom comes in torrents but generally falls at a moderate rate. The cold, drizzling rains are depressing. Consequently, rainy days are many and drawn out. It is due to these rainy days that Keelung is called "rainy port." The rainfall in the south, caused by local convectional storms and typhoons is characterized by frequent thunderstorms and tremendous downpours. On the east coast, south of Hualien, the northeast monsoon blows nearly parallel to the shore, and

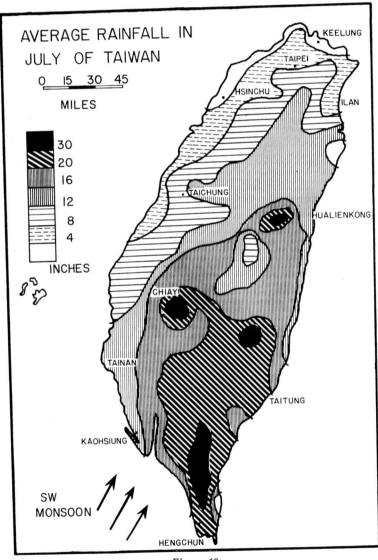

Figure 12

brings hardly any rain in spite of the dull weather. The western coastal plain lies within the rain shadow of the Central Mountains, and as a result, the central part of the west coast is the driest part of the island.

The rainfall in Taiwan varies not only from place to place and from season to season, but has also been very irregular from year to year. The rainfall variability ranges from 14.8 per cent at Ilan, 21.7 per cent at Taichung, 28.5 per cent at Tainan, to 34.4 per cent at Hengchun, increasing from north to south. The high rainfall variability in the southern and eastern parts of Taiwan is due to the typhoons which strike the southern and eastern parts of the island more often than other parts.

Table 10. Comparison of Rainfall in Winter and Summer between Keelung (North Part) and Hengchun (South Part)

	Keelung		Hengchun	
	winter (Oct.–March)	summer (April–Sept.)	winter (Oct.–March)	summer (April–Sept.)
Rainfall (inches)	63.5	50.0	10.5	79.2
Percentage of annual rainfall	55.9%	44.1%	11.8%	88.2%
Heaviest rainfall	11.7 (March)	13.1 (Sept.)	5.4 (Oct.)	22.1 (Aug.)
Lightest rainfall	8.5 (Oct.)	5.1 (July)	0.59 (Dec.)	1.6 (April)

As to the distribution of rainy days (Table 11) there are more rainy days in mountain regions than in the nearby lowlands. For example, the rainy days in Ali Shan total 208.3 days, but in the nearby cities of Chiay-i or Tainan there are only 110 or 121.3 days. In Tatun Shan the rain lasts for 268 days, while in Taipei, it lasts only 187.1 days. If we compare the rainy days between the western coast and the eastern coast, we find that the east coast has more rainy days, and the Penghu group of islands

Table 11. Monthly Rainy Days*

	Jan.	Feb.	Mar.	April	May	June	July	Aug.	Sept.	Oct.	Nov.	Dec.	Average	Years of Record
Keelung	22.3	20.7	21.2	17.6	18.2	15.6	10.2	12.3	14.8	17.5	19.9	22.7	213.0	43
Taipei	16.7	16.7	17.5	15.1	16.5	16.0	14.2	14.5	14.1	14.6	14.8	16.3	187.1	49
Hsinchu	10.5	15.5	18.0	14.8	15.3	14.1	12.4	10.9	8.4	5.8	7.6	9.8	142.9	8
Taichung	7.6	10.1	12.7	11.1	13.0	16.6	16.0	17.3	8.5	3.4	4.7	6.2	127.2	49
Ta-an	5.4	6.1	8.3	8.5	11.6	16.9	19.4	20.2	11.8	4.6	3.8	4.6	121.3	49
Hengchun	8.9	7.8	7.4	7.6	12.8	18.4	21.3	21.5	17.6	11.5	9.1	7.9	151.8	49
Taitung	11.0	10.4	12.8	15.1	18.6	13.2	13.1	14.0	15.3	12.0	9.9	9.6	155.0	45
Hualien	17.2	18.3	19.1	18.1	22.2	16.3	11.4	12.4	14.9	15.4	15.6	16.5	197.6	35
Ilan	21.7	19.7	20.8	16.4	20.9	18.3	11.9	14.2	16.9	21.6	22.0	21.9	226.3	10
Penghu	6.1	8.0	9.9	9.1	10.2	11.6	10.3	10.8	6.6	3.8	4.2	5.7	96.3	49
Ali Shan	10.4	11.0	16.3	15.7	22.8	24.8	26.8	26.0	21.4	14.3	8.4	10.3	208.3	12

* Fifty-one Years of Statistical Abstracts in Taiwan, Taiwan Governor's Office, Taipei (1946).

have the least number of rainy days. For example, the average number of rainy days in Ilan on the east coast is 226.3, while in Hsinchu on the west coast (in about the same latitude) there are only 142.9 days.

In comparing the annual rainfall of different cities with the annual number of rainy days, we find that these figures coincide with the exception of Tainan and Taitung. Tainan has fewer rainy days than Taichung, but the annual rainfall of Tainan is greater than that of Taichung. Similarly, Taitung has fewer rainy days than Hengchun, but the annual rainfall of the former city is greater than that of the latter.

The rainfall intensity refers to the amount of rain in a given unit of time and is closely related to the actual utility of the rainfall. If the rainfall intensity is too great it will not only increase the surface running water, but will also induce soil erosion. The rainfall intensity in Taiwan is greater in summer than in winter. In the northeastern part of the island the rainfall intensity is more evenly distributed in terms of seasonal variation than it is in the central and southern parts of Taiwan, where the rainfall intensity in one month can be as much as five times that of another. For example, in Taichung and Tainan the average rainfall intensity in June is 0.88 and 0.97 inch respectively, but it is only 0.145 inch for Taichung in November and 0.149 inch for Tainan in January. By comparison, in the northeastern part of the island at Keelung the rainfall intensity in June is 0.67 inch and in November it also reaches 0.45 inch. At Ilan the greatest rainfall is in October with 0.89 inch and the smallest is in February with 0.30 inch. The maximum rainfall intensity occurs in the months of July, August and September, as shown in *Table 12*.

Table 12. Rainfall in Northern, Southern and Central Taiwan (in inches)*

	Jan.	Feb.	Mar.	Apr.	May	June	July	Aug.	Sept.	Oct.	Nov.	Dec.
Northern												
Keelung	11.65	11.26	11.73	8.22	10.70	10.23	5.15	6.49	9.17	8.50	8.97	11.37
Taipei	3.50	5.51	7.20	6.65	8.93	11.96	8.97	11.81	8.85	4.44	2.36	2.87
Ilan	6.88	6.61	6.22	4.68	8.46	9.01	6.61	7.99	12.99	10.63	9.52	9.56
Southern												
Hengchun	0.86	1.18	0.94	1.69	7.00	15.82	21.57	22.12	10.98	5.47	1.53	0.59
Tainan	0.74	1.41	2.04	2.67	6.92	14.80	16.65	17.36	6.41	1.37	0.62	0.66
Taitung	1.45	1.73	2.51	2.79	6.69	7.79	13.74	11.81	11.37	6.81	2.40	1.41
Central												
Hsinchu	2.51	6.37	7.51	7.67	10.98	14.29	6.65	9.37	3.62	0.90	1.06	1.69
Taichung	1.29	2.67	4.48	5.11	8.97	14.60	11.61	13.30	5.47	0.86	0.70	1.01
Hualien	2.36	3.54	4.56	4.48	8.18	7.08	11.41	9.05	10.70	9.25	4.44	2.63
Penghu	0.90	1.49	2.71	3.26	4.33	6.37	7.36	7.08	3.93	1.14	0.86	0.90
Ali Shan	2.63	6.14	9.80	10.35	21.61	28.70	31.29	32.95	17.40	5.15	1.73	3.97

* *Fifty-one Years of Statistical Abstracts in Taiwan*, Taiwan Governor's Office, Taipei (1946).

WINDS

Being located on the eastern side of the great land mass of Asia and on the western edge of the Pacific Ocean, Taiwan's wind patterns are largely determined by the monsoons. In winter the cold Asiatic continent develops an immense thermal anticyclone from which great surges of dry and cold air spread oceanward; this is the northwest winter monsoon of China. Owing to the deflection force caused by the earth's rotation in the Northern Hemisphere, these northwest winds become a northeast monsoon bringing moisture from the ocean by the time it reaches Taiwan. In summer, on the other hand, a thermally-induced low pressure replaces the winter anticyclone over Asia. The pressure gradient is consequently the reverse of that which prevails in winter and moist tropical and subtropical maritime air masses originating over the low latitudes of the Pacific Ocean converge upon eastern Asia. This is China's weaker and more intermittent southeast summer monsoon. This southeast wind changes to a southwest monsoon when it reaches Taiwan, due to the deflection force of the earth's rotation. Therefore, the winds in Taiwan prevail from the northeast, having originated over the cold land mass of eastern Siberia (throughout the winter months; from the end of October to the end of March). During this period the northeast winds coincide with the northeast trade winds and the velocity increases immensely, especially in the north coastal region. For example, the wind velocity at Taipei reaches 153.5 inches per second in November, and at Hsinchu it is 157.4 inches per second in December (*Table 13*). These strong winds cause much damage to crops. In the northwest coastal area of Taiwan, which is directly exposed to the northeast gales, the farmers have set up lines of windbreaks composed of trees in order to protect their crops.

In the Taiwan Strait the wind velocity in winter is extremely great because of the lack of friction over the water. In Penghu, the average annual wind velocity is 255.5 inches per second, but in December it is 366.1 inches per second. The island off the north coast has an average annual wind velocity of 291.6 inches per second, but in December it reaches 348 inches per second. During the winter the Penghu Islands always have strong winds, with a velocity of more than 360 inches per second. The strong

Table 13. Monthly Wind Velocity (inches/second)*

	Jan.	Feb.	March	April	May	June	July	Aug.	Sept.	Oct.	Nov.	Dec.	Average	Years of Record
Keelung	145.6	129.9	114.1	106.3	86.6	82.6	114.1	110.2	122.0	141.7	149.6	145.6	120.4	29
Taipei	133.8	129.9	137.8	122.0	110.2	86.6	98.4	110.2	122.0	141.7	153.5	145.6	124.3	49
Hsinchu	141.7	129.9	106.3	94.4	90.5	106.3	98.4	90.5	98.4	137.8	145.6	157.4	116.4	8
Taichung	86.6	82.6	74.8	62.9	55.1	59.0	59.0	59.0	62.9	70.8	74.8	78.7	68.8	48
Tainan	153.5	153.5	137.8	114.1	98.4	102.3	106.3	102.3	98.4	106.3	122.0	141.7	119.7	49
Hengchun	208.6	185.0	177.1	141.7	118.1	106.3	110.2	110.2	122.0	188.9	236.2	240.1	162.0	49
Taitung	141.7	141.7	129.9	110.2	94.4	90.5	94.4	90.5	106.3	133.8	141.7	145.6	118.3	45
Hualien	122.0	114.1	110.2	98.4	86.6	86.6	90.5	86.6	90.5	106.3	114.1	122.0	102.3	35
Ilan	66.9	66.9	70.8	62.9	55.1	51.1	82.6	70.8	70.8	70.8	70.8	59.0	65.8	10
Penghu	342.5	318.9	271.6	212.6	177.1	165.3	149.6	157.4	216.5	330.7	358.2	366.1	255.5	49
Ali Shan	70.8	78.7	78.7	74.8	70.8	70.8	70.8	70.8	62.9	59.0	55.1	59.0	68.5	12

* Fifty-one Years of Statistical Abstracts in Taiwan, 1946, pp. 32–33.

wind days in Penghu total 138, of which 110 days are in the winter season from October to March and only 28 strong wind days occur from April to September. Because of this strong northeast monsoon in winter, northward sailing in the Strait becomes very difficult.

In summer (from the early part of May to the later part of September) the winds in Taiwan are from the southwest, having originated over tropical seas. The wind velocity of this southwest wind is far less than that of the northeast monsoon. For example, the average annual wind velocity at Hengchun is 162 inches per second with an average wind velocity for both the months of July and August of only 110.2 inches per second. At Tainan, the annual wind velocity is 119.7 inches per second, and only 102 inches per second for the summer months. Since the southwest monsoon is gentle and brings with it some rainfall, it has a favorable effect on the crops in this dry area.

In *Table 14* it is noticed that in January the prevailing wind direction in Taiwan is from the north, and in July from the south, such as is exemplified by the cities of Taichung, Tainan, and Taitung. However, in the cities of Hengchun and Penghu the prevailing wind direction in January is from northeast and in July from the east and south respectively. In Taipei the prevailing wind direction, both in January and July, is from the east.

Table 14. Prevailing Wind Frequency in the Months of January and July*

Site	Month	N	NE	E	SE	S	SW	W	NW	Average wind direction
Taipei	January	4	5	61	3	5	3	6	7	N 78 E
	July	9	5	22	11	15	7	16	6	
Taichung	January	58	4	1	1	1	2	3	4	N 48 E
	July	13	2	6	5	22	10	13	6	
Tainan	January	80	7	2	1	0	1	2	6	N 11 W
	July	11	5	17	12	22	9	14	7	
Taitung	January	44	20	5	1	1	1	3	24	N 7 W
	July	10	14	11	5	21	6	13	15	
Hengchun	January	16	52	22	2	1	1	2	3	N 45 E
	July	9	6	85	13	8	5	14	13	
Penghu	January	29	66	1	0	2	1	0	0	N 38 E
	July	15	6	2	4	39	19	9	4	

* P. J. Tsiang, *Étude sur la Direction du Vent à Taipei, Taiwan.* National Taiwan University, Taipei (1953).

In Taipei, there are two seasons for wind direction. In winter, the prevailing wind is from the northeast and in summer it is from the southwest. If we take the most frequent wind, ENE, as an example, the frequency of the wind starts to increase from October until March. During these six months, the frequencies are all over 100, culminating at 168 in December. After March the frequency of the ENE wind starts to decrease and in the months of June, July, and August the frequency drops to below 40. The west wind starts to increase from June until September. In the months of June, July and August the frequency of this wind is more than 50, while it is less than 30 during the winter season.

P. J. Tsiang has analyzed the wind direction in the city of Taipei in more detail. From his study we notice that Taipei has been dominated by monsoon winds as shown in *Table 15*.

From *Tables 15* and *16*, we notice that the prevailing wind of Taipei comes from the northeast quadrangle, especially the east-northeast (ENE) wind which accounts for more than 40 per cent of the whole wind frequency. The second prevailing wind is from the west, which accounts for 12 per cent of the total wind frequency.

Table 15. Taipei, Wind Frequency (1933–1942)*

N	51	NNE	52	NE	564	ENE	1259
E	326	ESE	106	SE	61	SSE	11
S	16	SSW	22	SW	19	WSW	19
W	406	WNW	88	NW	82	NNW	32

* P. J. Tsiang, *Étude sur la Direction du Vent à Taipei*, National Taiwan
University, Taipei (1953)

Table 16. Taipei, the Percentage of Different Wind Direction*

N	1.9%	NNE	1.8%	NE	18.1%	ENE	40.2%
E	10.4%	ESE	3.4%	SE	2.0%	SSE	0.4%
S	0.5%	SSW	0.7%	SW	0.6%	WSW	0.6%
W	12.8%	WNW	2.9%	NW	2.7%	NNW	1.0%

* P. J. Tsiang, *Étude sur la Direction du Vent à Taipei*, National Taiwan
University, Taipei (1953).

The wind direction in Taipei has certain effects on the various climatic elements such as temperature, rainfall, and wind velocity as shown in *Tables 17* and *18*.

From *Table 17* it will be seen that the temperature in Taipei is lowest (66.3°F.) when the wind comes from ENE, and is highest when the wind comes from south or southwest (79.7 and 78.0°F., respectively). This shows that the temperatures of the city are strongly influenced by the northeast monsoon in winter and by the south or southwest monsoons in summer.

It is evident from *Table 18* that the most rainfall in Taipei comes with the NE, ENE, E, W, and WNW winds. The rainfall of the NE, ENE, and E winds constitutes about 70 per cent of the total rainfall. W and WNW winds which prevail in summer carry only about 30 per cent of the total rainfall, being less than half that transported by the winter prevailing winds.

*Talbe 17. The Relationship Between the Prevailing Wind and the
Temperature at Taipei (°F.)**

N	76.4	NNE	74.8	NE	71.6	ENE	66.3
E	71.4	ESE	74.1	SE	74.6	SSE	72.6
S	79.7	SSW	73.7	SW	78.0	WSW	77.7
W	76.4	WNW	77.7	NW	75.1	NNW	73.0

* P. J. Tsiang, *Étude sur la Direction du Vent à Taipei*, National Taiwan
University, Taipei (1953).

Table 18. The Relationship Between the Prevailing Wind and the Rainfall
at Taipei (inches)*

N	2.3	NNE	1.28	NE	11.96	ENE	25.54
E	3.97	ESE	0.64	SE	0.61	SSE	0.38
S	1.12	SSW	1.36	SW	1.49	WSW	0.92
W	9.4	WNW	3.28	NW	1.52	NNW	0.77

* P. J. Tsiang, *Étude sur la Direction du Vent à Taipei*, Taiwan Governor
General's Office, Taipei (1953).

Table 19. The Relationship Between the Prevailing Winds and the Wind Velocity
at Taipei (inches per second)*

N	27.5	NNE	27.5	NE	55.1	ENE	70.8
E	66.9	ESE	59.0	SE	31.4	SSE	19.6
S	19.6	SSW	11.8	SW	19.6	WSW	15.7
W	31.4	WNW	23.6	NW	27.5	NNW	23.6

* P. J. Tsiang, *Étude sur la Direction du Vent à Taipei*, Taiwan Governor
General's Office, Taipei (1953).

The wind velocities at Taipei (*Table 19*) are greatest among NE, ENE, and E winds which are 55.1, 70.8, and 66.9 inches per second, respectively. The northeast monsoon which originates over the land mass of eastern Siberia has a great pressure gradient, which naturally results in higher velocity. The lowest wind velocities come from SSW, WSW, and SW, which are the summer monsoons. Since the summer monsoon develops over the tropical sea it has a smaller pressure gradient, resulting in smaller velocities.

TYPHOONS

Typhoons are tropical cyclones of a certain degree of intensity. In North and Central America they are known as *hurricanes*, and in India as *cyclones*. In the Philippines these storms are called *bayuios*, and in Australia, *willy-willies*. The Chinese name for typhoons is *chu-feng*, meaning "wind from all quarters."

Despite the different names, these tropical cyclones all have essentially the same origin, structure, and behavior. They are small low-pressure areas forming revolving storms and are very nearly circular in shape. They are the most violent storms experienced by the mariner.

Typhoons in East Asia have been studied by Jose Algue and Louis Froc, as well as by Charles I. Deppermann, Gherzi, Y. Horiguti, Co-ching Chu, and Haywood. Yet the exact origin of typhoons is not perfectly clear at present. The structure, energy supply, and the size and height of typhoons are still disputed subjects.

The tracks of typhoons are very hard to trace, but one can find many good charts illustrating the mean tracks of typhoons. Claxton's map[1] covers the period from 1884 to 1930, and it is one of the longest charted records we have. This chart shows the prevalence of typhoons in different regions of East Asia for each month of the year. This is an excellent chart of areas affected, but it does not show the actual tracks of typhoons.

Typhoon tracks can be divided into two directions: (1) those which move from east of the Philippines to the west (or northwest) and into the southern part of the China Sea (or to Indochina), and (2) those which have parabolic-shaped paths, moving first west then north. Upon crossing the latitudes 20°N. to 25°N., the latter typhoons curve to the east and northeast. These typhoons usually begin with a variable direction and low velocity. After moving to the middle latitudes and recurving their course, they begin to spread out and diminish in intensity, although they may still be quite violent.

As to the annual frequency in East Asia as a whole, there are several differences of opinion concerning the annual frequency of typhoons, for a storm which one person considers a true typhoon may not be regarded as such by another. The variation in the annual number of typhoons reported by different authorities for certain years is listed in *Table 20* .

Table 20. Variation in Annual Number of Typhoons

Author	Period	No. of years	Total number of storms	Number of storms for each year
Algue	1880–1901	22	468	21.3
Froc	1893–1918	26	619	23.8
Visher	1880–1920	41	917	22.4
Chu	1904–1915	12	247	20.5
Lu	1907–1936	30	637	21.2
Starbuck	1884–1896	50	989	19.7
	1905–1939			
	1946–1947			
Shih	1895–1945	51	875	17.1

From *Table 20* it appears that, on the average, the annual frequency of typhoons varies in number from 17.1 to 23.8. The figure varies considerably and there is no indication of any cycle. As a rule, at least 20 typhoons are detected each year in East Asia; however, only a small number of these reach Taiwan. In Taiwan, if we use the data recorded by the Weather Bureau of Taiwan and reported by Shih, of 875 typhoons in East Asia—an average of 17 per year—only 98 typhoons reached Taiwan, an average of about 2 per year.[2]

As to monthly distribution, typhoons are most frequent from July to October. This four-month period is commonly referred to as typhoon season in East Asia. The frequency of typhoons in each month is expressed in percentages of the annual total in *Table 21*.

As a whole, these figures, which have been gathered from various authorities, agree well in percentage, although there are a few discrepancies which are mainly due to the differences in the years recorded. The maximum frequency occurs either in August or September, and the minimum is recorded in February, March, and April.

The destructiveness of typhoons in Taiwan is great. The typhoon that visited the southernmost part of Taiwan on August 26th and 27th in 1911 was one of the most violent and destructive. The barometer at Kaohsiung fell to 27.67 inches, the lowest pressure ever registered. On this occasion the greatest wind velocity recorded was 161 feet per second; at this point the cups of the anemometer were blown away, making further observations impossible. The strength of the wind at that time could be judged from the force with which broken pieces of tile were driven like shrapnel into wooden boards and trunks of trees. It was estimated that the wind velocity reached nearly 230 feet per second, or 156 miles per hour during this storm in Taiwan. This storm inflicted terrible damage in the southern part of the island, taking a total of 305 human lives, with 378 persons wounded, 190 missing, and more than 30,000 houses destroyed.

When the typhoon reached the district of Taitung the pressure fell to a low of 28.59 inches and the velocity of the wind was registered at 152 feet per second, or 104 miles per hour, causing considerable damage to the district. However, when the storm appeared on the west coast after crossing the Central Mountain range, its strength had greatly decreased and its influence was scarcely felt in that part of the island. In Tainan the barometer fell to 29.35 inches, but the wind velocity reached only 61 feet per second, or 42 miles per hour.[3]

Another violent and destructive typhoon struck the island on September 25th and 26th in 1946. The pressure of the center fell to 27.68 inches as the storm approached the east coast of the island. The average maximum wind velocity was 132 feet per second, and the extreme maximum recorded was 180 feet per second. This great storm destroyed 373,748 houses, damaged 1,393,730 acres of crops and forests, and 28,448 animals were reported lost, 154 persons killed, and 618 persons injured.[4]

Table 21. *Percentage of Monthly Distribution of Typhoons from Various Authorities**

Authorities and the periods covered by them (number of years given in parentheses)

Month	Algue 1880–1901 (22)	Okada 1897–1911 (15)	Froc 1893–1918 (26)	Visher 1880–1920 (41)	Chu 1904–1934 (31)	Lu 1907–1936 (30)	Starbuck 1884–96 1905–39 1946–47 (50)	Shih 1895– 1945 (51)
Jan.	2	0.4	5	4.0	1.6	1.9	0.9	—
Feb.	0	0.0	3	1.9	0.8	0.9	0.3	—
Mar.	1	1.2	3	2.3	1.2	0.8	0.7	—
Apr.	2	0.8	2	2.6	1.2	2.0	1.2	—
May	5	3.6	5.5	5.1	4.1	3.5	4.4	4
June	9	4.5	5.5	6.1	5.7	5.5	6.2	6
July	16	11.7	14	15.4	16.4	16.2	17.9	19
Aug.	17	22.3	15	16.0	21.2	19.2	20.1	22
Sept.	19	22.7	18	18.3	19.2	18.6	19.9	21
Oct.	14	21.1	16	14.4	15.1	15.6	19.5	14
Nov.	11	8.9	8	8.6	8.2	10.3	9.7	9
Dec.	5	2.8	5	5.2	5.3	5.5	4.1	5

* Algue, *Cyclones of the Far East*, Manila, 1904, p. 86; T. Okada, "The Present Status of Typhoon Investigation in Japan," *Proceedings of the Fifth Pacific Scientific Congress (Canada)*, Vol. 3 (1933), p. 1981; Louis Froc, *Atlas of the Tracks of 620 Typhoons*, Zi-Ka-Wei Observatory, Shang-hai, 1920; S. S. Visher, "Notes on Typhoons, with Charts of Normal and Aberrant Tracks," *Monthly Weather Review*, Vol. I. (November, 1922), pp. 584-589; Co-Ching Chu, "Climatology of China," Meterological Institute of China, Vol. 7 (1936); A. Lu, "The Typhoons of the Far East," *The Meteorology Magazine*, Vol. 14, No. 6 (1939), p. 263; Hen-han Shih, "Typhoons Which Have Raided China within 51 Years," *Hsueh-i Tsa-chih*, No. 8 (1946), p. 5.

The occurrence of typhoons has had certain effects on the rainfall pattern in Taiwan. Although the wide variation in the amounts of annual rainfall and even the monthly means are sufficient to mask any correlation between it and typhoon occurrences, further investigation using the five-day means of rainfall shows that such a correlation does exist.

Typhoons are the most destructive natural force, apart from earthquakes, in the island of Taiwan. Their destructiveness is due to strong winds and heavy rainfall. Horizontal pressures during squalls may reach 100 pounds per square foot and typhoons may carry two quarts of rain per cubic yard of air.

The combination of strong winds, low barometric pressures, and the pounding force of the typhoon generates sea swells and destructive waves which cause major damage in coastal areas.

The sudden heavy rainfall brought by typhoons makes many rivers flood, destroying houses, damaging crops, and even causing injury to persons. In Taiwan hardly a year passes without the occurrence of typhoons. It is impossible to prevent typhoons from visiting the island, but it is possible to make accurate forecasts of their coming, and to predict the routes they will take. The government in Taiwan should invest money in a thorough study on typhoons. A detailed analysis of relationships between typhoon occurrence and rice cultivation in Taiwan is made in another section of this chapter (*pages* 68–72).

HUMIDITY, CLOUDINESS, SUNSHINE, AND EVAPORATION

HUMIDITY

Many places in Taiwan, outside of the Chungyang Shan area, have an absolute humidity of from 0.59 to 0.79 inch. In general, the absolute humidity is much greater in summer than in winter. For instance, in Taipei, the average humidity in July is 0.85 inch, while in February it is only 0.42 inch.

In the Chungyang Shan area, the absolute humidity is generally low. At Ali Shan the humidity in July is 0.33 inch, while in January it is only 0.22 inch.

The relative humidity in Taiwan averages between 75 and 80 per cent annually. The annual average relative humidity in Ilan is 85 per cent; Taipei, 82 per cent; Taichung, 81 per cent; Tainan, 81 per cent; Hengchun, 78 per cent; and in Taitung, 78 per cent (*Table 22*). From these figures it will be noticed that the relative humidity decreases from north to south. Also, the relative humidity in northern Taiwan is greater in winter than in summer. In Taipei, the relative humidity is 84 per cent, both in January and February. In July and August, it averages 78 per cent. Conversely, in southern Taiwan, the relative humidity is greater in summer than in winter. In Tainan, the relative humidity averages 84 per cent in August, but decreases to 79 per cent in January. In central Taiwan the relative humidity does not vary greatly from summer to winter: in Taichung, the relative humidity in August is 82 per cent and in January 81 per cent (*Table 22*).

Table 22. Monthly Relative Humidity (per cent)*

	Jan.	Feb.	Mar.	April	May	June	July	Aug.	Sept.	Oct.	Nov.	Dec.	Yearly Average	Years of Record
Keelung	84	84	84	83	83	83	78	77	79	79	80	82	81	29
Taipei	84	84	84	82	82	81	78	78	79	80	81	83	82	49
Hsinchu	82	85	85	84	83	82	81	80	80	77	79	78	81	8
Taichung	81	82	82	82	82	82	81	82	80	78	78	80	81	49
Tainan	79	79	79	79	81	84	83	84	82	78	78	79	81	49
Hengchun	73	74	74	76	79	84	85	85	81	75	73	72	78	49
Taitung	74	75	77	79	82	82	81	81	80	77	75	74	78	45
Hualien	78	81	81	82	85	84	81	81	81	78	78	78	81	35
Ilan	84	83	84	85	88	87	83	83	86	86	88	85	85	10
Penghu	82	83	84	84	85	87	85	86	83	77	78	80	83	49
Ali Shan	80	82	84	85	88	90	90	90	89	86	82	78	86	12

* *Fifty-one Years of Statistical Abstracts in Taiwan*, Taiwan Governor
General's Office, Taipei (1946).

CLOUDINESS

The cloudiness in Taiwan as a whole is between 6/10 and 7/10. The north-western part of the island and the eastern coast have the highest degree of cloudiness, averaging more than 7. Taipei and Taitung each have an average cloudiness of 7.2. The western and southern parts of the island are the least cloudy; for example, both Taichung and Hengchun have a cloudiness of 6 (*Table 23*). It is interesting to note that Penghu Island has the least rainfall of any place in Taiwan for which we have data, but its cloudiness averages 6.6, higher than that of either Taichung and Heng-chun. Penghu's disproportionately heavy cloudiness is due to the fact that the air over the Taiwan Strait rises and expands upward, producing little rainfall.

Table 23. Monthly Cloudiness (0/10)*

	Jan.	Feb.	Mar.	Apr.	May	June	July	Aug.	Sept.	Oct.	Nov.	Dec.	Year's average	Years of record
Keelung	8.7	8.8	8.6	8.1	7.8	7.4	5.8	5.7	6.5	7.9	8.3	8.7	7.7	43
Taipei	7.9	8.2	8.0	7.7	7.6	7.5	6.1	6.0	5.9	6.8	7.3	7.7	7.2	49
Hsinchu	7.2	7.8	8.0	7.4	7.6	7.6	7.0	5.9	5.6	4.8	6.2	6.4	6.8	8
Taichung	5.5	6.3	6.7	6.7	6.7	7.2	6.6	6.6	5.2	4.2	4.7	5.0	6.0	49
Tainan	5.3	5.5	5.6	5.5	5.9	6.6	6.4	6.7	5.4	4.4	4.6	5.0	5.6	49
Hengchun	5.7	5.5	5.6	5.6	6.3	7.0	6.6	7.0	6.2	5.6	5.5	5.7	6.0	49
Taitung	7.9	8.0	8.1	7.7	7.6	6.7	6.0	6.2	6.5	6.8	7.3	7.8	7.2	45
Hualien	8.8	8.7	8.7	8.4	8.3	7.7	6.3	6.3	6.9	7.8	8.2	8.7	7.9	35
Ilan	8.5	8.5	8.3	8.2	8.4	8.2	6.5	6.6	7.2	8.0	8.4	8.7	8.0	10
Penghu	7.7	7.7	7.5	6.8	6.5	6.6	5.8	6.0	5.3	5.5	6.6	7.4	6.6	49
Ali Shan	6.1	6.6	7.1	7.0	8.0	8.4	7.9	7.8	7.1	5.6	5.1	5.7	6.9	12

* *Fifty-one Years of Statistical Abstracts in Taiwan*, Taiwan Governor
General's Office, Taipei (1946).

The seasonal distribution of cloudiness varies from north to south. In northern Taiwan, winter is the cloudiest season and summer the least cloudy. For example, in February, the cloudiness at Taipei and Keelung is 8.2 and 8.8 respectively, while in September these figures decrease to 5.7 and 6.0. In southern Taiwan, the cloudiness is concentrated in the summer rather than the winter. The cloudiness of Tainan and Hengchun in August is 6.7 and 7.0 respectively, while in February the cloudiness at both places drops to 5.5 (*Table 23*). As previously mentioned, in southern Taiwan summer is the rainy and, therefore, the cloudy season. On the eastern coast of Taiwan and in the Penghu Islands, winter is the cloudiest season. On the western coast the heaviest degree of cloudiness occurs at the end of spring and at the beginning of summer. In the Chungyang Shan area summer is the most cloudy season. In Ali Shan the cloudiness in May, June, July, and August amounts to 8.0, 8.4, 7.9, and 7.8 respectively.

SUNSHINE

The northern and eastern parts of Taiwan are the areas which have the least amount of sunshine. For example, the average yearly sunshine in Taitung amounts to 1897 hours, Hualien 1671 hours, Taipei 1646 hours, and Keelung 1243 hours. Taipei and Keelung are the least sunny places in the island, with sunshine rates of less than 40 per cent. Places with more sunny days are located in the western coastal area: Taichung averages 2477 hours of sunshine, and Tainan 2593 hours per year. These coastal areas are important regions in the drying of salt.

The island does not generally suffer from many foggy days. The eastern and southern parts of the island have a few foggy days, but Taitung and Hengchun have practically none. Taichung has fog on an average of 13.4 days a year, Taipei 13.4 days, Keelung 12.6 days, and Penghu Island has only 2.8 days of fog a year. However, Ali Shan has 258.5 days of fog a year.

EVAPORATION

The actual efficiency of rainfall with regard to agricultural crops depends upon the evaporation rate, which in Taiwan as a whole, averages 59 inches per year and decreases from south to north. In Hengchun, at the southern tip of the island, the annual evaporation is 79 inches; farther north at Taichung, it becomes 61 inches; and at Taipei, it is only 51 inches. Ilan, in the northeast, has less evaporation, the amount being only 44 inches; and Ali Shan has the least evaporation with 32 inches (*Table 24*).

In the southwestern plain the rainfall in summer far surpasses the amount of evaporation, but in winter the evaporation exceeds the rainfall. Thus, in Tainan from October to March, the rainfall measures 7 inches, but evaporation during this same period amounts to 29 inches.

CLIMATIC CLASSIFICATION

Taiwan is situated in the subtropical latitude from 21°45′N to 25°38′N. Although the essential characteristics of the island's climate are heavy rainfall and high temperature Taiwan possesses various kinds of climate, ranging from the pre-humid and cold type up the high Central Mountain

Table 24. Monthly Evaporation (inches)*

Site	Jan.	Feb.	Mar.	Apr.	May	June	July	Aug.	Sept.	Oct.	Nov.	Dec.
Keelung	2.63	2.40	3.18	3.85	4.60	5.55	8.26	7.99	6.49	5.27	3.97	2.99
Taipei	2.24	2.20	2.99	3.81	4.84	5.59	6.96	6.73	5.63	4.33	3.07	2.36
Hsinchu	2.67	2.36	2.87	3.70	4.84	5.66	6.45	6.73	5.98	5.78	4.01	3.07
Taichung	3.70	3.46	4.01	4.72	5.63	5.82	6.57	6.14	6.02	5.98	4.64	3.81
Tainan	3.93	4.01	5.15	5.98	6.61	5.98	6.18	5.70	5.98	5.70	4.48	3.81
Hengchun	6.06	5.82	7.32	7.63	7.67	6.37	6.18	5.66	6.10	7.08	6.69	6.41
Taitung	4.64	4.37	4.96	5.39	5.86	6.45	7.12	6.73	6.10	6.10	5.19	4.68
Hualien	2.71	2.48	3.22	3.81	4.60	5.23	6.89	6.45	5.55	4.84	3.58	3.18
Ilan	2.04	2.12	2.91	3.38	3.81	4.44	6.18	6.10	5.00	3.42	2.24	2.00
Penghu	3.74	3.34	4.09	4.92	5.86	5.86	6.49	6.26	6.33	6.85	5.27	4.25
Ali Shan	2.55	2.32	2.51	2.83	2.79	2.67	2.71	2.63	2.59	3.07	2.95	2.75

* *Fifty-one Years of Statistical Abstracts in Taiwan*, Taiwan Governor
General's Office, Taipei (1946).

range to the warm, even very hot, tropical climate found down in the
coastal area. Thus both latitude and landforms play an essential part in
the island's climatic factors.

Even though Taiwan is small, the climate differs markedly from place
to place, as well as from season to season. There are various methods of
classifying climatic types, but Köppen's and Thornthwaite's systems are
particularly noteworthy, because they are qualitative systems which use
numerical values for defining the boundaries of climatic groups and types.

Köppen's system of climatic classification

Köppen's classification is based upon annual and monthly means of
temperature and precipitation. Native vegetation is looked upon as the
best expression of the totality of a climate so that many of the climatic
boundaries are selected with vegetation limits in mind. A unique and distinctive feature of the system is the employment of an ingenious symbolic
nomenclature in designating the climatic types. This makes unnecessary
the employment of cumbersome descriptive terms. Each type of climate is
described by a formula consisting of a combination of letters, each one of
which has a precise meaning.

Köppen recognizes five principal groups of world climate which are
intended to correspond with five principal vegetation groups. The five
climatic groups, each designated by a capital letter, are as follows:

A—tropical rainy climate with no cool season
B—dry climate
C—middle-latitude rainy climate with mild winters
D—middle-latitude rainy climate with severe winters
E—polar climates with no warm season

Each of these in turn is subdivided into climatic types based upon the
seasonal distribution of rainfall or the degree of dryness or cold. The small
letters, *f,s,w*, indicate the seasonableness of precipitation;

f—no dry season
s—dry season in summer
w—dry season in winter

In the Köppen system of classification, as applied to Taiwan, two different regimes can be distinguished. Symbol *A* represents the climate which has high temperature and abundant rainfall throughout the year, appearing in the southern tip of Taiwan. Symbol *C* stands for a climate of moderate temperatures and adequate rainfall, but with long, hot summers and mild winters, covering most parts of Taiwan (*Figure 13*).

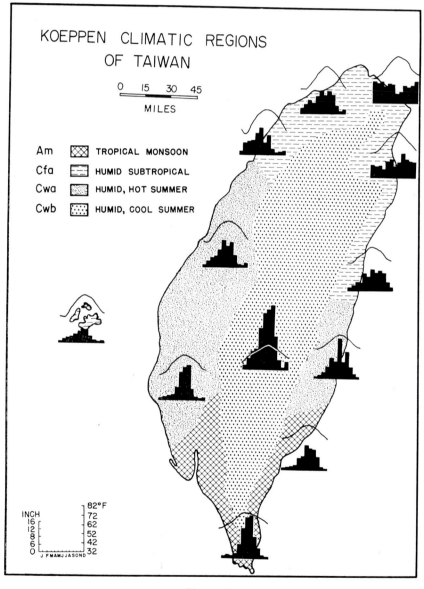

KOEPPEN CLIMATIC REGIONS
OF TAIWAN

0   15   30   45
MILES

Am   TROPICAL MONSOON
Cfa   HUMID SUBTROPICAL
Cwa   HUMID, HOT SUMMER
Cwb   HUMID, COOL SUMMER

INCH   82°F
16   72
12   62
8   52
6   42
0   32
  J FMAMJJASOND

Figure 13

64

These two major groups are modified by small letters as follows:

m—monsoon influence
f—always moist, with no dry season
w—dry winter
a—hot summers, temperature more than 72°F.
   in the warmest month
b—cool summers with four months having temperatures
   of more than 50°F.

With the combination of the above letters, four types of climates result in Taiwan. They are:

Am—tropical monsoon, in the southern part of the island
Cfa—humid subtropical, in the northern part of the island
Cwa—humid, hot summer, in both eastern and western coastal areas
Cwb—humid, cool summer, in the Central Mountain ranges

However, the Köppen system of classification, as applied to Taiwan, fails to bring out certain important climatic features. First, this system overlooks the climatic differences between the east and west coast of Taiwan. For example, in Köppen's system, Hualien and Taipei both belong to the same climatic group, having the symbol of Cwa. In reality, the climates of the paired cities are quite different. Second, in Taiwan the Chungyang Shan region has higher humidity, clouds, rain, and annual temperature range than that of the coastal lowland. But in Köppen's classification both the coastal lowland and the high Chungyang Shan region belong to the Cw group, and the difference between them is shown only in the symbols a and b. Third, places such as Tainan and Kaohsiung each have the same type of climate—sunny, rainfall concentrated in summer, high rate of evaporation, and so on. But in Köppen's scheme the climates of these two cities have been widely separated. One belongs to the A climate classification, while the other is included in the C group.

Thornthwaite's system of climatic classification

Thornthwaite's system is another method in classifying climatic regions. Instead of employing simple temperature and precipitation values as limiting boundaries (as Köppen does), the new concepts of precipitation effectiveness, seasonal concentration of rainfall, and thermal efficiency are introduced. Both annual potential evapo-transpiration and the moisture index are adopted as entities among climatic factors and are considered essentials of a rational classification of climate. Curves comparing water needed and precipitation at twelve key stations in Taiwan are given in *Figure 14.* Amounts of water surplus and deficiency, soil moisture utilization, and soil moisture recharge through the year have been shown. There are water surpluses up in the mountains and northeastern stations, but distinct water deficiencies can be observed over the coastal and southwestern lowland station in winter months. Penghu is the only station with annual potential evapo-transpiration slightly exceeding the amount of precipitation.

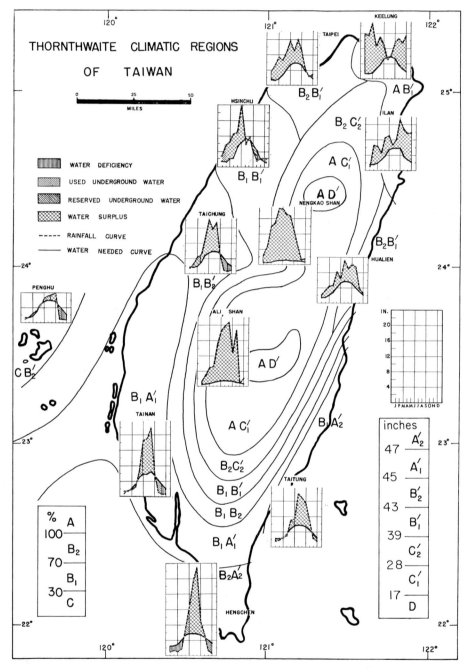

Figure 14. (After CHI-HSUN HSUEH)

Taking moisture index and annual potential evapo-transpiration as the criteria of moisture and thermal efficiency respectively, the climatic types of the Thornthwaite system are classified as follows:

Climatic type	Moisture index (%)
A—prehumid	100 and above
B_2—humid	70–100
B_1—humid	30–70
C—subhumid	0–30

Climatic type	Annual potential evapo-transpiration (inches)
A_2^1 A_1^1 —tropical	41.5 and above 44.5–47.5
B_2^1 B_1^1 —subtropical	43.5–44.5 39.5–43.5
C_2^1 —warm temperate C_1^1 D^1 —cold temperate	27.5–39.5 16.5–27.5 0–16.5

Although Taiwan is limited in area, the climatic types, according to the Thornthwaite classification, are very complicated, due to the variety of landforms. Eleven climatic types can be observed. They are AD', AC_1, AB_1', B_2C_2', B_2B_1', B_2A_2', B_1A_2', B_1A_1', B_1B_2', B_1B_1', and CB_2'. Generally speaking, Taiwan possesses the prehumid cold temperate climate (AD^1) on the summit of the Central Mountain range, prehumid warm temperature climate (AC_1') over most mountainous districts, from humid warm temperature (B_2C_2') to humid subtropical ($B_1B_1'-B_1B_2'$) climate along the foothill region, and from humid subtropical (B_1B_2', B_1B_2') to humid tropical (B_1, B_2, A_1', A_2') climate over the coastal plain. The only prehumid subtropical climate (AB_1') is observed over the northeastern corner, and the only subhumid subtropical climate (CB_2')is observed over the Penghu island group.

TYPHOONS AND RICE CULTIVATION IN TAIWAN

In the agricultural subsistence economies of the Far East, Taiwan is a "rice bowl," for rice production on the island has developed to a point where it exceeds the considerable demands of the more than 11 million people living there. In 1954, rice comprised about 48 per cent of the total value of agricultural crops, and the paddy field occupied about 63 per cent of the cultivated land. Compared to other crops, rice ranks high not only in the value of product and proportion of crop land utilized, but also in terms of the number of people engaged in rice-growing. Of about 716,600 farm households in 1954, there was an agricultural population of about 4,488,763, constituting about one-half of the total population. Among the agricultural population, the rice farmer is the leader.

High temperature, abundant rainfall, long growing season, and the fertile alluvial plains in the west combine to provide Taiwan with excellent agricultural environment. However, the island is not without natural handicaps: earthquakes and typhoons are two powerful calamities. About twice a year an earthquake can be expected, and, on the average, two typhoons strike the island annually. While both earthquakes and typhoons inflict widespread damage to the island, it is the typhoon which brings tremendous ruin to the rice crop. No other rice cultivation area in the Far East has suffered so much from typhoons as has Taiwan.

In this section we shall analyze the effects of typhoons on rice cultivation in Taiwan, and suggest some ways by which the magnitude of the damage caused by typhoons might be reduced from catastrophic proportions in the future.[5]

The widespread cultivation of rice in Taiwan began with the immigration of large numbers of Chinese farmers to the island in the 17th century. Wherever Chinese farmers found plains, rice paddy fields were developed. While the cultivation of paddy rice requires a high degree of agricultural skill, the local climatic conditions greatly affect the rice growing schedule. Rice in Taiwan is double-cropped, that is, the first crop is planted in February or March and is harvested in late June or early July; the second crop is planted from late July to early August and is harvested from late October to early November.

While the rice cultivating process generally remained the same, significant changes took place in rice cultivation in Taiwan during the period of Japanese rule (1895–1945). In 1922 the Japanese introduced a new kind of rice to Taiwan, named "Ponlai" rice (the Japanese called it "Horai rice"), which is round-grained in contrast to the long-grained native rice of Taiwan. Before the introduction of Ponlai rice in Taiwan the area used for rice cultivation slowly expanded, but the yield per acre remained almost stationary. However, from 1922 to 1935, the area of rice cultivation rose from 1,235,000 acres to 1,539,060 acres, and the yield per acre increased by 72%. During this twelve-year period production almost doubled.[6] The area brought under Ponlai rice cultivation expanded especially rapidly, for the new rice gave a higher yield per acre than the native variety, and it was also more acceptable to Japanese consumers, who found the native Taiwan rice unpalatable. A graphic comparison of Ponlai rice and native rice with respect to production and area of cultivation is presented in *Figure 15*. Both curves for native rice fall after 1922, while both curves for Ponlai rice rise steadily; the production curve showing an extremely sharp rise until the effects of war were felt.[6] From 1945 to 1956 the area of cultivation of Ponlai rice did not exceed the 988,000 acres which it occupied in 1945. In 1956 the area of cultivation of native rice was 800,796 acres.[7]

During the 11-year period from 1944 to 1954, much more rice land was damaged by typhoons than by any other natural cause. The total area of farm land damaged by natural causes was 6,706,779 acres, and of this total, typhoons were responsible for 2,850,936 acres, or 42.5 per cent. Damage to rice by disease was responsible for 2,727,249 acres, or 40.6 per cent of the total, second only to the damage wrought by typhoons. Among the diseases rice blast was the leading cause for crop loss. Crop losses due to typhoons exceed by 2½ times the losses caused by drought, flood, and other causes combined. The rice lost during this period amounted to 1,424,722 tons.

with more than 50 per cent of this total due to typhoons, as shown by *Table 25*.[8]

Since the typhoons have such a serious effect on the rice crop, it would be a great boon to the rice farmers in particular, and to the island economy in general, if some of this damage could be avoided. However, before going into the matter of reducing rice losses due to typhoons, it is necessary to know more about the frequency of typhoons in Taiwan.

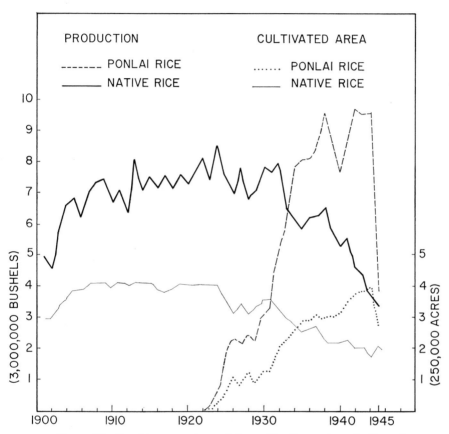

Figure 15.—Graphic comparison of the cultivation and production of native and Ponlai rice from 1900 to 1945

Table 25. Causes of Damage to Rice Crops in Taiwan From 1944 to 1954 Inclusive

Paddy rice	Typhoons	Disease	Drought	Flood	Others	Total
Damage in acres	2,850,936	2,727,249	777,724	334,388	16,485	6,706,779
Per cent of area	42.5	40.6	11.6	5.0	0.3	100
Rice lost in tons	811,041	326,013	191,468	91,795	4405	1,424,722
Per cent of rice lost	56.9	22.8	13.6	6.4	0.3	100

Taking the data recorded from 1895 to 1945 by the Weather Bureau of Taiwan and reported by Shih, of 875 typhoons in East Asia, only 98 typhoons reached Taiwan, an average of about two per year.[9] As to monthly distribution during these 51 years, typhoons are most frequent from July to September. The earliest typhoon visited Taiwan in May and the latest arrived in November. No typhoons were recorded for the months of December through April. Of the 98 typhoons about 86 per cent of them were concentrated in July, August, and September. One-third of the total number of typhoons occurred in August, and about one-fourth occurred in July and one-fourth in September. *Table 26* shows the monthly distribution of typhoons during the 51 year period.[10]

Table 26. *Monthly Distribution of 98 Typhoons Striking Taiwan from 1895 to 1945 inclusive*

Month	May	June	July	Aug.	Sept.	Oct.	Nov.
Number of typhoons	1	7	25	36	25	3	1

So far we have dealt only with average figures of typhoon occurrence. However, climatic data, especially that which deals with catastrophic features, may be more meaningful if frequency figures are used. *Table 27* shows the annual frequency of typhoons in Taiwan.[11]

Table 27 reveals that within a span of 51 years no typhoons occurred for 12 of those years; they occurred once a year for 9 of the years, twice a year in 18 of the years, three times in 6 of the years and four times in 3 of the years. Going further, typhoons occurred 6 times in one year, 7 times in another year, and even 10 times in a third year.

Table 27. *Annual Frequency of Typhoons in Taiwan*

Occurrence of typhoons	0	1	2	3	4	5	6	7	8	9	10	Total typhoons:	98
Number of years	12	9	18	6	3	0	1	1	0	0	1	Total years:	51

After the study of the frequencies of typhoons in Taiwan, we may now compare this with the growing schedule of the rice crop and try to find out whether there is any coincidence between the two. At first glance, there seems to be little chance for the rice crop to avoid the typhoon calamity, for the typhoon season in Taiwan is also the cultivating period for rice. However, the amount of damage done to the rice crop by typhoons greatly depends upon the stage of rice growth during which the typhoon occurs. Typhoons do only slight harm to rice in the seed bed stage, and rice in the mature stage is strong enough to resist such storms. The most serious damage is done to rice in the heading stage, for at this point the rice kernels are just beginning to form and are most adversely affected by typhoons.

Figure 16, which was prepared by an agronomist, illustrates possible damage to rice by typhoons.[12] If a typhoon were to strike when the rice was just heading, 75 per cent of the crop would be destroyed, but if the typhoon struck four or eight days before the heading time, only 20–50 per cent of the crop would be destroyed, and if it struck four or eight days after the rice had headed, only 5–25 per cent of the crop would be lost. Thus, we may conclude that the possible typhoon damage to rice crops is greater in the days before heading than in the days after heading.

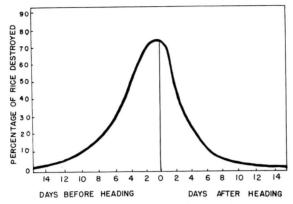

Figure 16.—Possible damage to rice crop from typhoons striking at different stages of the growing process

With the above fact in mind, let us glance now at the growing schedule of the rice crop (*Figure 17*). Typhoons have little effect on the first rice cropping of the year because of their limited occurrence during this period. The great damage done to rice crops by typhoons is during the second cropping. In both northern and southern Taiwan the rice enters the heading stage in September, which is one of the months during which a typhoon is most likely to occur. The picture of rice damage done by typhoons is more complicated if we consider native rice and Ponlai rice separately. In comparing the lengths of growing time required by each, we notice that the total number of growing days for Ponlai rice is much less than for the native rice—especially for the second cropping—and that the time from transplanting to heading for the second crop of Ponlai rice is much shorter than for the native rice, since the second crop of Ponlai rice heads out much earlier, as shown by *Table 28*.[13]

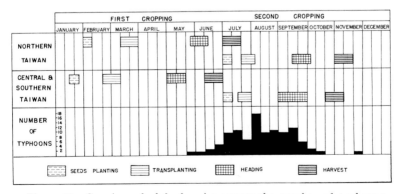

Figure 17.—Growing schedule for rice versus the number of typhoons

One should pay special attention to the earlier heading of the second cropping of the Ponlai rice. From 1933 to 1940, the second cropping of Ponlai rice averaged its heading in late September in northern Taiwan, and in mid-September in the southern part. Since most typhoons in Taiwan occur in July, August, and September, and since about one quarter of the total number of typhoons may be expected in September, the second cropping of Ponlai rice enters the heading stage at a rather inopportune time. The second cropping of native rice, on the other hand, heads out in late September or in October, and thus it has a better chance to escape typhoon damage, since the number of typhoons decreases after September.

Table 28. Comparison of the number of growing days required by native rice and Ponlai rice (1935–1938)

	Nursery period	Transplant-ing to heading	Heading to harvest	Total grow-ing days
Native rice	1st cropping, 44.1	84.2	34.7	163.0
	2nd cropping, 32.5	75.2	34.3	142.0
Ponlai rice	1st cropping, 34.7	74.4	38.9	148.0
	2nd cropping, 16.2	58.6	42.3	117.1

In addition, in the first cropping of Ponlai rice, the crops are also damaged by diseases. Therefore, the amount of native rice is more stable in harvest than is Ponlai rice. Nevertheless, because of the fact that Ponlai rice is usually planted in the most fertile fields and receives more fertilizer than native rice, the yield of Ponlai per acre is much more than that of the native rice, as shown by Table 29.[14]

Since the rice harvest in Taiwan depends more on Ponlai rice than on native rice, the earlier heading of the second cropping of Ponlai rice in typhoon-prone September is most critical.

Table 29. Comparison of the harvest of the first and second cropping of native rice and Ponlai rice in Taiwan (1924–1943)

	Native rice		Ponlai rice	
	first cropping	second cropping	first cropping	second cropping
Average production of rice in bushels per acre	3.44	3.05	5.30	3.39

To summarize briefly, it appears that the disastrous effects of typhoons on the rice crop in Taiwan can be minimized by shifting the planting time. The first crop of both native and Ponlai rice should be started earlier, so that the crop will mature before the end of June; the second crop should be planted later, so that its period of heading will fall in October. In this way, the rice would not be in its most vulnerable stage during the main typhoon season.

However, several problems arise with this solution. While it would not be difficult to have the first croppings of both native and Ponlai rice mature before the end of June, both would be more subject to disease if grown earlier, Ponlai rice being weaker in this respect than the native variety. Therefore, a new kind of rice more capable of resisting disease should be developed.

To escape the September typhoons, the second crop of rice must be headed after the beginning of October. This program can be followed easily with the native rice, but it would be more difficult to delay the heading of Ponlai rice. Some agricultural answer might be applied to this problem, but the difficulty might be solved by a concentration on native rice during the second cropping season, with a decrease in the amount of Ponlai rice. In other words, Ponlai rice should be encouraged for the first cropping and native rice for the second cropping.

REFERENCES

[1] T. F. CLAXTON, *Isotypes* (Hong Kong, 1932).

[2] Y. H. SHIH, "Typhoons which have raided China within 51 years," *Hsueh-I-Tsa-Chih* **17, 5** (1945). [In Chinese with English abstract.]

[3] *The Climate, Typhoons and Earthquakes of the Island of Formosa* (Taihoku Meteorology Observatory, Taihoku, Japan, 1914).

[4] Report of the weather bureau of Formosa (1946).

[5] CHIAO-MIN HSIEH, "Typhoons and rice cultivation in Taiwan," *Proc. I.G.U. Regional Conf. in Japan,* (1959), pp. 326–331.

[6] *Fifty-one Years of Statistical Abstracts of Taiwan (1895–1945)* (Taiwan Governor's Office, Taipei, 1946), pp. 538–545.

[7] *General Report of the Joint Commission on Rural Reconstruction* (Taipei, 1956), p. 68.

[8] *Taiwan Agricultural Year Book* (Taipei, 1944–1954).

[9] Y. H. SHIH, "Typhoons which have raided China within 51 years," *Hsueh-I-Tsa-Chih* **17, 5** (1945). [In Chinese with English abstract.]

[10] *Ibid.,* p. 5.

[11] *Ibid.,* pp. 9–16.

[12] *Agriculture Report* (Taiwan Agriculture Research Institute, 1947), Vol. I, No. 5, p. 3.

[13] EIKTCHI ISE, "Summary of the studies on the correlation phenomena among the characters of rice plant and its application in practice," *Bull. Taiwan agric. Res. Inst.* **1, 20** (1946).

[14] *Ibid.,* p. 15.

FIVE

Hydrography

RAINFALL, DISCHARGE AND FLOODS

SECOND ONLY TO THE AIR WE BREATHE, water is the earth's most important resource—it is also the earth's most changeable material. Part of the water which falls on the earth's surface as rain, snow, dew, and sleet is evaporated and transpired; another part runs off into streams; and a third part seeps down through the porous rocks of the surface and is added to the immense underground water reservoirs. This sequence of events—precipitation, run-off, evaporation, transpiration, and underground infiltration—constitutes the main part of the hydrologic cycle. The study of hydrography is concerned with the phenomenon of water. This includes its origin, distribution, flow, influence on the earth, and relation to biology.

Water and land are Taiwan's two great natural resources, but land is obviously of little value without water. In industry coal and iron are the basic necessities, while water and soil are the keys to agriculture. The management of the water supply for agriculture is a complex task. The rainfall of Taiwan, as in other places, is either too much or too little, comes too early or too late, or falls in the wrong places. Flood and drought are simply manifestations of the same problem of too much or too little water. The problem of supplying water to agriculture thus involves two factors: time—the storage of water from rainy season to dry season; and place—distribution from source to place of use.

Because of the central-backbone mountains, steep slopes, short and swift rivers, intensive rainfall, and unevenly distributed rainfall, the retaining of water on the ground has been a great problem throughout Taiwan's history. During the rainy season much rain runs off into the rivers and from there empties into the ocean. In the dry season river channels are dry and irrigation becomes a necessary practice for agricultural production in Taiwan, especially in view of the fact that the major agricultural products of the island have been rice and sugar cane, both relatively thirsty crops.

After decades of effort by the inhabitants of Taiwan, the management of water of the island has a good foundation and the island has become the granary of the Far East. Comparing the agricultural environment of Taiwan with that of Japan and South Viet Nam for instance, it can be seen that Japan has an adequate rainfall but, being located in a higher latitude, it is not warm enough to have a year-round growing season. South Viet Nam is located in a subtropical region, as is Taiwan, and has a year-round growing season; however, the country has not yet developed its irrigation system to the same extent as has Taiwan and cannot maintain abundant agricultural production in drought periods.

In this section we will examine Taiwan's rainfall characteristics, discharge, and floods. The basic data on water resources comes from the rainfall records. There are 279 rainfall stations in Taiwan with an average of 50 square miles covered by each station. Most of the rainfall stations are located on the plains. Among the 279 stations, there are only 92 stations (32 per cent of the total number) which are located above 1640 feet. Since most of the land area in Taiwan is above 1640 feet, and since additional rainfall is more varied in mountainous areas than in the lowlands the need for more rainfall stations in mountainous areas is apparent.

RAINFALL

Rainfall is the ultimate source of surface water and is closely related to the hydrology. Taiwan's rainfall is abundant, but very unevenly distributed. The average annual rainfall over the whole island is about 98.4 inches, ranging from 258.9 inches in the mountainous regions to 39.4 inches in the coastal areas of the plains[1]. For example, the Houshao-liao section of the northeast, with an elevation of 1377.6 feet has an annual average of 258.9 inches with the maximum annual rainfall attaining 331.2 inches. Thus this site has the highest rainfall in Southeast Asia, with the exception of Cherrupanji in East Pakistan[2]. On the other hand, on Penghu Island and in the Western coastal plains of the island, the average annual rainfall is only 39.4 inches, and in the driest years, only 16.3 inches.

The rainfall in Taiwan is not only unevenly distributed in location, but also varies with the seasons. The maximum daily rainfall at different places varies from 11.8 to 39.4 inches, and the maximum hourly intensity varies from 2.8 to 3.9 inches. Rainfall in Taiwan is mostly concentrated in short periods during the rainy seasons. In the winter half-year from October to March the total rainfall in some locations amounts to only 20 per cent—or even less—of the annual value.

DISCHARGE

In addition to the record of rainfall, the record of discharge of various rivers provides the basic data for water resources. The discharge survey of Taiwan was begun in 1937 with 46 stations distributed among 17 rivers.

The places of high mean discharge are located at the Tamshui River in the north, the Ilan-Choshui River in the northeast, and at both sides of the Central Mountains. The southwest part of the coastal plain has the lowest discharge. This is the result of the winter dry season of this area.

The mean discharge of 130 cubic feet per second or 51.4 inches of the run-off in Taiwan is a much higher rate than that found on the mainland of China; such a high rate is very rare even in the rainy part of the world. For example, Cherrupanji, in East Pakistan, is reputed to have a heavy rainfall—818.9 inches in one record twelve-month period —the highest record in the world, yet the area's highest run-off record is only 46.1 inches. Ceylon, separated from the sub-continent of India, is comparable to Taiwan in location. Its average yearly rainfall is 82.7 inches in the rainy season, but its run-off is only 41.9 inches. In the mainland of China, the areas in which the amount of rainfall can reach 51.2 inches are limited to the southeastern part, but their run-off figures are so much less as to be negligible. According to the record of Taiwan's Bureau of Water Conservation, water for urban areas and home use reaches 264 cubic feet per second, industrial use varies from 260 to 307 cubic feet, and irrigation uses vary from 13,494 to 29,702 cubic feet. Thus the total utility of the water ranges from 13,994 to 30,273 cubic feet per second and occupies from 30 to 64.6 per cent of the mean discharge. Taiwan is one of the few places in the world which has such a high rate of water utilization. Since the water usage for irrigation is so much greater than the other uses, this should be examined in more detail.

Irrigational use of the water supply averages only 100 days per year. The average irrigational use of water is about 10,531 cubic feet per second. This figure is a minimum estimate, but it accounts for 23.7 per cent of the mean discharge. Based on these estimations, it can be safely stated that Taiwan has the highest rate of water usage for irrigation in the world. For instance, in India the amount of water used for irrigation is only 5.6 per cent and in the United States it is 13.8 per cent. This figure also shows that the utilization of surface water in Taiwan has been exploited to the utmost, and that the island must begin to consider the water reservoir of the future in view of the increase in population and urbanization.

FLOODS

The rapid run-off, the overall steepness of mountain slopes, the composition of the alluvial plain which is easily affected by water, and the highly intensive storm rainfall all are factors in Taiwan's susceptibility to floods.

Rainstorms in Taiwan mainly come from typhoons, which in turn contribute to floods. Since the Philippines and Taiwan are located on the main route of typhoons, these two areas have a high record of rainstorms.

Regardless of the character of the soil or vegetation covering, only a small fraction of this intensive rainfall can percolate downward or be absorbed. As a result, volumes of water must be disposed of chiefly by surface run-off.

Destructive floods in Taiwan are almost always caused by exceptionally severe summer thunderstorms or by infrequent typhoons. In general, about 30–40 per cent of flood damage is attributable to typhoon rainfall. Since the island is small, no part is particularly subject to or free from flood hazards. Because of the limited drainage areas of all rivers, however, the most severe floods tend to occur on the largest streams. The northern part of the island, particularly the important Tamshui drainage basin, is to some extent sheltered from the typhoons by mountains; it is also visited less by intensive convectional thunderstorms, the source of heavy rainfall. The east coast, in contrast, is exposed to the usual approach of typhoons from the southeast, and is also subject to extremes of flooding and debris downflow from the especially short rivers of the area.

Except as an incidental product of irrigation works and the development of power sites, the flood control structure in Taiwan consists almost exclusively of river dikes or levees. Unlike the earth-filled levees characteristic of Japan, most levees in Taiwan are of stone construction, surfaced with masonry or wire cylinders, and have wire-cylinder or concrete reinforcement on the river side. Earth levees are used only on smaller streams whose loads consist of fine gravels or sand. The levee function in Taiwan is three-fold: to contain flood crests within established channels, to check stream meandering, and to reduce the number of seaward distributaries. All three objectives are designed to bar stream encroachment upon adjacent land. However, achievement of this goal is not possible unless comprehensive control of upstream erosion is successfully accomplished.

GENERAL CHARACTERISTICS OF THE RIVERS

SHORTNESS

Since the general configuration of Taiwan is that of a tilted block with all the streams originating from the high Chungyang Shan, the island presents a radial drainage pattern. With less than 60 miles between the high mountain peaks and the coastal margins, the rivers in Taiwan are naturally short and swift. The Choshui, the longest river in Taiwan, is only 105 miles long. Only six rivers exceed 60 miles in length (*Table 30*), and only 20 are more than 30 miles long. Among these 20 rivers, 16 flow toward the west and only four toward the east. (*Figure 18*). Since the main divide of the island lies near the eastern coast, and since the surface of the eastern part is much steeper than that of the western part, the rivers of the east are shorter and swifter than those of the west. The rivers of Taiwan are shorter even than those of Japan, which are notoriously lacking in length. The shortness of the rivers is an important characteristic in Taiwan.

STEEPNESS

A second characteristic of the rivers in Taiwan is their steepness. Most rivers in Taiwan originate from peaks of more than 6,000 feet elevation, and empty into the sea within a short distance from their source. A steep gradient and a high velocity result as a consequence of this fact. For example, the lower part of the gentle Tsengwen-Chi has a gradient of 1/820 and the steep stream of Taan gives a figure of 1/90. In Europe, the steepest is that of the Rhone River which has a gradient of 1/2,200. In China, the Gold Sand River has a very large gradient of 1/1,000. However, in comparing these figures to those of the rivers of Taiwan, we find that the gradient of the Tsengwen-Chi is greater than that of both the Rhone and the Gold Sand Rivers. The gradient of the Taan is 120 times as great as that of the Gold Sand River and 25 times greater than that of the Rhone River. Thus the gradient of the rivers in Taiwan may be the greatest in the world[3].

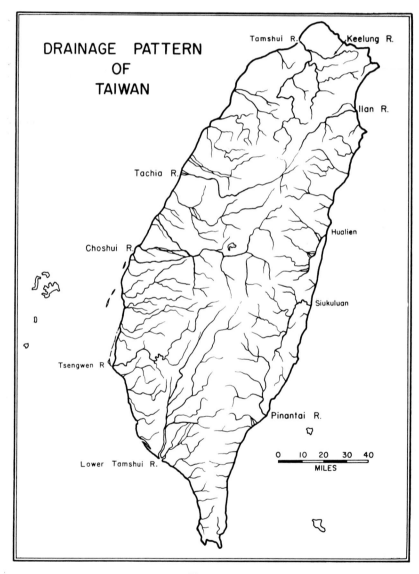

Figure 18

SEASONAL HYDROGRAPHIC CHANGES

The third characteristic of the rivers of Taiwan is the distinct seasonal change of hydrography. Except in the northeastern part of the island, the rainfall is concentrated in the summer, and the water level in the river rises to its highest level from June to September, and reaches its lowest point from December to January. In the summer, the stormy nature of rainfall, aided by the steep gradient of the rivers, causes great flooding of all the rivers. For instance, the Choshui river and the Lower Tamshui river have drainage areas of only about 1160 squares miles respectively, yet both have the greatest flood volume at high flood level, reaching 778,000 cubic feet per second. The Yellow River—the sorrow of China—drains an area of 270,270 square miles, but its greatest extent of flooding is not more than 955,000 cubic feet. For the other rivers in Taiwan, such as the Tachia, Wu and Siukuluan rivers, the flood volume of all exceeds 354,000 cubic feet per second. There are not more than forty rivers in the world, the flood volume of which exceeds this figure. On the small island of Taiwan, the number of rivers which have a flood volume of more than 354,000 cubic feet accounts for one-seventh of the world total. This great flood during the summer destroys many fields and causes great damage.

*Table 30. The Hydrography of the Main Rivers in Taiwan**

River	Length (miles)	Height of source (feet)	Average gradient	Drainage area (sq. miles)	Minimum discharge (cu.ft./ sec.)	Maximum discharge (cu.ft./ sec.)
Choshui	105.6	11.33	1/59	1204.1	2.9	734,022
Lower Tamshui	98.7	13.11	1/48	129.6	35.3	746,065
Tamshui	89.4	9.96	1/50	1043.2	—	688,266
Tsengwen	85.1	7.75	1/69	470.8	7.1	391,467
Tachia	77.0	10.70	1/46	497.2	—	404,074
Wu	70.2	7.99	1/55	778.4	176.6	559,460
Taan	54.0	11.92	1/29	278.8	7.1	283,862
Peikong	51.5	1.29	1/24	299.2	3.5	284,392
Peinanta	50.9	10.70	1/30	585.6	70.1	486,100
Siukuluan	47.8	4.72	1/64	712.8	738.1	509,701
Pachuang	45.9	4.72	1/62	184.9	14.1	210,442
Putzu	44.1	3.54	1/79	110.2	7.1	152,172
Ilan Choshui	42.2	5.11	1/52	392.0	483.8	345,343
Chishui	39.7	3.93	1/64	123.2	7.1	172,867
Erhtsenghang	38.5	.39	1/62	139.2	3.5	174,491
Touchien	36.0	8.34	1/27	201.6	7.1	230,784
Houlung	37.9	6.29	1/38	222.0	3.5	236,116
Hualien	34.7	4.72	1/47	585.6	—	451,290
Chungkong	32.3	6.29	1/33	153.7	—	—
Hsinhuwei	31.6	.23	1/85	64.0	14.1	—

* Based on *Fifty-one Years of Statistical Abstracts of Taiwan*, Taiwan Governor General's Office, Taipei (1946), p. 58, and data from K. C. Chang, "Hydrography of Taiwan," *Taiwan Hsin-chih*, 1954, pp. 109–11. [In Chinese].

On the contrary, during the winter season, the rainfall decreases and the water level in rivers is also lowered, the rivers thus becoming dry creeks. Because of this seasonal change of hydrography, the rivers in Taiwan are not navigable and the lack of water in winter is a great handicap in irrigation.

SAND CONTENT

Another characteristic of Taiwan's rivers is that they contain a great volume of sand (*Table 31*). On this subtropical island, the stormy rainfall, together with the fragile rock base and the destruction of the forest cover in mountain areas all combine to create a great erosive force. The rivers contain a great volume of sand and gravel during flood time. In mountain areas the rivers cut deep gorges and waterfalls and rapids often occur. On reaching the gentle slopes, the velocity of the rivers decreases and

Table 31. Sand Content of Taiwan's Main Rivers*

River	Station	Maximum content (per cent of total weight)	Minimum content (per cent of total weight)	Average content (per cent of total weight)
Choshui	Tzumeikouyuan	0.628900	0.019800	0.144550
Lower Tamshui	Lukweili	0.014730	0.000412	0.000227
Tamshui	Chuchiui	0.001118	0.000058	0.000278
Tachia	Shihkantze	0.010480	0.000005	0.000446
Wu	Saunton	0.006470	0.000015	0.000383
Ilan Choshui	Niutou	0.014720	0.000011	0.002226
Houlung	Waishihtan	0.003504	0.000106	0.000953

* K. C. Chang, "Hydrography of Taiwan," *Taiwan Hsin-chih,* 1954, pp. 99–100. [In Chinese].

the carrying capacity of the rivers also diminishes. Thus, the rivers deposit their debris and build up alluvial fans in the outlets of the mountain area and in the delta near the sea. On the western coast along the mouths of the rivers, there are sand deposits of various widths, from 1.5 to 3 miles. This indicates that deposition is still in process.

SUMMARY

In summary, the rivers of Taiwan are short, swift, flooded, and sandy. All these characteristics are unfavorable for navigation. With the exception of the Tamshui, which is navigable for a small steamboat of 50 tons between Tamshui and Taipei, none of the other rivers in Taiwan is navigable. In spite of the fact that the rivers of Taiwan are difficult to manage, as these rivers descend rapidly from steep slopes, they are, on the other hand, able to supply a large amount of power for the production of electricity, an important factor in the industrial development of Taiwan. Also, the rivers have been utilized to the benefit of agriculture, that is, by providing the means for irrigation. The southwestern plain of Taiwan is noted as the island's granary, but the dry season during the winter has prevented it from producing large amounts of agricultural products. From the early days, the rivers in this part of Taiwan have been used efficiently for irrigation. The Chianan irrigation system is a good example of the utilization of the waters of Tsengwen river and the Choshui river.

WATER-BEARING CAPACITIES OF ROCK LAYERS

The nature of the underground rocks greatly affects their water-bearing capacity. The size and structure of the rock is closely related to its capacity for containing water. A good water-containing rock must first have volume to retain the underground water; second, the rock must be highly permeable. Spaces within the rock must allow the ground water to permeate freely. There are three kinds of rocks which have differing capacities for containing water. The rocks which can contain much water are sandstone, gravels, and other loosely-compacted rocks, while the rocks which contain the least water and which are impermeable are clays, shales, crystalline, and other compactly-structured rocks. In some rocks, such as limestone, granite, basalt, and other igneous types, there are few spaces, yet fissures and joints enable them to contain much water. The various types of rock in Taiwan have different water-bearing capacities.

TYPES OF ROCKS[4]

Recent alluvium

This rock is mainly composed of layers of unconsolidated clay, silt, sand, and gravel. Because of its loose structure its permeability is great. The sand and gravel in the alluvium are the most important aquifers in Taiwan and are the best deposits for containing groundwater. These alluviums exist along the west coastal plains and along the river valleys and have supplied the largest amounts of groundwater for various uses up until the present time. The value of development of these alluvial deposits depends on the thickness of the alluvium, the size of the sand and gravel which compose the alluvial deposits, the amount of clay, and the recharge of water source.

Gravel tableland

Gravel tableland forms the deposit on the terraces. Most of these deposits are distributed along the west coast area. They are comprised mostly of coarse-textured, poorly-sorted gravel with considerable admixture of silt and fine sand. The pebbles are mostly of hard sandstone and are commonly capped by red laterite on the surface. With loose structure and good permeability, these gravels are of importance as a water-bearing formation in Taiwan.

Tertiary volcanic rocks

The tertiary volcanic rock usually is compact and not permeable. However, there are some fissures in the rock which can contain a certain amount of water. In the volcanic area there are usually vertical joints and gas fissures in such formations as basalt which also contain large amounts of water. Also, certain porous bodies of volcanic detritus may be filled with water to a certain degree, depending on the extent of fracturing and weathering as well as on the conditions of recharge.

Plio-Pleistocene Toukoshan formation

The Toukoshan formation of rocks may range from poor to excellent as an aquifer. The poorest portion is the massive claystone, siltstone, and muddy sandstone laid down during the early stage of deposition (Hsiang-shan facies); the best section is the conglomerate (Houyenshan facies) that is composed of loosely-cohering pebbles with adequate porosity and permeability for water storage and transmission. This conglomerate may, in places, be only a fair water-bearer if the matrix contains much clay or if the rock is located in an area where conditions are unfavorable for recharge. The coralline limestone lenses in the Plio-Pleistocene beds in southern Taiwan exhibit the same water-bearing characteristics as those of the Pliocene limestone.

Pliocene Miaoli formations

The Miaoli formation possesses little value as an aquifer because it is predominantly dark shale and fine dense sandstone or siltstone. The Pliocene coralline limestone lenses in southern Taiwan may hold some water in caverns or crevices, but the limestone lenses are generally known to be locally "tight" due to the lack of lateral continuity.

Miocene Haishan series

The Haishan series is composed of alternating beds of shale, sandstone, and sandy shale. Some important sandstone beds have been found in this series which show considerable thickness and areal extent, but most of them are muddy and water-tight. Only the coarse-grained white sandstone in the coal-bearing formations may constitute adequate aquifers. They might possibly yield water for domestic or industrial requirements if favored by good recharge conditions.

Eocene slate formations

The Eocene slate formations consist largely of dark slates and hard sandstones that are impervious and water-tight. Small amounts of water, controlled only by minor features such as cleavages and fractures, may be stored in these rocks.

Pre-Tertiary metamorphic complex

The metamorphic complex in the eastern flank of the Central Mountains is composed mostly of crystalline rocks that are tight and unfavorable to the supply of ground-water except for negligible amounts which are found in the fractures, joints, or weathered zones of the rocks.

GROUND WATER

Rainfall is the ultimate source of both the surface and underground water. As a natural resource, the essential difference between ground water and surface water is that the former is not only hidden, but it tends to travel much more slowly—through rock interstices—with the result that the technical problems of utilization are somewhat complex.

The existence of ground water reserves depends on three factors: availability of rainfall to fill the storage space, the rock capacity for underground water storage, and the means of access whereby water can move from surface sources to the underground reservoir.

AVAILABILITY OF RAINFALL

The annual average rainfall of 98.4 in. in Taiwan is enough to keep all potential ground water reservoirs filled. However, this rainfall is not always favorably distributed in terms of space and time. The winter drought in the southwestern part of Taiwan regularly restricts the potential amount of water available for ground water recharge. Although summer rainfall is abundant, it is so concentrated in short, heavy downpours that a large proportion of the water runs off rapidly over the surface rather than replenishing the ground water reservoirs.

OCCURRENCE OF UNDERGROUND WATER

The occurrence of underground water requires layers of permeable underground rock through which water can slowly travel. As a rule, the thicker the potential aquifer and the greater its lateral extent, the more abundant will be the potential groundwater supplies. Gravel beds or coarse-grained sandstones are examples of excellent aquifers. On the other hand, very fine-grained shale or dense granitic rocks may be almost entirely impermeable to water and constitute non-aquifers even though surface water is abundant.

Taiwan has never used ground water systematically and extensively. Before the 20th century, digging shallow wells for domestic use was the only way of utilizing ground water. The water level of these wells represents only a pressure surface rather than a water table. They are usually cased with hollow bamboo and have a life span of up to ten years. During the Japanese occupation, modern drilling rigs were introduced and about 80 wells were drilled with a diameter ranging from 6 to 15 inches. From these ground water wells scattered over the island, the water is used chiefly for municipal and industrial purposes and very little is used for agricultural ends. Only recently has irrigation become a popular practice and the irrigation areas have extended year after year with a proportionate reduction in the quantity of surface water. Water is needed not only for farm lands, but also for public use in large cities, factories, schools, airfields, and military establishments. For example, residents of the cities of Taipei and Tainan complain a great deal about the shortage of water during the summer season, the industrial factories in Tainan are forced to cease operation during the dry season, and the shortage of water greatly affects agricultural production—especially sugar cane output. Since the development of additional supplies of surface water has become increasingly difficult and costly, attention has gradually been turned to water stored in underground reservoirs.

Fortunately, the island of Taiwan is favorably endowed with conditions for developing the underground water reservoir. First, the ground water can be found at a reasonable depth in most alluvial plains. Second, it can easily be pumped to the surface at rather low expense without too much engineering work. Third, the ground water in Taiwan is of good chemical quality, especially after having flowed through several layers of rocks. The water is quite pure and clear and can be used directly for irrigation, and for industrial and drinking purposes in the metropolitan areas. Fourth, since surface water in Taiwan is not available in sufficient quantities during the dry season, the underground water of the island is not affected by the seasons[5].

The greatest impetus to well-drilling came after World War II, and the number of modern wells was tripled between 1948 and 1952. The first large-scale ground water development on the island was commenced by the Taiwan Sugar Corporation in 1950 when the company made a contract with the Johnston International Company of the United States to drill wells on the sugar cane farms owned by various sugar factories of the corporation. The drilling of these wells was specifically intended to increase the yield of sugar cane by proper ground water irrigation. Most of the wells drilled are located on farms in the two favorable ground water basins: the Choshui River alluvial fan and the Pingtung Valley. By 1951, about 120 wells had been completed with diameters ranging from 14 to 18 inches. Besides the sugar cane company, the Chinese Petroleum Corporation has also drilled wells to help develop Taiwan's ground water reservoirs. About 50 wells have been completed and 23 of these are water wells while 27 are testing wells for geological information. The depths of these wells range from several score to a thousand or more feet and they have an average diameter of 6.5 inches[6].

Although direct data on ground water in Taiwan are generally lacking, available geological information provides a useful key to the location and probable richness of the various aquifers. Of the total island area of 13,884 square miles, about 2085 square miles are underlain with alluvial material having potentially high water-yielding capacities. The thick alluvial deposits tend to have the highest ground water potentialities, since they normally combine the two major geologic and hydrologic requirements: storage space in permeable materials and access to adequate supplies of water for recharge. About 2699 square miles consist of Pleistocene gravels and conglomerates (partially permeable volcanic deposits and partially poorly-recharged coastal plain sediments). These regions have fair to doubtful ground water possibilities. A vast remaining area of 9100 square miles is underlain with fine and close-grained shales, sandstones, and limestones or massive dense metamorphic rocks—all of which are essentially non-water bearing[7].

DISTRIBUTION OF GROUND WATER

The distribution of ground water in Taiwan (*Figure 19*) can be described as follows:

THE COASTAL ALLUVIAL PLAINS.—They include the western coastal plain and the northeastern Ilan plain. The western coastal plain starts from Hsinchu in the north and stretches to Chiayi, Tainan, Kaohsiung, and Pingtung in the south, reaching a maximum of 149.1 miles in length and 24.9 miles in width.

In these plains the rivers have deposited clay and gravels which are characteristically loose in structure and great in permeability. Thus a good foundation for reservoirs of ground water is provided.

The Choshui River between Changhua and Chiayi and the Lower Tamsui River near Pingtung are the best ground water areas. The former has many distributaries and has built broad alluvial fans, while the latter is rich

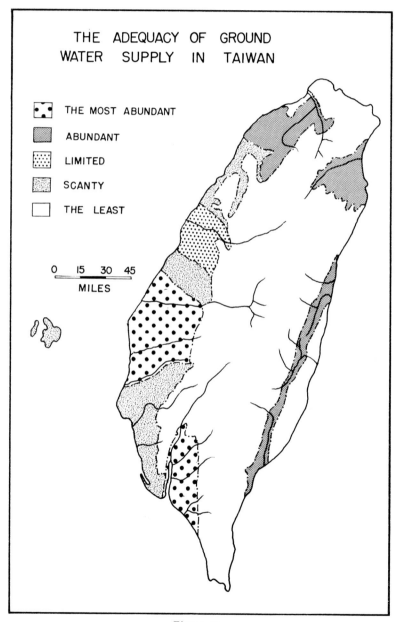

Figure 19

85

in water supply and has a good geological structure. The northeastern Ilan coastal plain covers about 144 square miles, but the ground water is not yet well developed.

THE FOOTHILL BELT AND THE TABLELAND.—From the western coastal plains to the Central Mountains the foothill belt and the gravel tablelands are encountered, extending from Taipei to Kaohsiung. Between Taipei and Hsinchu there is a large gravel tableland which is a dissected upland with a thickness from 164 to 328 feet. These tablelands consist of gravels of different sizes which are loose in structure and good in permeability, and which provide a good layer for ground water. However, in these elevated uplands the water table is far below the tableland and it is therefore necessary to dig the wells deep; this however, raises the cost of pumping. The pumping cost could be reduced if artesian aquifers were encountered. The capacity to store ground water would be considerably increased if Toukoshan conglomerate rather than bedrock were found below the tableland gravel.

THE CENTRAL MOUNTAINS OF METAMORPHIC COMPLEX.—The Central Mountains are underlain by crystalline rocks, hard sandstones, and dense slates which are so compact that they generally do not contain ground water. Small amounts of water may be held in fissures and joints in these hard rocks, but they are not apt to form a large ground water reservoir. The Central Mountain area is the poorest region for ground water development.

THE COASTAL VOLCANIC RANGES.—The Tatun coastal range in the north and the Taitung coastal range in the east are built of andesitic lava flows and agglomerates, with occasional exposures of intruded sandstones and shales. The conglomerates and the agglomerates are fair water-bearers. Other rocks yield water only in fractures, joints, and weathered zones. Although the ground water supply is generally small here, parts of the public water supplies for the municipalities of Taipei and Keelung are obtained from the water seepages in open fractures and cavities found in the pyroclastic rocks of the Tatun volcanic group.

THE INTERMONTANE BASINS AND VALLEYS.—This area includes several important drainage basins and intermontane valleys of Taiwan, including the Taipei basin and the Taitung rift valley. Since these depressions are located in the lower part of the surrounding mountains, each contains a ground water body in the alluvial deposit of sand and gravel which is fed by drainage from the encircling mountains. The most important aquifers are the alluvial sand and gravel of the valley fill. Wide recharge areas are provided as major streams cross or flow through these valleys or basins. The Taitung rift valley provided a great depth for the accumulation of thick alluvial deposits. The valley fill is characteristically pervious and will yield good supplies of ground water. The area constitutes, as a whole, an important ground water reservoir for Taiwan, though little development of it has occurred thus far.

THE PENGHU ISLANDS GROUP.—The Penghu group is composed of sixty-four volcanic islands made up of basalt with sandstone and shale interbeds underneath. The fissures and joints common to these volcanic islands could be useful for storing ground water, but water supplies on these islands are obtained chiefly from the sandstone aquifers below the basalt cap. Surrounded by sea, there is no important river on Penghu and the supply of fresh water has been a real problem. In addition, there is a serious problem with sea water encroachment in the wells of these islands. Thus the ground water reservoir is limited and the development potential is negligible.

Penghu Island has a semi-arid climate and the evaporation is greater than precipitation. The only water source which can be utilized is ground water. There are, however, three major unfavorable conditions for digging deep wells to the ground water of the island.

First, the ground water table of the island is rather low, averaging 32.8 feet below the surface; therefore, air pumps must be used for getting the ground water. However, these air pumps are expensive; their efficiency is only 30 per cent and maintenance costs are high.

Second, if the deep-well pumping machine of the American Johnston International Company is to be used, the diameter of the wells must be more than 20 inches. Since the island's rock layer is capped by the basalt for about 131.2 feet, the digging of these deep-wells would be very costly. Also, the underground water is not found in large quantity and the resultant water supply would be limited.

Third, since Penghu Island is surrounded by seas, and since its basalt is an extremely porous rock, the over-pumping of fresh water in the deep ground may result in the seepage of salt sea water from the basalt to the fresh water layer. After a period of time, the water in the well may change its quality. This phenomenon has occurred in both Hawaii and Makun Island with rather undesirable results.

For the above reasons it is not practicable to dig deep wells in the Penghu Islands. Nor is it practical to build a reservoir on the ground since the island's rainfall is not great and there is excessive evaporation which may dry out the reservoir. In addition, the wind over the island contains salt and silt which would accelerate the drying up of the reservoir. The only feasible method for obtaining underground water in the Penghu Islands seems to be the development of shallow wells.

SUMMARY

To summarize, three broad ground-water regions in Taiwan can be recognized: the mountain region, the foothill area, and the coastal plains. The storage of ground water is limited in the mountain region and the foothill area, making the coastal plains the sole storehouse for ground water. In the mountain region and foothill area not only is the reservoir of ground water limited, but also cultivated land and settlement are sparse. Thus, these two areas have less demand and less value for developing ground water, while on the coastal plain the rich ground-water reservoir, together with the large population and great amounts of cultivated acreage, make the area promising for the development of underground water resources.

In the coastal plains two proved favorable ground-water areas are noted; one in the Choshui River alluvial fan in the central western Taiwan area between Changhua and Chichow, and the other in the Pingtung Valley in southern Taiwan, stretching from Chiwei and Meimung down to Chaochow. The large amount of stored ground water in these two areas was indicated by numerous bamboo artesian wells in the early days and has been recently proved by some 125 wells drilled by the Taiwan Sugar Corporation during 1950 and 1951. These two ground-water areas have thick deposits of alluvial material containing good aquifers in both the artesian and unconfined zones. These alluvial materials are evenly-sized rounded gravels without too much fine clay which might prevent the flow of the ground water. Recharge conditions on the fans are excellent. The great run-off, which derives from the high precipitation, the watersheds in the lofty mountains, and the long rivers, assures a large safe yield for ground water.

Pingtung Valley is the best reservoir for ground water in Taiwan. This is an alluvial fan with a length of 32.3 miles and a total area of 355 square miles. It contains pebbles, gravels and sands, but there is very little fine silt which would create an unfavorable condition for ground water. Porous rocks and uncompact structure have favored the reserves of ground water. Water will appear at only 350 inches. The water table of the area varies with the season. During the rainy season the water table is 20 inches from the surface, while in the dry season it is 120 inches.

The Choshui River alluvial fan is the other rich ground water reservoir. With a total area of 907.3 square miles the area is covered with gravel and sand. As in the Pingtung Valley, one only needs to dig 300 inches to reach water. However, in contrast to Pingtung Valley, the deposits here are mostly fine sand and silt. In developing the ground water, care must be taken to avoid the large amounts of fine sand which could affect the well volume as well as its longevity.

REFERENCES

[1] LEE-TANG HSUEH, "Hydrology of Taiwan," In *A Scientific Review of Taiwan* (Educational and Cultural Association, Taipei, 1956).

[2] S. T. HSU, "Hydrography of Taiwan," In *The Gazeteer of Taiwan* (The Historical Research Commission of Taiwan Province, Taipei, 1956).

[3] K. C. CHANG, "Hydrography of Taiwan," *Taiwan Hsin-chih*, 1954. [In Chinese].

[4] C. S. Ho, *Mineral Resources of Taiwan* (Hsinchu Research Institute, Chinese Retroleum Corporation, 1953).

[5] K. C. CHEN, *Groundwater in Taiwan* (The Bank of Taiwan, Taipei, 1952). [In Chinese].

[6] C. S. Ho, "Groundwater of Taiwan and its Utilization," *Taiwan Reconstruction Monthly*, No. 7 (1951). [In Chinese].

[7] WILLERT RHYNSBURGER, *Area and Resources Survey, Taiwan*. (International Cooperation Administration, U.S. Mutual Security Mission to China, Taipei, 1956).

SIX

Soils and
Natural Vegetation

FACTORS IN SOIL FORMATION

SOIL IS THE RESULT OF MANY FACTORS, including climate, parent material, landforms, and the vegetation cover. Temperature, precipitation, and humidity are the critical climatic elements in forming soil types. Parent material refers to the physical properties and mineral composition of the rock from which the soil is derived. Landforms affect drainage, erosion, and air movement within the soil. The native vegetation supplies nutrition to the soil.

CLIMATIC FACTORS

In Taiwan's humid climate, physical weathering, chemical decomposition, and leaching are strong, and soil microorganisms are very active. Soluble minerals, organic materials, calcium carbonates, and other basic salts have been well leached from the mature soil, leaving only a concentration of iron and aluminum in the B horizon. This condition is typical of pedalfer soils. Consequently, all mature soils in Taiwan are acid in degree, varying from slight to strong in reaction (pH values from 6.5 to 4.5), and are rather low in fertility.

Laterization and podzolization are the two most important soil-forming processes in Taiwan; the former occurs in the lowlands while the latter appears in the mountainous areas. In lateritic genesis the soluble bases are quickly released and are subject to removal by leaching; the silica content is dissolved and leached away, while elements of iron, aluminum, and manganese remain. Sometimes the iron and aluminum concentrate in the upper part; thus, as weathering proceeds, a red and yellow soil high in sesquioxides and low in silica results.

Although the red lateritic soils are widely distributed, there are few well-developed profiles. This lack is the result of climatic conditions.

89

Taiwan has a high annual temperature of 71.6°F. and the annual rainfall exceeds 98 inches. With this abundant rainfall the iron and aluminum in the soil are well-soaked, and the soils tend to be yellow in color. The connection between heavy rain and yellow soils explains why the more rainy northeastern part of the island has more yellow soils than do other parts of Taiwan. In the south the winter is rather dry, but the annual rainfall is still quite high in relation to average temperature. Excessively heavy rainfall here does not encourage the development of lateritic soils. The ideal climatic conditions for its formation are an average temperature of more than 77°F. and an annual rainfall between 40 and 60 inches. Lateritic soils in Taiwan are usually developed from parent rock. Quaternary red terraces which contain a great deal of iron are good examples of this process. This leads some pedologists to believe that these lateritic soils were not evolved under Taiwan's present climate, but that they are relic soils, from a much hotter and drier climate which prevailed in a former geological period[1].

The red mature soils of the warm lowlands contrast sharply with the gray mountain soils. With the increase in altitude, laterization yields gradually to podzolization which is typically carried out in a cool, humid climate with concomitant coniferous or mixed forest cover. In this environment the decaying of tree leaves is retarded, giving rise to a large amount of organic acid. Also, in this humid, dark, forested area, there is enough water carried along with these organic acids to dissolve the iron and aluminum to the bottom, leaving the silica content in the subsoil. A well-developed profile of podzolized soil should fit the following description: the top of the A horizon is a layer of decayed leaves; next is a layer of dark humus; the third layer, having been drastically leached, is bleached and gray in appearance and has been left in a highly acidic siliceous condition. The B-horizon subsoil is yellowish-brown in color, loamy in texture, and compact in structure.

PARENT MATERIAL

The formation of soils in Taiwan has been affected not only by climate, but also by their parent materials. The parent materials of Taiwan's cultivated soils are primarily derived from sedimentary rocks and alluvium, which determine the soil texture. The soils derived from these parent rocks are of a loamy texture. In Taiwan loamy soil covers more than 70 per cent of the island's cultivated land. Soils of the upper parts of alluvial fans, however, are derived from coarse detritus carried down by summer rains; they are usually stony, unirrigable, and have a low potential yield. The sand dunes along the coast present another kind of problem. These sandy soils require the addition of organic materials in order to improve water retention, to stabilize the surface against wind erosion, and to enrich the content of plant nutrients. Most of the lacustrine soils in the Taipei and Taichung basins have a clayish texture which is ideal for cultivation. Igneous and metamorphic rocks appear only in the forest-clad mountains of the central part of the island. Here, heavy rains result in torrents which flow down the steep slopes, bringing about severe erosion and exposing the parent rock. The resultant soil is characterized by a shallow profile and a coarse texture.

LANDFORMS

Landforms also affect the formation of Taiwan's soils. For example, the Chungyang Shan area, with its cool temperatures, heavy rainfall, and dense forest cover, should be an ideal place for the development of pod- zolic soils. But the steep slopes (usually more than 15 degrees in steepness, and sometimes as much as 80 degrees) cause rapid soil erosion and expose the parent rock and drainage pools. Thus it is difficult to develop a well- preserved soil profile in this area.

The steep and high mountains make rivers in Taiwan short and swift. The heavy rains flow down from the mountains carrying a great amount of sand and gravel, which is then deposited on the flat land. Since the de- posits were irregular, and since these coastal plains were often flooded, the soils have had little chance to develop a normal and clear profile; they exhibit only differences of texture.

Marine-deposit soil is a special kind of soil in Taiwan. It is not definitely known whether this soil is derived from clay deposits on the deep sea floor which later rose above sea level, or whether it represents old deposits in still water. The clear layers of its profile indicate that there has been little soil development. From the soil profile the salty soil of the coastal area belongs to neither the solonchak nor the solonetz group, for the climate of Taiwan is not dry enough to produce a true salty soil. The appearance of salt soil is due to the low elevation and high water table, the poor drainage, and the salty material produced from siliceous parent materials. During the typhoon season the sea water leaves a great amount of soluble salt on the land. This soil, then, is only another kind of alluvium.

VEGETATION COVER

In forested areas the soils are usually covered by a layer of decomposed leaf mold called humus. This humus, if used in agricultural areas, could not only provide sulfur and nitrogen for plants, but could also improve the physical characteristics of the soil. However, after long periods of settle- ment and cultivation in Taiwan the average content of humus in cultivated soils is less than two per cent. This could be remedied through the use of green manure, and especially by legumes which have a narrow carbon to nitrogen ratio. This suggestion has often been emphatically raised by agriculturalists in Taiwan.

SOIL GROUPS

The interplay of different soil-forming factors gives the soils in Taiwan a great diversity. *Figure 20* shows the horizontal distribution of the soils in Taiwan. However, as a result of the island's landforms the soils vary more according to vertical zonation than horizontal. In traveling from the western coast to the Central Mountain area all the various soil groups are encountered. In the west are encountered first salines (solonchaks) and planosols (paddy soils), then alluvial soils. Next, the hills and terraces where the lateritic soils are found are crossed. Proceeding ahead, the red and yellow soils are seen, and after climbing this hilly land, it will be noticed that the podzolic profile is more prominent, recognizing the characteristic gray-brown soils. When the top of the mountainous area is finally reached, podzolic and stony mountain soils are encountered.

Because of the various soil groups which exist in this cross-section, land use differs accordingly, from the coastal flatlands to the interior mountains. In the west to east journey, one sees only salt fields and some fish culture along the coast; proceeding inland sugar cane, rice and paddy fields, citrus

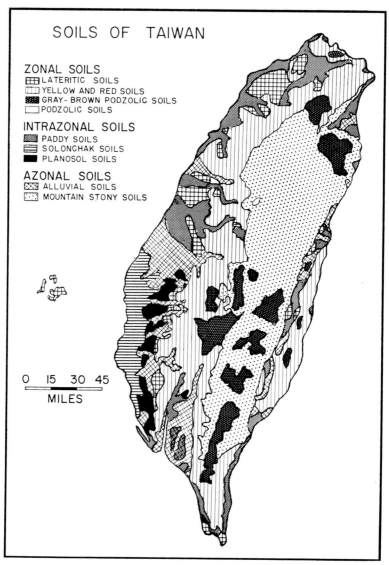

Figure 20

fruit, and barren steep slopes are encountered; climbing to the high mountains one is surrounded by huge forests or waste lands.

There are three soil orders and nine soil groups. The distribution and characteristics of each soil group will be discussed briefly below[2, 3].

ZONAL SOILS

Zonal soil is mature soil with a relatively well-developed profile, formed under the strong influence of climate and vegetation cover. There are four groups of zonal soils found in Taiwan:

Lateritic soil

Lateritic soil is predominant in the lowlands, that is, from 328 to 1640 feet above sea level. This soil developed from diluvial deposits and is characterized by its dark red color. Well-leached and acidic in reaction (pH 4.5) and poor in fertility, it needs an adequate application of chemical fertilizers to increase the crop yield. It appears from north to south along the Chungyang Shan area and is found mainly on the tableland of Hsinchu, to some extent in Taichung and Tainan, and sporadically in Kaohsiung and Taitung. Almost without exception all the lateritic soil has been cultivated wherever there is a good water supply or well irrigation, and it is most important for growing rice, tea, and citrus fruits. The soil depth is about 6.5 feet. The surface soil, which is loam and clayey loam, turns grayish-brown as a result of cultivation. In Taoyuan and Chungli the soil is cultivated and paddy fields are created. After soaking in water for a long period, the soil profile changes considerably and dispersion occurs.

It is interesting to note that although the soil of the Penghu Islands should belong to the lateritic family since it is red in color and derived from basalt, this soil is coarse and sandy in texture, and neutral or slightly alkaline in reaction. These characteristics are typical of dry lands. As a matter of fact the climate of Taiwan is quite different from that of the Penghu Islands, where, although the rainfall is heavy, the wind is strong, making the evaporation rate half as great as the rate of precipitation. Thus the climate is semi-arid, and the soil should be classified as a transitional type between lateritic and red desert soil.

The yellow and red soil

Yellow and red soil covers a large part of the hilly lands which flank the Central Mountains of Taiwan. It prevails between 984 and 2624 feet above sea level, where both podzolization and laterization have been at work. Temperate mixed forest, often remarkably deciduous, still covers most of this soil, while in the cultivated areas bananas, pineapples, tea, and citrus fruits are often grown. Thus this soil is one of the most productive zonal soils in Taiwan. It developed from parent material which contained silicas; it is very acidic in reaction and lacks sufficient mineral nutrients. Like lateritic soil, when yellow and red soil appears on a gentle land with a sufficient supply of water for irrigation it is used for paddy fields. The Taipei basin and Taoyuan terraces are good examples of such paddy lands. After the yellow and red soil has undergone prolonged soaking as paddy fields it exhibits an interesting change: the surface layer (about

93

five inches deep) becomes gray-brown in color; below the cultivated layer there is a thin solid layer from 1.47 to 3.15 inches in thickness and dark-gray and pinkish-brown in color. The heavy subsoil is a light blue or light yellow clay—the deeper the soil, the lighter the color. The soil is very acidic in reaction and much resembles the planosol of the United States.

Gray-brown podzolic soil

The gray-brown podzolic soil, which is found at elevations between 2624 and 6560 feet, is mildly podzolized. The parent materials include many kinds of rocks, most of which are covered by needle-leaved forest or mixed forest. The soil is very acidic, having a pH value of 5.0. Organic matter is incorporated with content mineral in a mull layer of several inches. Considerable calcium still occupies the colloidal complex. Were it not for the rugged terrain, which restricts the land use, the soil would constitute a zonal group of great agricultural value.

Podzolic soil

Podzolic soil appears only in the mountain areas at elevations above 6560 feet and is derived mainly from sandy shale. This soil is so sporadically distributed that it is difficult to discern on a small-scale soil map. The soil is shallow, usually having a thickness of less than 23.6 inches, and its reaction is strongly acidic. Its profiles often show signs of poor drainage. Since it occupies an area which is extremely small and is under forest cover it is of little agricultural importance.

INTRAZONAL SOIL

Intrazonal soil is distinguished from zonal cover by the fact of it being that soil which reflects the influence of local conditions, such as parent rock, drainage, alkali salts, or some unique inherited characteristic. Three groups of intrazonal soils are recognized in Taiwan:

Paddy soil

Paddy soil is that soil which has been devoted to rice cultivation for so many years that it has developed some unique characteristics. Being irrigated most of the year, its top-soils are highly dispersed and are usually structureless. As a result of the dispersing action of soil water much of the soluble material is conveyed to different parts of the solum, forming a great number of rusty streaks and mottlings. The paddy soil appears in the coastal plains, local basins, and along the river banks. When properly handled, paddy soil is second only to alluvial soil in productivity.

Solonchak soil

Solonchak exists along the southwest coast of Taiwan, where the invasion of tidal water adds to its salinity. It is formed through the action of salts in the sea water and those released from the base-bearing parent rock. On the average, the salt content seldom exceeds 0.2 per cent. The predominant salts are usually calcium and sodium sulfates, while sodium chloride exists in great amounts in the soil along the immediate coast.

The carbon content is very small. Mildly alkaline to neutral in reaction, solonchak is unsuitable for most crops unless the injurious effects of soluble salts are offset by special treatment. If the soil has an extremely high salt content it is used as salt field. Most of the saline soil which has already been degraded is used for planting rice or for fish culture.

Planosol soil

Planosol is found on the Tainan and Kaohsiung alluvial plains and connects with solonchak on the western side. Its subsoil is brittle and neutral in reaction. It is formed on marine deposits and is heavy in texture. This soil group is used mainly for growing sugar cane. Its structure is compact, tending to resist penetration by water or by the roots of vegetation. When dry this soil becomes very hard and when wet it becomes heavy and muddy. Thus it is very difficult to cultivate, and in addition, the area occupied by this soil suffers from a shortage of water. The farmers in Taiwan have much trouble with planosols, calling it *K'an-t'ien t'ien*, or "look-at-the-sky-fields," since its productivity depends to such a great extent upon the weather.

AZONAL SOIL

Azonal soil is immature soil which is derived from various parent materials and which lacks well-developed profiles. Two groups of the azonal order are found in Taiwan.

Alluvial soil

In Taiwan the widely-distributed alluvial soil constitutes the most important soil for agricultural purposes. This soil appears in such locations as plains, basins, river banks and alluvial fans. Different parent materials have given rise to different types of alluvial soil. Slate alluvial soil is found between the Tatu and Silo Rivers in Taichung, on the eastern side of the Lower Tamshui River in Kaohsiung, and in the alluvial fans of Ilan and Taitung. It is characterized by a dark color, a depth of 3.28 feet, high calcium content, and neutral reaction. This soil contains abundant nutrients, making it the most fertile soil on the island. The alluvial soil areas of Pintung, Yuanlin, and Ilan have become Taiwan's granary. Tobacco and rice are the dominant crops in these areas.

Sandstone and shale alluvial soil occupies the major part of the cultivated area, extending from north to south. In the north, the alluvial soil is acidic in reaction, whereas that in the south is slightly acidic to neutral, or even slightly alkaline. In the north most of these soils have become paddy fields, while in the south they are used for dry farming and rotated crops because of the shortage of water supply. The main crops produced on alluvial soil are rice and sugar cane. Schist alluvial soils are found in the eastern part of the Chungyang Shan area, which is composed of old crystalline schist. The rivers flowing down from this area to the Taitung rift valley deposited disintegrated schist, thus forming the alluvial soil which is high in lime content and alkaline in reaction. Rice, sugar cane, and peanuts are the principal crops. Though derived from different sorts of parent rock, alluvial soil is generally high in fertility and is the most productive soil in Taiwan.

Stony mountain soil

Stony mountain soil is found on high mountain slopes, usually at elevations above 9840 feet. Under the cool climate and coniferous cover it has become distinctly podzolized, but because of the steep slopes erosion has continually removed the surface soil before it is able to form more than a thin layer of loose material. Therefore, this soil does not have a well-developed podzolized profile. In spite of its large extent, covering the entire Chungyang Shan area, the stony soil has little agricultural value.

OTHER SOILS

Along the sea coast of Taiwan, wave action has caused the accumulation of a narrow sandy ridge a little more than three feet in height. These sandy deposits, mixed with shell and broken coral reef, are more or less acidic in reaction. In areas such as the northwestern coast area in Taoyuan and Miaoli, where strong winds occur, these sand deposits have become relatively larger.

Muck occurs in poorly-drained lowland swamp areas. Muck soil is a dark bluish color and is acid in reaction. The surface layer contains rich organic matter and extends to a depth of 7.87–11.81 inches. This soil covers a very small area. It is found in Taoyuan, Lotung and Lukong.

Rendzina soil, which was formed in the limestone area, contains much calcium, and appears in Hsinkong or Taitung. It contains about 4 per cent organic matter, is fragile and granular in structure, and is slightly acidic in reaction.

Another minor group is gritty soil, which is derived either from coral reef or basaltic rock. The former occurs near Hengchun, the latter in Taitung. Both are young soils.

Because of the influence of erosion, deposition, and human factors, one can hardly find a well-developed soil profile in Taiwan. Also, since alluvial soil and stony mountain soil occupy a large area, soils developed in the mountain area contain much broken stone, while the alluvial soils developed on the plain have been under cultivation too long to permit the formation of distinct soil profiles.

As for the size of the area occupied by each soil group the stony mountain soil and red and yellow soil cover the largest areas, while paddy soil and alluvial soil are less extensive. Solonchak, along with gray-brown podzolic soil, occupies still smaller areas, while the planosol and podzolic soil cover only scattered patches. In terms of agricultural value the alluvial soil and paddy soil are the most extensively farmed, and are, therefore, the most productive; lateritic, planosol, solonchak, and red and yellow soils are less productive, and the rest are either forested lands or waste lands.

SOIL FERTILITY

In view of the fact that agriculturists and farmers are more interested in soil fertility than in whether the soil is lateritic or podzolic, a discussion of soil fertility in Taiwan is called for. Soil fertility is closely related to

soil productivity, but has a more limited meaning. In agriculture, productivity is synonymous with crop yield. In the soil sciences, soil productivity refers to the capacity of the soil to grow plants, and this capacity is
dependent upon air, water, and mineral nutrients in sufficient quantities
for plant growth. Texture, structure, and moisture characteristics are the
three chief criteria of soil productivity. Texture refers to the various
size groups of individual soil grains. Structure is the arrangement of the
various size clumps or aggregates of finer-sized particles in a mass of soil.
With regard to predominantly clayey or silty soils, structure is the key
factor; with regard to predominantly sandy or gravelly soils, texture and
moisture are of major importance. Soil productivity is controlled not only
by the properties of the soil, but also by climatic and biotic conditions.
Soil fertility refers to the soil factors themselves, of which perhaps the
most important are texture, pH value, organic matter content, nitrogen,
available phosphorus, and available potash. Although these six factors
are not the only ones used in evaluating the capacity of the soil to grow
plants, they are the essential ones.

In spite of a continuing effort to maintain or increase the fertility of
the soil, such qualities as the texture, the pH value, and the organic matter
content of the soil are more or less stable features controlled by nature;
that is, by climate, parent material, surface features, vegetation, and the
like. On the other hand, the available nitrogen, phosphorus, and potash of
the soil are more subject to change by human activities. But even these
available contents of the soil are determined to a great extent by natural
forces rather than by human activities, such as fertilizing and manuring.
For example, we cannot expect a richer available phosphorus content in
an acid lateritic soil than in a neutral soil under similar farming practices.
Thus, a map of soil fertility factors would have the same general pattern
as a map showing soil groups. This section on soil fertility was mainly
derived from Chang's valuable survey of the island[4].

TEXTURE

Texture is one of the most important qualities of soil, for it influences not
only the physical properties but also the chemical behavior of the soil.
Generally speaking, most soils in Taiwan are loamy in texture. Those in the
north are sandy loams, while those in the south are loams and silty loams.
But there are exceptions: the heaviest soils in Taiwan are slate alluvial
soil (in Tainan and Kaohsiung). These clay soils cover a large area, but
few of them are more than 40 per cent clay, the general range being from
30 to 40 per cent. Marine-deposited soil, which has long aroused the complaints of farmers because of its heavy texture, is also a loamy clay soil.
The lateritic soil in Hsinchu is likewise very heavy in texture, and is also
primarily clay loam.

REACTION

Soil reaction is considered to be the most important factor in soil fertility.
A very acidic soil can never yield a good crop, while a slightly acidic to
neutral reaction is generally an index of fertility. Soil reaction is measured
in terms of pH (hydrogen potential), that is, whether it is acid, neutral, or

alkaline. Values below 7.0 indicate acidity; those above 7.0 show alkalinity. The pH values of soils in Taiwan are determined by the nature of the parent materials and by the geological time of their deposition. Alkaline rock always forms alkaline alluvial soil, and acidic rock always derives an acidic alluvial soil. Given two soils derived from the same kind of parent material, the earlier deposit will have a greater acid reaction, because the older deposit has been subjected to climatic influences for a longer time. For example, yellow and red soil is an older deposit; it has been exposed to high temperatures, heavy rainfall, and strong leaching longer than has alluvial soil. As a result, yellow and red soil is very acidic in reaction.

Also, soils along the sea coast or along river banks are higher in pH value than are those more distant from such bodies of water. Slate is a calcareous rock. The alluvial soils derived from slate are, on the average, 0.97 per cent lime (CaO) and 1.15 per cent magnesia (MgO). The soil reaction is mostly neutral (as in Taichung). Although the reactions of the slate soils in Taipei, Ilan, Kaohsiung, Pintung, and Taitung are slightly acidic, their subsoils are neutral. The sandstone and shale alluvial soils contain much less calcium and magnesium, and their reactions are acidic. The shale in southern Taiwan, however, has a higher marl content than has that of northern Taiwan. The sandstone and shale alluvial soils in the south are therefore a little higher in pH value. Schist is also an alkaline rock, and schist alluvial soils are consequently alkaline in reaction. The marine-deposited soils vary from acidic to neutral in reaction. The saline and alkaline soils are slightly alkaline in reaction; however, their pH values are rarely above 8.5. Acidic soils with pH values below 6.0 are estimated to cover about one-fourth of the cultivated area of Taiwan. It is thought that liming the soil will create a great increase in crop production. This practice has been entirely neglected in the past; however, recent experiments with sugar cane and rice indicated that these two crops respond well to liming.

ORGANIC CONTENT

The organic matter content of the soil not only supplies plant nutrients but also constitutes the essential factor in improving the physical, chemical, and biological properties of the soil. Climatic elements greatly influence the organic content. High temperature causes greater activity of the soil microorganisms, and thus hastens the decomposition of organic matter. On the other hand, heavy precipitation always retards the decomposition of the organic matter, permitting it to accumulate. The relationship between climate and organic matter can be clearly seen by travelling from the northern to the southern tip of Taiwan, or from the coastal plain to the mountainous regions. In Taiwan, temperature does not vary greatly from north to south. However, the difference in amount of rainfall is much greater. Annual precipitation at Taipei and Keelung averages between 98.43 and 118.11 inches, while that along the coastal plain of Tainan is around 56.06 inches. The difference may be as much as 75 inches. As a result, the organic content of the soil in Taiwan decreases from north to south. In Taipei the organic matter is generally more than 3.5 per cent of the total, but it decreases southward gradually to less than 1.5 per cent in the coastal plain of Tainan. Since the mountain area of Taiwan receives more rain than the coastal lowland, the organic matter of the soils thus decreases from the mountains to the lowland.

In addition to climate, soil texture plays a very important role in the decomposition and accumulation of organic matter. A heavy texture slows down decomposition, while light texture quickens it. Heavy clay loam always contains more than 2.5 per cent organic matter, while lighter, sandy loam usually contains less than 2.0 per cent. An extreme example of soil with a low organic content is found in the Tainan coastal plain, where decomposition of organic deposits is speeded by both light-textured soil and relatively light rainfall.

NITROGEN

Nitrogen exists in the soil mainly in organic form. The organic matter content of the soil serves roughly as an estimation of soil nitrogen; where soil organic matter is high, the nitrogen content is also high. Most soils in Taiwan are 0.1–0.15 per cent nitrogen. The availability of nitrogen may be judged from the carbon-nitrogen ratio of the organic matter. A high C/N ratio means that the nitrogen is in a more available form. Generally, the C/N ratio of soil organic matter in Taiwan is around 10, but the ratio varies from one soil group to another. The slate alluvial soils rate comparatively low, having a C/N ratio of 6 to 8. It seems that a high lime content stimulates the activity of soil microorganisms and rapid decomposition of the organic matter, and at the same time the heavy texture retains the released nitrogen. On the other hand, decomposition of organic matter proceeds more slowly in a heavy-textured soil with an acidic reaction. Thus the C/N ratios of organic matter in the Taipei basin and of the marine-deposited soils are generally more than 10. For the rest of the soils, the figure is usually between 8 and 10. The C/N ratio of the soil is a very good index of productivity.

PHOSPHORUS

Phosphorus is one of the primary nutrient elements. A statistical study of soil samples revealed that the total phosphorus content of alluvial soils derived from northern tertiary sandstone and shale is 0.08 per cent, that of southern tertiary sandstone and shale alluvial is 0.11 per cent, that of lateritic soils on the diluvial deposit is 0.1 per cent, that of slate material soils and saline soils is 0.15 per cent, and that of schist alluvial soils is 0.12 per cent. A high lime content is always accompanied by a high phosphorus content. It is also clear that the available phosphorus content varies indirectly with pH values of the soil. In acidic soils the amount of available phosphorus is very low, and it increases as the pH value increases. The amount of available phosphorus in the soil is only a relative value, and must be checked by field experiments in order to diagnose the deficiency of the soil. Experiments with sugar cane and rice have revealed that in the acidic soil in Hsinchu, the slightly acidic soil in Taitung, and the alkaline sandy soil along the coast in Tainan and Kaohsiung, these two crops respond significantly to phosphorus. The study showed that by testing the soil for its phosphorus content, pH value, and texture, a fairly reliable diagnosis could be made and suitable fertilizer recommended.

POTASH

Potash is another primary plant nutrient, and the amounts in which it is present in the soil vary according to the nature of the parent material of the soil. The lateritic soils on the diluvial deposit contain 0.17 per cent potash, the north tertiary sandstone and shale alluvial soils contain 0.18 per cent, the slate alluvial soils 0.31 per cent, the alkaline soils 0.22 per cent, and the schist alluvial soils 0.10 per cent. It seems that the potash content of the soil, like the phosphorus content, is connected with the lime content. The relation between the available potash of the soil and pH value or texture is not apparent, but in soils with pH values of less than 5.0, the amount of available potash is always low, while in soils with pH values of more than 7.5, a high amount of available potash is frequently found. Generally speaking, the yellow and red soils respond most significantly to potash fertilizer.

SUMMARY

From the above discussion, soil fertility in Taiwan can be briefly summarized as follows: Cultivated soil in Taiwan is mainly of the alluvial type. The fertility of this alluvial soil is rather high and its physical properties are well-suited for growing crops. As to the soil texture, loamy soil occupies a large area, while the extent of sandy soil is limited. The area occupied by clay soil is by no means small, but the clay soil is somewhat loamy in texture; thus it does not have the disadvantage of being too heavy. In Taiwan there are no soils which are excessively acidic or alkaline, most of them ranging from slightly acidic to neutral in reaction. The organic content of the soil is, in most places, around 2.0 per cent, which cannot be considered low. In general, then, Taiwan's soils are in good condition. If these soils are well managed, they can provide a sound foundation for the increased development of agricultural production.

The less productive soils in Taiwan are the lateritic and the red and yellow soils which are distributed in the Hsinchu and Taichung foothills along the western side of the Chungyang Shan area. Of the two, lateritic soil is the poorer. Having developed under a hot and humid climate, its base content has been thoroughly leached, and it is strongly acidic. In addition, the calcium, potash, and phosphorus content is a reliable index of the soil's productivity, and the low productivity in southern Taiwan soils mainly due to their deficient supplies of organic matter. However, with proper treatment this soil still can be made fertile. The soils along Taiwan's coastal areas are also low in productivity, mainly because of their strong alkalinity.

The most productive soils in Taiwan are the alluvial soils, which show a slightly acidic or neutral reaction. Some examples of these soils are found along river banks in Taichung and Kaohsiung, and in the plains of Pintung. These fertile soils have these three very salutary qualities: first, they range from slightly acidic to neutral; second, they are loamy in texture, some being loamy clay; third, they have a high organic content—around 3.0 per cent. With these three characteristics, these soils are structurally sound and have an abundance of effective plant nutrients, including calcium, potash, nitrogen, and phosphorus.

The soils of Taiwan react very well to nitrogen, phosphorus, and potash fertilizers. The soils which react most noticeably to phosphorous are the lateritic and salt soils, while those which can be effectively treated by potash fertilizer are the lateritic and the red and yellow soils.

SOILS AND AGRICULTURE

Agricultural practice in any region cannot ignore the soil types. The pedologist can explain soil properties, formulate fertilizers and aid in designing the regional plan of soil management. Thus, the agriculturist and the pedologist can certainly work cooperatively to increase crop yields.

Natural forces, aided by human activities, have caused serious soil erosion. High mountains, steep slopes, and torrential rains have combined to make the soil profile in Taiwan never complete or well developed, but immature, eroded, or dissected. Taiwan's rugged terrain limits the amount of land suitable for cultivation, but with the rapid increase of population in recent years, much land which should be used as pasture land or to cultivate non-food crops has been diverted for food crops. This extensive misuse of marginal lands and the devastation of mountain forests has contributed to making the soil erosion problem much more acute. Once the thin soils on the steep slopes have been cleared of their protective vegetation and have been turned under by the plow, a few torrential showers can wash them away and the terrain may become rocky and barren within four or five years. In many coastal foothill areas one finds rock talus on which even grass can hardly grow. If this situation is allowed to continue, many wastelands will result. Therefore, proper soil management and the prevention of soil erosion are of primary importance in planning the future agricultural development of Taiwan.

As to fertility, the soil in Taiwan, though not excellent, is generally good. Temperatures do not limit the growing period nor is the rainfall insufficient. Although the nutrient content is not high, it can be remedied by fertilizers. In short, effective soil management is bound to improve agricultural production on the island.

Admitting that improved soil management is vitally necessary, it remains now to make some specific suggestions in connection with agricultural practices in Taiwan.

Farmers in Taiwan have long suffered from the heavy texture of the marine-deposited soils, for these heavy soils are rather difficult to work. During sunny weather they become dry and hard, while in rainy weather they become muddy and sticky. Along with the improvement of the irrigation systems to meet the water shortage, the structure of this marine-deposited soil could be improved by adding lime and organic matter. The introduction of agricultural machines may also greatly help in solving the difficult problem of plowing.

The soils of southern Taiwan are very low in organic matter content, and this is the main reason for their low productivity. Therefore, green manure should be widely used in order to maintain a level of organic matter necessary to raise the capacity of the soil to support plant growth.

On the island as a whole, soils with a pH value of less than 6.0 should be treated with lime to neutralize the acidity; in addition, base-forming fertilizers such as calcium cyanamide and fused phosphate should be applied.

Since Taiwan is quite humid there is considerable leaching of soluble nitrogen. In order to build up the nitrogen content economically and effectively, organic and chemical fertilizers should be used. The steady depletion of plant nutrients, by the leaching process and by heavy cropping throughout the year, can be remedied by heavy application of chemical fertilizers, growing of green manure crops, and turning under of compost.

Phosphorus deficiency occurs primarily in acidic soils. Since an acidic soil usually has a strong phosphorus fixation power it is usually better either to lime the soil before applying phosphorus, or to mix phosphate fertilizer with organic manure before applying it, in order to avoid the fixation of the phosphorus by the soil. For row crops such as sugar cane, sweet potatoes, and jute, a rational method of local placement should be carefully studied.

The potash supply in soil is generally rich in Taiwan, but certain crops, such as sugar cane, jute, sweet potatoes, and tobacco respond to potash more noticeably than others. Therefore, potash fertilizers should be used particularly on these kinds of crops to increase production. The potash supply is also more important in the acidic soils.

In short, basic practices in soil management in Taiwan should include readjusting the soil reaction, increasing the organic matter content and improving the structure. Although hundreds of thousands of tons of chemical fertilizers are used annually in Taiwan, more study of soil fertility is urgently needed.

NATURAL VEGETATION

With high mountains, high temperature, and abundant rainfall, Taiwan has a rich flora. However, different groups of settlers who came to the island at various times cleared the natural vegetation from all the western plains suitable for agriculture. At present, approximately 68 per cent of the island, estimated at 6,158,975 acres, is still forested. About 80 per cent of this forested acreage is covered with trees, while the remaining 20 per cent is covered by shrubs.

Four main types of vegetation are dominant (*Figure 21*), namely, broad-leaved evergreen forests, mixed forests, coniferous forests, and steppe and shrub and bamboo. The total number of species of commercial importance reaches about 100, ranging from tropical hardwood growing at sea level to spruce, hemlocks, and firs occurring at higher elevations.

Of the total forest area in Taiwan (4,563,115 acres), the broad-leaved evergreen forest has an area of 3,356,235 acres or 73 per cent of the total. Next comes the mixed forest which has 665,157 acres or 14 per cent of the total. The coniferous forest, which is the most important economically, represents only 417,967 acres, or 10 per cent of the total. The bamboo has the least area in the total forest in the island, with 123,755 acres, or about 3 per cent (*Table 32*).

Table 32. Forest Area of Different Hsiens in Taiwan (acres)*

Hsien	Broad-leaved green forests	Mixed forests	Coniferous forests	Bamboo forests	Total
Taipei	464,322	96,855	133,170	9,535	703,882
Hsinchu	472,047	61,537	34,982	13,552	582,142
Taichung	628,557	157,932	94,785	46,292	929,885
Tainan	259,285	6,612	9,760	40,942	316,600
Kaohsiung	523,492	100,222	25,995	9,775	659,485
Taitung	591,382	31,330	23,200	1,732	647,642
Hualien	416,250	210,517	95,982	1,927	724,835
Penghu	897	—	—	—	897
Total	3,356,235	665,157	417,967	123,755	4,563,115

* According to data from the Provincial Government of Taiwan.

The vertical distribution of Taiwan's forests demonstrates an unusual rich variety and distinct zonations, which include the tropical, sub-tropical, temperate, and cold temperate zones[5, 6, 7].

Because of the latitudinal extension of the island, the climatic condition in Taiwan is quite different between the north and south. The effect of latitudinal differences on the vertical distribution of the natural vegetation in Taiwan is shown in Table 33.

Table 33. Vertical Distribution of Natural Vegetation Zones in Taiwan*
(altitude in feet)

Zone	North	Middle	South	Per cent of the total forest area
Tropical	below 300	below 2500	below 3300	56
Subtropical	below 4900	below 6600	below 7500	31
Temperate	below 9500	below 9800	below 11,000	11
Cold-temperate	above 9500	above 9800	above 11,000	2

* According to data from the Provincial Government of Taiwan.

VEGETATION ZONES

THE COLD TEMPERATE ZONE (CONIFEROUS FORESTS).—This natural vegetation zone is to be found above 9800 feet. Pure stands of the dominant species of firs (*Abies Kawakamii*) are widespread. The higher slopes are covered by grasslands on which are to be found junipers (*Juniperus squamata*) and numerous deciduous shrubs.

Towards the crest of the Central Mountains a second area of grassland vegetation appears in the form of Alpine meadows[8].

THE TEMPERATE ZONE (MIXED FOREST).—This natural vegetation zone is to be found on the mountain slopes at an elevation of from 5900 to 9800 feet. It includes mixed forests which contain deciduous and coniferous trees. The dominant trees include spruce (*Picea Morrisonicola*

Hay) and cedar and cypress (*Chamaecyparis formosensis Matsam, Chamaecyparis taiwanensis Mas,* and *Taiwania cryptomeriaides Hay*). The Chamaecyparis forests are most important from the economic point of view, not only because of the large area they cover, but also because of their straight, enormous trunks which produce valuable construction timber. Others include *Rhododendron spp.* (*Juniperus formosana,* and *Acer kawakamii*). The coniferous forests are to be found on the upper slopes of the zone, the dominant varieties being hemlock (*Tsuga formosensis*) and pine (*Pinus armandii*).

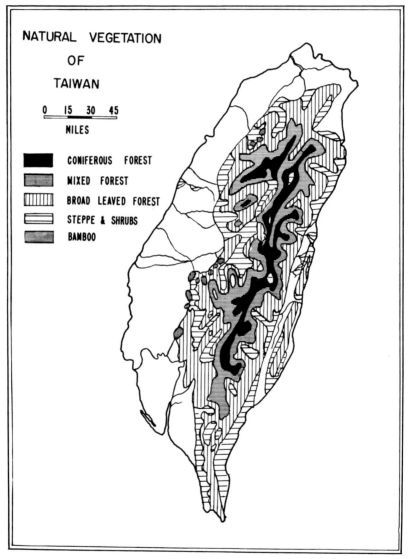

Figure 21

SUB-TROPICAL ZONE (BROAD-LEAVED FOREST).—This zone lies between 1640 and 5900 feet. It is the region of the broad-leaved evergreen forests with dense undergrowth. These forests are the most luxuriant vegetation of the island; the predominating species belong to the *Lauraceae*, *Fagaceae*, and *Betulacease*. Within these forests there are three broad subdivisions.

On the lowest slopes of the mountains the following species are dominant—*Bischoffia javonica*, *Cleyera ochnaceo*, *Lagerstroemia subcostata*, evergreen oaks, palms (*Calarmus Margaritae*) and tree ferns (*Cyathea* and *Alcophila*).

On the middle slopes of the mountains are found some of the largest trees of the island—camphor trees (*Cinnamonum Camphora*), *Engelhardia formosana*, and *Machilus kusanoi* and *Tetradenia konishii*.

On the upper slopes deciduous varieties such as oak, maple, and chestnut are to be found along with the broad-leaved evergreen trees and shrubs.

In the disturbed area the secondary growth area of this sub-tropical zone often contains pure stands of deciduous oak (*Quercus variabilis*). Large alders (*Alnus formosana*) are also to be found.

THE TROPICAL ZONE (MANGROVE TREES AND BAMBOO).—This zone lies below 1640 feet in the north and 2625 feet in the south of Taiwan. The natural vegetation of this zone appears in two areas, one along the seacoast and the other on the plain. The natural vegetation along the seacoast can be represented by mangrove, while on the plain it can be represented by the banyan tree (*Ficus retusa*).

In the south there are a number of large tracts covered with palm trees, in particular the *Phoenix hancona*, a relative of date palm.

Because of the cultivation on the plains, where the natural vegetation disappeared it was replaced by rice paddy fields, sugar cane, sweet potatoes, tea, peanuts, and beans.

In the foothills between the mountains and plains, there are steppes and shrubs. Here neither soil nor climate is adverse to tree growth. Rather, it represents secondary and subsequent growth in those broad-leaved and mixed forest areas where cutting and burning of forests has resulted from the pressure of population on the island.

REFERENCES

[1] L. T. Hsi, "Soils of Taiwan," *Taiwan Hsin-chih*, pp. 137–8 (1950). [In Chinese].
[2] C. Y. Chow, "Soils of Taiwan," In *A Scientific Review of Taiwan* (Educational and Cultural Association, Taipei, 1956).
[3] L. T. Hsi, *Key to the Soils of Taiwan* (Taiwan Fertilizer Company Bulletin, Taipei, (1950). [In Chinese].
[4] S. C. Chang, *A General Study on the Soil Fertility of Taiwan* (Taiwan Fertilizer Corporation, Taipei, 1951).
[5] Tang-Shiu Liu, *Illustrations of Native and Introduced Ligneous Plants of Taiwan* (National Taiwan University, Taiwan, 1962).
[6] Ryozo Kanehira, *Formosan Trees Indigenous to the Island* (Government Research Institute, Formosa, 1936).
[7] Wei-Fang Lin, "Forests of Taiwan," In *A Scientific Review of Taiwan* (—, Taipei, 1956).
[8] G. Massamune, "On the Alpine Vegetation of Formosa and its Origin," *Geogr. Rev. Jap.* **14**, No. 7, 565–72 (1938). [In Japanese].

| # Mineral Resources

CHARACTERISTICS AND GEOGRAPHICAL DISTRIBUTION OF MINERAL DEPOSITS

THE MAIN RESOURCES of Taiwan are agricultural rather than mineral. The chief minerals produced on the island are coal, gold, and sulfur; other mineral resources of importance include copper, petroleum, and salt. While agricultural production depends on climatic conditions and soil fertility, the mineral resources are related to geological basis. The low mineralization in Taiwan is chiefly due to a lack of widespread igneous intrusion, which is usually associated with mineral-forming processes. Despite the diligent survey by the Japanese under their colonial policy between the years 1920 and 1940, and the efforts of today's Chinese geologists to discover more mineral wealth, the widespread distribution of sedimentary rock of recent age which might have more petroleum reserve makes it unlikely that important mineral reserves still remain to be discovered. The most important rock formations in terms of minerals are the Tertiary beds of shale and sandstone. Bituminous coal is found interbedded with shales and sandstone in the northern part of the island. These rocks contain pools of petroleum and reserves of natural gas. Gold veins are located in the extreme northeast's metamorphic rock; copper reserves are found in the crystalline schist formation on the east flank of the Central Mountains; and sulfur in economic quantities is available throughout the areas of volcanic rocks (*Figure 22*)[1, 2].

GEOLOGICAL STRUCTURE OF MINERAL DEPOSITS

Geologically, three important epochs associated with certain types of mineral deposits are recognizable in Taiwan[3].

Pre-Tertiary period

The Pre-Tertiary period includes all the mineral deposits in the metamorphic complex of eastern Taiwan. Intrusions of both acidic and basic character brought with them deposits of mica, feldspar, manganese ores, and many bedded copper-bearing pyrite deposits. Other basic to ultrabasic intrusions brought about the formation of some asbestos and talc deposits near Hualien and Taitung. There are also widespread deposits of limestone, dolomite, and serpentine which were formed in this epoch.

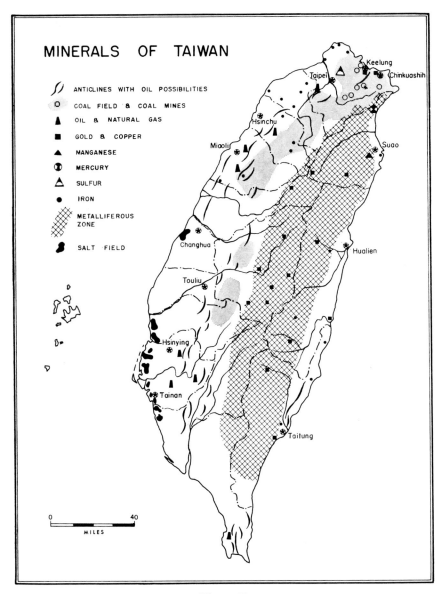

Figure 22

Late-Tertiary organic period

The Late-Tertiary period was marked by the formation of organic minerals in Taiwan. It was responsible for the oil and gas deposits in the western foothill belt of the Central Mountain Range and for all the coal deposits in northern and central Taiwan. At least three intervals of coal formation are known in this period.

Post-Tertiary period

The Post-Tertiary period was an epoch of extensive mineralization in Taiwan. Extrusions of dacitic or andesitic composition gave rise to gold and copper veins with accessory deposits of alunite, barite, and pyrite. Representative localities are the Chinkuashih and Juifang districts in Taipei County. Vast extravasations of andesitic lava flows occurred around the Tatun volcanic group. These rocks are closely related to the mineralization of sulfur, alunite, and some gold veins found in the surrounding region.

GEOGRAPHICAL DISTRIBUTION OF MINERAL DEPOSITS

Geographically, the parts of Taiwan where the various mineral deposits are found may be specified as follows[4]:

The northern part is characterized by dacite and andesite, results of volcanic activities. The important deposits are sulfur, gold, and copper.

EASTERN CENTRAL MOUNTAINS.—The eastern flank of the Central Mountain Range is characterized by various schists and by crystalline limestone intruded with acidic and basic igneous rocks. The special minerals found in this region are mica, asbestos, manganese ores, chalcopyrite, pyrite, and pyrrhotite.

WESTERN FOOTHILL BELT.—The western foothill belt is composed of Miocene sedimentary rocks, which contain hydrocarbon deposits of petroleum and coal.

EASTERN COASTAL RANGE.—The eastern coastal range, so far as is known, has less important workable mineral deposits than the other areas. Here occur the andesitic volcanics which give rise to deposits of gold, copper, gypsum, and the serpentinized peridotite carrying traces of nickel ore. The Miocene rocks are known to be petroliferous, but no producing field has yet been developed.

AVAILABILITY OF MINERAL RESOURCES

The availability of Taiwan's mineral resources can be grouped into three classes:

(1) Minerals existing in sufficient quantities to fulfill domestic needs include gold, copper, sulfur, salt, silver, limestone, serpentine, building stone, coal, and glass sand.

(2) Minerals capable of meeting some domestic requirements are divided into those available through (a) introduction of new extractive processes, these include iron from pyrites and heavy sands, gypsum from brine and magnesium material; or (b) through discovery of additional deposits; included here are such minerals as asbestos and talc.

(3) Minerals known to exist in small amounts and some that have been used but which are not in current production. They include mica, manganese, mercury, nickel, quartz crystals, phosphate and graphite.

(4) Minerals needed by domestic industry but which are not available. Included in this category are iron, bauxite, tin, lead, zinc, and potash.

THE DIFFERENT MINERALS

COAL

Coal deposits are found in the northern parts of the island where 90 per cent of the total output is produced. The coal-bearing area stretches from the northeastern coast southwestward for a distance of 75 miles with a 12-mile width. The estimated area is about 900 square miles[5].

With a few exceptions the coal in Taiwan is of Tertiary age and occurs mostly in the Miocene formation. Three important coal-bearing formations—upper, middle, and lower—are distinguishable in the Miocene formation. The upper formation is of comparatively inferior grade, owing to the high water and ash content and low fixed carbon percentage (*Table 34*). It is rather moderate in calorific value. The coal in the lower formation is highly carbonized, probably owing to thick cover and deep burial before cropping out. It contains a relatively high percentage of fixed carbon and less volatile matter. Most of the coal can be transformed into commercial coke. This is the chief source of coke in Taiwan. The middle coal-bearing formation is intermediate or transitional in character.

*Table 34. General Properties of Taiwan's Coal**

Content	Upper coal-bearing formation	Middle coal-bearing formation	Lower coal-bearing formation
Water	3–7%	2–4%	1–2%
Ash	6–10%	1–10%	1–10%
Volatile matter	36–40%	36–40%	26–40%
Fixed carbon	41–50%	46–55%	51–60%
Sulfur	0.6–2.0%	0.6–1.5%	0.6–3.0%
Phosphorus	0.02%	0.02%	0.02%
Calorific value	6,100–7,000 cal./kg.	6,600–7,500 cal./kg.	6,600–8,000 cal./kg.

* Condensed from T. P. Yen, "The properties of the Taiwan coal; *Formosan mining Industry* **2**, No. 3 (1950). [In Chinese].

The coal produced in Taiwan is used in various ways according to its grade[6]. That from the upper coal-bearing formation, owing to its inferior quality, is used mostly in minor industries such as brick-making, and in agricultural industries such as tea-firing. The middle coal-bearing formation has produced good steam coal which is used on ships, in

109

locomotives, and for stationary boilers. The lower coal-bearing formation has been used for the manufacture of coal gas. Owing to its low content of volatile matter, it does not respond rapidly to stimulated firing and for steam coal use it is often blended with the coals of the middle formation.

Consumption

Consumption of coal in Taiwan can be divided into three categories: domestic consumption, ship use, and export. Domestic consumption includes use by alcohol plants, cement factories, ceramic kilns, textile mills, powerhouses, railways, and so on, as well as by households. Ships sailing between Taiwan and foreign seaports consume a considerable quantity of coal, and much of it is purchased in Taiwan. Coal from Taiwan is exported mainly to Hong Kong, Japan, and the South Sea Islands.

Domestic consumption in Taiwan accounts for the use of about 30–60 per cent of the total coal output in each year; ships' bunkers absorb 20–40 per cent; and another 20–40 per cent is exported. An increase or decrease of consumption in any of these categories would affect the coal production of the island, and since domestic consumption of coal is without any marked fluctuations, the coal industry in Taiwan is affected more by the consumption in the other two categories. Both have fluctuated widely from year to year, and the mining industry has exhibited correspondingly irregular changes.

Despite the significance of coal production to industrial development in Taiwan, the per capita coal consumption is low in comparison with that of Japan and the United States. Domestic coal utilization between 1951 and 1960 averaged about 397–419 pounds per capita as compared with 1212 pounds in Japan, and 7714 pounds in the United States. This low per capita rate of coal consumption is the result of greater dependence on hydrogenerated power and of fairly low levels of household use. Between 85 and 95 per cent of the electricity used in Taiwan is supplied by water power compared with 70–85 per cent in Japan and 35–40 per cent in the United States.

Mining

Geological features have affected coal mining in the island. Taiwan experienced tremendous tectonic disturbances in Tertiary and Quaternary times, which affected the coal-bearing rocks after their formation. Not only are the coal seams thin, ranging from about 0.8 to 2.4 feet in thickness, but most are steeply dipping. Large parts of the coal fields exhibit complex patterns of folds and faults that affect the coal deposits and make mining rather difficult. A great deal of dislocation has been the result of faulting, which makes the coal seams discontinuous. As the result of folding, many coal beds are repeatedly compressed and pinched off, and coal is easily pulverized after such continued stress. In spite of these difficulties in coal mining, there are some advantageous features in the coal deposits, resulting from the crustal movements. Large-scale overthrust may bring several widely-separated coal beds close together, so that they are more profitably mined. Also, some deeply buried coal bodies have been brought upward by successive tectonic adjustments; this makes them readily accessible.

Reserves

Although coal is the leading mineral resource of Taiwan and has been mined there longer than any other mineral, the coal reserve figure is still not accurately known. The early Japanese estimation of the coal reserve was 461,647,428 tons, but recent estimates of Taiwan's coal reserves are 737,000,000 tons[7] (*Table 35*).

A total of 66,138,600 tons of coal was produced in 85 years in Taiwan, according to mining records from 1873 to 1958. If the recovery rate of coal mining is given as 60-65 per cent, production of 66,138,600 tons will mean a corresponding reduction of 110,231,000 tons of coal in the total workable reserves. The remaining tonnages left in the coal fields would thus be 626,769,000 tons[8].

Table 35. Geologically Proved Coal Reserves of Northern Taiwan (in Tons)*

Coal region	Coal-bearing formation			Total
	Lower	Middle!	Upper	
Keelung	99,000,000	176,000,000	6,600,000	281,600,000
Taipei	88,000,000	132,000,000	9,900,000	229,900,000
Hsinchu	27,500,000	60,500,000	66,000,000	154,000,000
Chunan	—	38,500,000	33,000,000	71,500,000
Total	214,500,000	407,000,000	115,500,000	737,000,000
Per cent	29	55	16	100

* Converted from C. S. Ho, *Mineral Resources of Taiwan*, (Ministry of Economic Affairs, China, Taipei, 1953), p. 45

In comparison, technically workable coal reserves were estimated at 236,500,000 tons. At present rates of exploitation, approximately 2,700,000 tons per year, and assuming an average mining loss of 35-40 per cent, current reserves may be expected to last somewhat less than 62 years.

There are altogether 181 operating coal mines in Taiwan at present. Almost all of them are located in the northern section, about 70 per cent of the number being located in the Keelung and Taipei regions. A part of these mines is owned by the government and the rest by private investments or by joint stock corporations.

GOLD

Gold is often used in alloy with silver. Thus the two industries of gold and silver mining in Taiwan are intimately related. Silver is not very important in the island in terms of mineral production value, but gold provides about one-third of the total value of the mineral production.

Deposits of gold ore in Taiwan are of two types: gold-bearing quartz veins called lodes, and deposits along the rivers called placers. The former appear in the northern part of the island, the latter along the rivers of the eastern coast[9]. More than 95 per cent of the total output of gold in Taiwan comes from three gold mines, all located near Keelung. In all three the gold is found in lodes[10]. The output from one of these mining areas has continued without interruption since 1897; its total production over the past half century is reported to be almost half that of the Chinese mainland during the same period. The important gold deposits, concentrated in an area of less than two square miles, are estimated at 5,534,202 tons, 3,083,371 tons, and 456,524 tons respectively.

Gold has been obtained for a long time from placers along the Keelung River. The alluvial gold came from the original deposits in northern Taiwan, and it led to the discovery of the important gold lodes.

SULFUR

The important sulfur-producing districts of Taiwan are concentrated around Tsaisin Shan in the Tatun volcanic group in the northern part of Taiwan.

The economically workable deposits of native sulfur are of volcanic origin[11]. They are formed by solfataric action in the craters of volcanoes or on the slopes in the Tatun volcanic group, and also in the volcanic islet of Kuei Shan off the coast of Ilan. The sulfur content ranges from 20 to 40 per cent and averages about 26 per cent. The sulfur was used in early days as raw material for gunpowder, and a large part of the production was exported[12]. With expanded industry on the island in recent years, the domestic consumption of sulfur has risen remarkably.

The sulfur has been used chiefly in the paper and sugar industries, and also in the manufacture of matches, firecrackers, and medicine, and for bleaching purposes. A recent important use of sulfur is in the manufacture of ammonium sulfate, a newly-established fertilizer industry in Kaohsiung.

The domestic consumption of sulfur is about 5512–7716 tons per year. Since the end of World War II a large tonnage of both cheap and high-grade sulfur has been shipped to Taiwan from the United States and Japan. With the outbreak of the Korean War in 1950, a stimulus was given to the domestic sulfur industry, as sulfur was a strategic mineral and was for a time barred from export by all the leading producing nations.

COPPER

Copper ore occurs in Taiwan in economically workable deposits. It is associated with igneous rocks, and it can be divided into two types: one form, called hydrothermal deposits, contains also gold and silver; the other type, called cupriferous deposits, is associated with workable minerals such as pyrite.

As for hydrothermal deposits, those in Chinkuashih are the only ones being actively exploited at present and which hold a prospect for the future. This type of deposit occurs in the lower part of the gold veins, is grayish black to iron black, and usually forms vertically-striated prismatic crystals which are commonly arranged in rows or clustered in small masses[13]. Current production is at the rate of 551–772 tons of metallic copper per year.

The cupriferous deposits are widely distributed in the crystalline schists on the eastern flank of the Central Mountains. They are composed chiefly of pyrite, with subordinate amounts of quartz, calcite, and magnetite.

The ore bodies show great variation in thickness and in extension. Generally several occur together like a string of sausages.

PETROLEUM AND NATURAL GASES

The petroleum in Taiwan is confined in Tertiary rocks, which appear in two zones[14]. One is the western foothill belt extending from Keelung to Pingtung along the west flank of the central range. In this zone, Oligocene, Miocene, and Pliocene sedimentary rocks are tilted, folded and faulted against Eocene and older rocks, which form the bulk of the central range.

The second zone is in the west. There, Tertiary sediments, deeply hidden beneath recent deposits, form a synclinal trough between the central range of Taiwan and Fukien old rocks.

Old gas seepage has long been reported from various localities within the Tertiary areas in Taiwan, and production of oil has been going on since 1861.

Crude oil and natural gas arise in the sedimentary rocks of Tertiary age on the western plain and in the foothill regions. The most productive area is the region from Hsinchu to Miaoli[15].

In Taiwan nearly 260 wells have been drilled. More than 100 seepages are distributed throughout western Taiwan and the eastern coastal range. Forty or more proved anticlinal folds with oil potentialities have been discovered on the island, but only six fields are producing either oil or gas at present.

Since 1945 the Chinese Petroleum Corporation has operated most of the fields. The production of crude oil from 1904 to 1951 was about 200 million quarts.

In the coastal plain area to the west of the exposed anticlinal folds, the existence of broader and more gentle folds, buried under alluvial deposits, could reasonably be expected.

Forty-six anticlinal foldings, either exposed or half exposed, show the areas with potentialities for oil or gas production in Taiwan. Twenty-one prospective structures have been explored and tested by wildcat drilling, of which only seven are now productive fields.

SALT

Salt is one of the most essential raw materials for chemical industries, as well as one of the primary necessities of life. No rock salt deposits occur in Taiwan, and the main production of salt on the island depends completely upon the natural brine of sea water. Six important salt fields are situated along the southwestern coast of Taiwan.

The salt fields have a total area of 11,014 acres, of which all but about 425 are producing salt; the rest are still under restoration.

Crude salt, produced by solar evaporation, is approximately 90 per cent sodium chloride. The most important salt-producing time of the year is from March to May, and about 45 per cent of the total annual output of salt in Taiwan is produced during this time.

Much of Taiwan's salt is used on the island in the household, in fish curing, in meat packing, and in agriculture and industry, but a larger part of the salt is exported to overseas markets, mainly to Japan, together with Hong Kong, Korea, Sakhalin, and the Ryukyu Islands. The costs of production of Taiwan's salt are high because of the seasonal character of its production, the high labor costs, the poorly coordinated and integrated production methods, and high local transport costs. Production of sea salt averages from 165,350 to 385,800 tons per year.

REFERENCES

[1] *The Underground Resources in Taiwan*, Research Series No. 3 (Bank of Taiwan, Taipei, 1951). [In Chinese].

[2] PING-FAN CHEN, "Mineral resources of Taiwan," In *A Scientific Review of Taiwan* (Educational and Cultural Association, Taipei, 1956).

[3] T. P. YEN, "Mineral resources of Taiwan," *Formosan Science*, No. 1. (1956). [In Chinese].

[4] C. S. Ho, *Mineral Resources of Taiwan* (Shinchu Research Institute, Chinese Petroleum Corporation, Taiwan, 1953).

[5] T. P. YEN, "The properties of Taiwan's coal," *Formosan min. Ind.* **2**, No. 3 (1950). [In Chinese].

[6] *Coal Mining in Taiwan* (Bank of Taiwan Research Monograph No. 38, 1950). [In Chinese].

[7] T. P. YEN, "Coal of Taiwan," *Quart., Bank of Taiwan* **III**, No. 2 (1950). [In Chinese].

[8] C. S. Ho, *Mineral Resources of Taiwan* (Shinchu Research Institute, Chinese Petroleum Corporation, Taiwan, 1953) p. 46.

[9] T. P. YEN, "The high terrace gold placers of Taiwan, "In *Gold in Taiwan*, Special Products Series No. 6 (Bank of Taiwan, Taipei, 1950). [In Chinese].

[10] C. C. LIN, "Geology and ore deposits of the Juifang mine," *Formosan min. Ind.* **1**, Nos. 1–2 (1949). [In Chinese].

[11] T. ICHIMURA, "Bedded cupriferous pyritic deposits in the crystalline schist region of Taiwan," *Taiwan Tigaku Kizi* **10**, No. 2 (1939). [In Japanese].

[12] T. P. YEN, "Sulphur of Taiwan," *Quart., Bank of Taiwan* **III**, No. 2 (1950). [In Chinese].

[13] M. SAITO, "Gold-copper deposits in Chinkuashih, Taiwan," *J. Geogr., Tokyo* **48**, Nos. 566–568 (1936). [In Japanese].

[14] C. S. CHANG, "Petroleum in Taiwan," *Quart., Bank of Taiwan* **III**, No. 2 (1950). [In Chinese].

[15] C. C. LIN. "Some problems on the Hsinchu and Miaoli oil fields," *Formosan min. Ind.* **III**, Nos. 3 and 4 (1951). [In Chinese].

| Geographical
Regions

TAIWAN IS SMALL, but its landscape is greatly varied. In order to understand and interpret the areal characteristics of the island, its subdivision into smaller geographical regions is a necessity. The most difficult problem in subdividing is to determine the criteria for making delimitations. As Ellen Churchill Semple has emphatically stated, "nature abhors fixed boundary lines and sudden transitions."[1] Geographical regions are separated by broad transitional zones, rather than by single lines.

Otto Maull has advocated a simple, yet objective method of regional delimitation.[2] His method is to select and map several basic physical elements such as structure, landforms, climate, soils, and vegetation. If maps which are based upon these criteria are superimposed, the resulting composite map will show certain aggregate boundary lines which, in turn, signify a synthetic geographical meaning. Where these lines overlap and correspond to each other, the resulting line-bundles are called *boundary girdles*. Delimitation of synthetic geographical regions is made relatively easy by following the major lines of division made by these boundary girdles. The closer such lines group together, resembling contour lines in a topographic map, the more dramatic is the divergence between adjacent regions. By using this same method a map of Taiwan's geographical regions can be derived (*Figure 23*).

In Taiwan five rather distinct regions can be separated and distinguished: (1) the northern hills and basins, (2) the southern plains, (3) the Central Mountains (Chungyang Shan), (4) the eastern coast, and (5) the Penghu Island group. Each of these five geographical regions has a significant amount of homogeneity within its boundaries and is considerably different from others, yet all are closely related in forming the integral whole that is the island of Taiwan.

115

Among the physical boundaries in Taiwan, there is one which is distinctive in its coincidence with the boundary girdle and which can be used as a major regional dividing line. This is the 1640-foot (500-meter) contour line which outlines the Central Mountains, separating them from the surrounding hills and coastal plains. It is this line which creates a vertical, north–south division of the island. It is interesting to note that this line also coincides roughly with the 118 inch (3,000 mm.) isohyet.

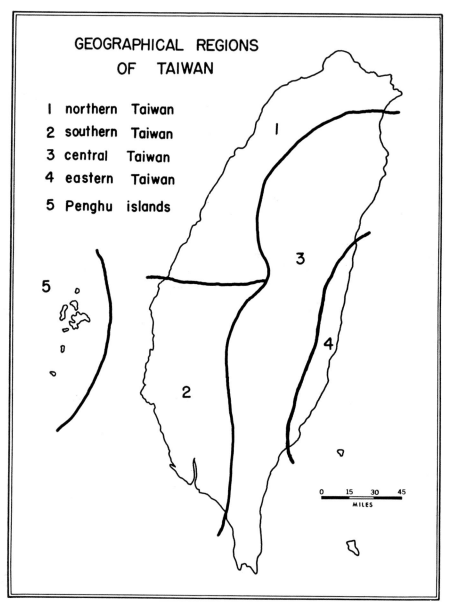

GEOGRAPHICAL REGIONS
OF TAIWAN

I northern Taiwan
2 southern Taiwan
3 central Taiwan
4 eastern Taiwan
5 Penghu islands

0   15   30   45
MILES

Figure 23

While the 1640-foot contour line divides the island vertically, the Choshui River bisects the western coastal area horizontally into northern and southern parts. It is also the climatic boundary between north and south. For example, the rainy season occurs at opposite times in these two areas. From October to March the northern hills and basins receive their greatest amount of rainfall, while in the south these months are characterized by sunshine and generally delightful weather to the extent that irrigation is a necessary practice. The character of the rainfall also differs on either side of the Choshui. In the north the monsoons are cold, drizzly, and drawn out over long periods of time; in the south the rains are caused by local storms and typhoons, occurring as frequent downpours.

The river also serves as an agricultural divide: rice and tea are prevalent in the north, while sugar crops dominate the south. Not only do the types of crops differ, but the cultivation times and crop rotation schedules do not coincide in north and south. It should also be noted that population settlement in the north is of a diversified nature, while the south shows a conglomeratic pattern.

With this understanding of the criteria and methods employed in regional delimitation, each geographical region will be briefly characterized.

THE NORTHERN HILLS AND BASINS

The northern region is a hilly land with an elevation of less than 2000 feet, except in the extreme northwestern part, where volcanic peaks rise to 3700 feet; none of those volcanoes is active at present. In this hilly land there are scattered tectonic basins and tablelands.

Taipei Basin presents a clearly defined physical unit. It is a triangle bordered by fault lines. The basin is drained by the Tamshui River, the third largest river of the island. The floor of the basin is covered by alluvium deposited by the Tamshui River and its tributaries. It is believed that the basin was formerly the site of a lake (*Figure 24*).

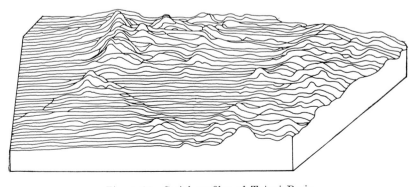

Figure 24.—Serial profiles of Taipei Basin

117

Ilan Plain is the delta of the Choshui River—an equilateral triangle, each side about 20 miles long. The base of the plain is the coast and its apex lies in the Central Mountains. The Ilan River originates in these mountains and bisects the plain from its apex to the sea. Erosion has curved the coast of the plain toward the west. The most prominent features in the coast landscape are sand dunes.

Taichung Basin is surrounded by scarps. It has an elongated form and the city of Taichung is located in its center.

The dominant climatic feature of the region is the northeast monsoon. The region has rainfall the year round, with the maximum in winter. Ilan, with an average annual rainfall of 100 inches, receives 40 per cent of its rain from September to November. This results in an extremely large number of rainy days. The many rainy days in Ilan are as famous as are the strong winds in Hsinchu. Since the last syllable of *Ilan* has the same sound in Chinese as the word for orchids, and *Hsinchu* has the same sound as the Chinese word for bamboo, "orchid rain" and the "bamboo wind" are well known in the island. However, these poetic names are not as pleasant as they sound, for the strong winds in Hsinchu make the sand fly and destroy the buildings, and the rain in Ilan causes floods. The city of Keelung, with an average annual rainfall of 114 inches, has an average of 213 rainy days a year and it is called the "rainy port."

The well-drained, reddish, acid soils of this hilly land are particularly suitable for growing the tea shrub. Tea shrubs, together with other cash crops, usually cluster in patches on the hill slopes; the basin bottoms and plains are planted in food crops, of which rice is dominant. Around Hsinchu, orange trees are important and in Miaoli, citronella is prominent.

In Taoyuan and Hsinchu there is a tableland slightly more than 1300 feet in height. Citrus fruit and tea are the main products. Near Hsinchu and Miaoli, besides agricultural and forest products, petroleum and natural gas are important.

The northern region of Taiwan developed much later than did the southern. Not until the 17th century did the northern city of Keelung become the island's main seaport and Taipei its political, economic, and cultural center. Before that, Tainan, located in the south, was the most important port, and the second and third most important cities also were in the south. Keelung's rias type of coast enabled it to rise in importance. Also, the economic development of this region has been helped by the fact that it is rich in agricultural products and mineral resources. The most important agricultural product is tea, for the cultivation of which the northern region is well suited. The growth in economic status of the region depends on its tea production. The north does not produce as much sugar cane as does the south, but the leading export of the island is tea. The mineral resources in the north include coal, gold, copper, and sulfur. Among these, coal is especially influential.

THE SOUTHERN COASTAL PLAIN

The southern coastal region is a low, flat, alluvial plain formed by more than 10 rivers flowing from the interior hilly land westward. Each river as it flows out of the foothills divides into a number of channels. Because of the gentle slope of the alluvial plains, the rivers meander on it until they empty into the sea. Many of them have been linked by irrigation and drainage canals. At the edge of the plain, where it meets the sea, appear wide tidal flats. The coastline, generally speaking, is rather swampy. Many shallow lagoons have been formed where the sandbars have shut off the river mouths from the sea. These shallow swampy lagoons are the fishing ponds of the island. Although the offshore waters are shallow there are a number of good ports along the coast, of which Kaohsiung leads.

The region has a tropical climate—no month has an average temperature of less than 68°F. Between 80 and 90 per cent of the rainfall occurs in summer, and total average annual rainfall on the plain ranges from 60 to 100 inches. The winter dry season is characterized by gales.

The alluvial soils of the region are grayish in color and high in mineral content. They are fertile but low in humus and they are from neutral to slightly alkaline, being among the least acid of Taiwan's soils. Because these alluvial soils are formed by the coalescing of many alluvial fans they include large areas of coarse, infertile sand and cobblestone washes. Along the coast are found saline soils that developed on tidal flats. The strong winds, the heavy deposits of sand, and the early settlement of the region combined to cause the disappearance of the original vegetation.

At the present the southern coastal plain is the most productive agricultural region in Taiwan. But in early days, the salinity of the soil in the immediate coastal zone and the prolonged dryness in winter constituted a great obstacle to the development of agriculture. The situation has been remedied by construction of irrigation systems, resulting in a phenomenal increase of crop yields. A great variety of crops are grown here: rice, jute, soybeans, wheat, sweet potatoes, pineapples, bananas, and vegetables; but sugar is the main crop. The continuous rows of compact villages, strung like beads along the streams, indicate the productiveness of the region. In this region dwell about 70 per cent of the total population of the island.

THE CENTRAL MOUNTAINS

The Central Mountains consist of anticlinal mountains, which form the backbone of the island. The region, ranging from 10 to 35 miles in width, runs 255 miles along the length of Taiwan. The mountain bedrock is the old, hard, resistant schist and gneiss. The relief is marked and the forest-clad mountains with their extreme ruggedness are almost impenetrable. The heavy rainfall has deeply eroded the mountains into a large number of peaks, of which more than 30 attain heights of more than 10,000 feet and river valleys and canyons cut the mountainsides. During the winter the high mountains are covered with snow, a rare feature in the lowlands. The vegetation on the mountains includes coniferous and mixed forests. Stony soils are found on the slopes of these high mountains. With the cool climate and coniferous forest cover, the soils are distinctly podzolized, and the soil profiles are thin and shallow. Because of the low temperature, steep slopes, and severe erosion, the mountains have had little cultivation, but the region is rich in water power and forestry.

Most of the aborigines live in this region, and their primitive dancing, along with the beautiful scenery have attracted many vacationists. The tourist center is Sun-Moon Lake, in the central part of the mountains.

THE EASTERN COASTAL HILLS

The eastern coastal region is perhaps the least developed part of the island. A great variety of landscape is found there. The region's isolated position rather than any uniform features makes it a geographical unit. The area includes mountains and the Taitung rift valley. The coastal mountains are partly folded and partly volcanic in origin. In the south they rise steeply from the water to an elevation of more than 7000 feet. In the north they are less than 3000 feet high. The base of the mountain chain is extremely narrow; it is only from 10 to 15 miles wide, and as a result the mountains are extremely rugged. The coastline has few indentations and few harbors, but has deep offshore water. Generally speaking, the shoreline is marked by steep cliffs, which are cut by the short and swift-flowing rivers.

The Taitung rift valley is of tectonic origin. The west side of the valley is formed by the steep cliff of the Central Mountains. Since the valley averages only from 5 to 9 miles in width, it looks like a deep cut into the mountain surface of the island. The floor of the trench is covered by thick deposits of alluvial material brought down from the mountains. Much of the western part of this alluvial plain is formed by coalescing alluvial fans. At the two ends of the valley are deltas that are occupied by the cities of Hualien and Taitung. The area has a heavy rainfall due to its exposure to the ocean and the sharp relief of the elevations.

A great variety of crops are grown in this region—rice, sugar cane, fruits, sweet potatoes, tobacco, peanuts, and millet. In general, rice cultivation is concentrated in the flood plains of the river along the rift valley or along the narrow coast, sweet potatoes are on the terraced fields, and fruit trees are farther up the slopes. Almost all the crops produced here are consumed locally. The population density of the region is low and about 22 per cent of the population are aborigines.

THE PENGHU ISLANDS

Penghu consists of 64 isles, which have a total area of 50 square miles. The largest isle is Penghu, which has an area of 25 square miles. Located in the Taiwan Strait, the isles have the earliest colonization history and are of strategic importance. The isles are composed of dark basalt, which is resistant to erosion, and the landforms are featureless except in a few places where basaltic columns assume fantastic shapes. The shallow, warm waters of the Strait favor the growth of coral. Around the Penghu Islands are many fringing reefs, which provide good shelter for ships. Makun, the biggest town in this region, is a great naval base. Rice and sugar, the major crops of Taiwan, are not found here; fruit crops are negligible, sweet potatoes and peanuts are the only staple crops.

REFERENCES

[1] ELLEN CHURCHILL SEMPLE, *Influence of Geographical Environment* (Constable, London, 1914) p. 204.
[2] OTTO MAUL, "Staatsstruktur und Staatsgrenzen," *Kartogr. schulgeogr. Z.* **VIII**, 129 (1919).

PART TWO

THE OCCUPANCE

NINE | Sequential Occupance in Taiwan

THE LOCATION OF TAIWAN, near the Malayan Archipelago, the Chinese mainland, and Japan, has attracted different cultural groups, including aborigines of Malayan or Indonesian origin, the Dutch and Spanish, the Chinese, and the Japanese.

Each of these peoples brought with it its own cultural traits, customs, beliefs, moral values, types of agricultural crops, and technical abilities. The cultural influences of each group have left their mark on Taiwan. Today we find remnants of every culture that has appeared on the island.

Various peoples living in the same environment at different times may use the land in entirely different ways, build quite dissimilar houses, settle in various patterns, travel on different kinds of roads, and lead various types of economic lives. Although the environment is a limiting factor, it can be overcome to a greater or lesser degree by use of man's technical ability to change the landscape to suit his purposes. Primitive people may exert little influence on their surroundings, but people with advanced technological skills may greatly transform the landscape by such means as removing forests, damming rivers, draining swamps, and developing large cities. A given territory may thus undergo a series of changes in its landscape as successive people of varying abilities and objectives move in. This is called the "sequent occupance," one of the most important concepts in modern geography, which is exemplified widely in America and Europe, but seldom in Asia. Yet great changes have occurred, and are occurring, in the occupance of much of the Orient, and nowhere is this more apparent than in Taiwan. *Part Two* of this book points out some changes wrought by the successive inhabitants (*Figure 25*).

From the relics left by different economic activities, by changing settlement patterns, by successive house types, by development of transportation, and by evolution of place names, five periods of sequent occupance in Taiwan have been noted: (1) the primitive aboriginal period; (2) the Dutch commercial period; (3) the Chinese agricultural period; (4) the Japanese industrial period; and (5) the period of return of the island to the Chinese.

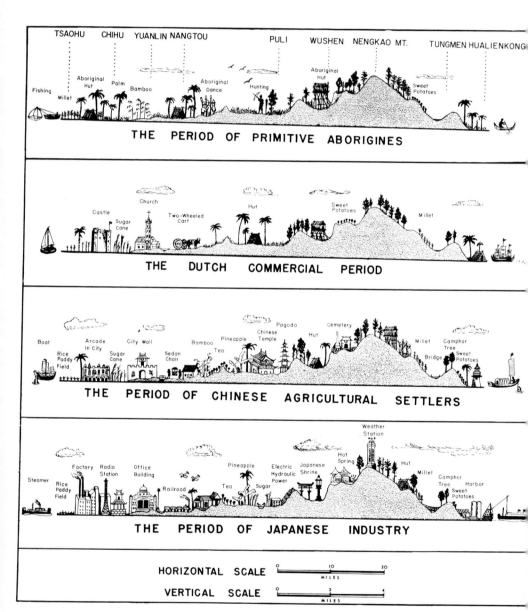

Figure 25

Period of the Primitive Aborigines

TEN

ORIGIN OF THE ABORIGINES

WE ARE NOT SURE where the original Taiwanese or Formosans—the aborigines—came from, nor when they arrived on the island. The 300 years of fragmentary written history of the aborigines cannot be relied upon, even with a knowledge of archaeology, ethnology, and linguistics.

There are two theories about the origin of the aborigines. Some scholars maintain that the aborigines came from Malaya, for from the standpoint of physical anthropology the aborigines belong to proto-Malaya.[1-4] The vocabulary and grammatical structure of the language of the aborigines belong to the Malayan-Polynesian family of Indonesia. Also, many cultural traits and customs of the aborigines resemble those of the Indonesians, such as tattooing, using identical names for father and son, rule by the old in the society, head-hunting, spirit worship, and indoor burials. These cultural characteristics are totally different from those of the three major cultures of Asia—those of Arabia, India, and China. On the other hand, after recent archaeological investigations, some Chinese and Japanese anthropologists suggest that the aborigines in Taiwan were closely related to the people of the mainland of China, for the prehistoric materials found on the island give evidence of that country's cultural traits.[5-7]

Both early Japanese archaeologists and recent Chinese archaeologists have undertaken such investigations.[8-14] As a result, archaeologists have identified some 450 sites, including many dwelling sites, tombs, shell mounds, and megaliths. These sites are distributed all over the island and on the adjacent islands; however, the main concentration is found on the western coastal plains. The sites are found in locations as high as 6600 feet—about the upper limit of the modern aborigines' settlements.

CATEGORIES OF ARTIFACTS

The main categories of artifacts recovered in Taiwan, as given by Chang[15], may be listed as follows:

STONE IMPLEMENTS.—Chipped stone implements are more frequently found in Taiwan than are polished ones. Normally they are made of hard, fine-grained sandstone. Chipped shouldered axes, arrowheads, and knives are occasionally found. The polished stone implements (which have a wide distribution in Southeast Asia) include round axes, shouldered axes, rectangular axes, and stepped axes. Other polished stone implements include flat axes, tembeling knives, chisels, spearheads and halberds, daggers, arrowpoints, rings, beads, pendants, awls, tapa-beaters, potter's tools, spindle whorls, sinkers, mortars and pestles, money-like discs, and statues.

POTTERY AND EARTHENWARE UTENSILS AND IMPLEMENTS.—On the basis of color and pattern, the prehistoric pottery found in Taiwan can be divided into: (a) red pottery with cord patterns; (b) red polished pottery; (c) black pottery with incised or impressed patterns; (d) gray pottery with incised or impressed patterns; and (e) unpolished and undecorated pottery of various colors. They are molded, coiled, or ring-built. Earthenware items include idols, rings, spindle whorls, earplugs, pipes, and others.

ARTIFACTS MADE OF ANIMAL MATTER.—Most of the artifacts made of antlers, teeth, and molluscans' shells are ornaments, but bone arrowheads and spearheads also are found.

METAL IMPLEMENTS.—Metal implements are rare; those found are of bronze, copper, iron, gold, and silver.

CONCLUSIONS

The above list is by no means exhaustive, but it indicates the range of Taiwan's prehistoric material discovered so far.

The people who left these items are assumed by anthropologists to be Stone Age men. Though chipped stone implements are widespread, they are generally accompanied by pottery, and it seems reasonable to associate them with some people who lived in this area during relatively recent times. Neolithic implements are rare, and many of these bear signs of having been made or retouched with metal tools. The prehistoric people of Taiwan are Eolithic for the most part; a real metal age never occurred in Taiwan, probably owing to scarcity of copper and tin.

From an examination of artifacts in Taiwan there is reason to believe that the major Stone Age people in Taiwan were Malaysian or Indonesians in their cultural relationship. The majority of the prehistoric finds are characteristic of the Indonesian region, such as the flat axes, red unpolished pottery, bronze implements with decorations, megalithic structures, and glass beads. On the other hand, there are also items connected with the Chinese mainland, such as painted red pottery, red polished pottery, chipped stone knives, polished saddle-shaped rectangular and leaf-shaped stone knives, black pottery, pottery tripods, incised designs of pottery decoration, stone halberds, bone arrowheads, bone spearheads, cord-impressed pottery, and the comb-technique of pottery decoration.

All of these have affinities with the painted pottery culture of China. This would indicate that the Chinese culture had diffused to Taiwan through the Taiwan Strait. It has been generally accepted that in the Pleistocene epoch Taiwan was an important spot, serving as a stepping stone on the Sino-Malayan faunal migration route. The same may be true with respect to the Neolithic ethnic migrations in southeastern Asia. Kano, a Japanese anthropologist, states that "The foundation of the prehistoric cultures of Taiwan is the mainland cultures of China, which entered Taiwan several times. Later the Eolithic culture arrived from French Indo-China, which included bronze and iron implements. Finally, the iron culture of the Philippines was introduced into this island."[16]

Were the prehistoric remains left by the ancestors of the modern aborigines in Taiwan? The question is a complex one, but we can make the following assertion: even though the latter part of the Stone Age culture does not correspond with the present aboriginal culture, the prehistoric culture remains were not all left by the ancestors of modern aborigines. Particularly, the many prehistoric materials discovered along the western coast have no proved relation with the present aborigines' culture. In the eastern part of the island also the prehistoric culture does not correspond with the present aborigines' culture. A recent excavation at the Yuan Shan shell mound near Taipei uncovered five human skeletons. The one skull available for examination clearly indicates the removal of both the upper lateral incisors and the canines during youth. Until a few decades ago this custom prevailed among several tribes in Taiwan. Also, the present settlements of the aborigines are in the locations where the prehistoric remains were discovered. Thus we may say that the culture of the aborigines in the northern and central parts of Taiwan is related to that of the Chinese mainland, while that of the southern and eastern parts is related to the South Sea Islands' culture. Also, as Kano has suggested, it is quite probable that the prehistoric peoples living in Taiwan included Negritoes.[17]

DISTRIBUTION OF MODERN ABORIGINES

There are seven tribes of modern aborigines in Taiwan: the *Ami, Yami, Taiyal, Saiset, Tsou, Bunun,* and *Paiwan.* The Ami live on the eastern coastal plain; the Yami, on Lanyu Island off the southeastern coast. The other five tribes are mountain inhabitants: the Taiyal live in the north, the Saiset in the northwest, the Tsou and the Bunun in the Central Mountains, and the Paiwan in the south (*Figure 26*).

HORIZONTAL DISTRIBUTION

We do not know in what parts of the island the ancient aborigines lived. But as for the modern aboriginal settlements, maps prepared by a Japanese scholar in 1939[18] showing the distribution of the settlements show 663 tribal villages, and indicate that the large ones, those having a population of more than 1000 persons were concentrated on the eastern coast and in the southern part of the Central Mountains. The eastern coast was the most densely settled area, with 1000 persons per 6 square miles.

Next in population came the southern part of the Central Mountains, with a density of 500 persons per 6 square miles.

With respect to the population density of the various tribes, the Ami on the eastern coast took first place. They had large settlements, often with populations of more than 1000 inhabitants, and with sometimes as many as 2,000. Next came the Paiwan group of tribes in the southern part of the island, with a total population of some 1700 persons. The areas

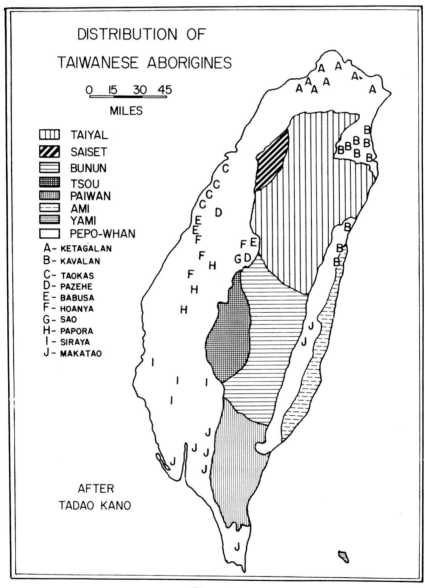

DISTRIBUTION OF
TAIWANESE ABORIGINES

0   15   30   45
MILES

TAIYAL
SAISET
BUNUN
TSOU
PAIWAN
AMI
YAMI
PEPO-WHAN

A- KETAGALAN
B- KAVALAN
C- TAOKAS
D- PAZEHE
E- BABUSA
F- HOANYA
G- SAO
H- PAPORA
I- SIRAYA
J- MAKATAO

AFTER
TADAO KANO

Figure 26

128

occupied by the Taiyal, the Saiset, and the Tsou were not so densely populated. The lowest in density were the areas occupied by the Bunun in the Central Mountain region. They had a total population of 18,000 people—the lowest population among the tribes—living in a vast area in the mountains. The Yami of Lanyu Island occupied only a little more than one square mile, and naturally the density of their population was high.

VERTICAL DISTRIBUTION

One of the most interesting features of the population distribution on the 1939 maps was the vertical distribution of the tribes. They lived at altitudes ranging from less than 160 feet up to 7500 feet. They inhabited areas of the tropical forest, the subtropical forest, the temperate forest, and the snow-covered open grass of the mountain summits.

The settlements situated at altitudes of less than 330 feet were, without exception, limited to the eastern coast. Those at heights of 330–1640 feet were found in the following four areas: the Taitung valley, the southern slope of the Central Mountains, the western slope of the Kaohsiung peninsula, and the edge of the northern part of the Central Mountains. Those living at heights of 1640–3280 feet were found throughout the Central Mountains. Habitation at 3280–6560 feet was limited to those mountains. Settlements at heights of more than 6560 feet were few and could be found only at certain points in the middle part of the Central Mountains.

With regard to the distribution of the tribes by altitude, the maps indicate that the Bunun, numbering 18,000 persons, were the high-mountain dwellers. They were found at altitudes from 490 to 7540 feet. One-third of them lived at 3280–4920 feet, a quarter at 4920–6560 feet, and 4 per cent above 6560 feet. The Taiyal, totaling 34,000 persons, lived at heights from 33 feet to 6560 feet. One-third lived at places between 3280 and 4920 feet high, a quarter at an elevation of 1640–3280 feet, and 10 per cent at 4920–6560 feet. The Tsou and the Saiset lived at somewhat lower elevations. The Tsou numbered 1100; they lived at altitudes between 755 and 4600 feet. Half of them were found at altitudes of 3280–4920 feet and the other half at 328–3280 feet. The Saiset numbered 1300; about 96 per cent of them lived at altitudes between 1640 and 3280 feet and the rest at 3280–16,400 feet. Half lived at heights of 1640–3280 feet, a third at 328–1640 feet, and a tenth at 3280–4920 feet.

The Ami and the Yami inhabited plains. The former had the largest population—42,000—and they lived in locations less than 1640 feet high. About half lived at altitudes of 328–1640 feet and the other half lived below 328 feet. The Yami, totaling 1700 persons, lived at no more than 328 feet in altitude.

With altitude as the ordinate and the population as the abscissa, the relation between the population and the altitude habitations of each tribe is shown in *Figure 27*.

If we consider the aborigines of Taiwan as a whole, their vertical distribution in 1939 was as follows: Approximately 25 per cent were living at altitudes of less than 330 feet, another 25 per cent lived between 328 and 1640 feet, and 25 per cent were found at elevations between 1640 and 3280 feet; 16 per cent inhabited regions between 3280 and 4920 feet in altitude; and 5 per cent were located between 4920 and 6560 feet. Fewer than one per cent were found at heights above 6560 feet (*Figure 28*).

The curves in the figure reveal the fact that more than one-third of the mountain aborigines were concentrated at the height of 1640–3280 feet. Both below and above this elevation, the number of aborigines was much smaller. During recent times they have gradually moved from the high mountains to the lowlands.

Comparing the altitudinal distribution of the aborigines with that of the zones of vegetation, we find that the Ami and the Yami tribes lived in the tropical forest, where the banyan tree is found. About 95 per cent of the Saiset tribe and half of the Paiwan were concentrated in the camphor tree zone, which is part of the subtropical forest. The Taiyal were scattered from the broad-leaved forest to the mixed forest, which includes tropical, subtropical, and temperate forests. About one-third of this tribe dwelt in the oak tree area.

The Bunun, inhabitants of the high mountains, lived in the camphor, oak, pine, and spruce regions. Only 4 per cent of the Bunun lived above 6560 feet in the temperate forests and in the coniferous tree zone where hemlock and fir are found.

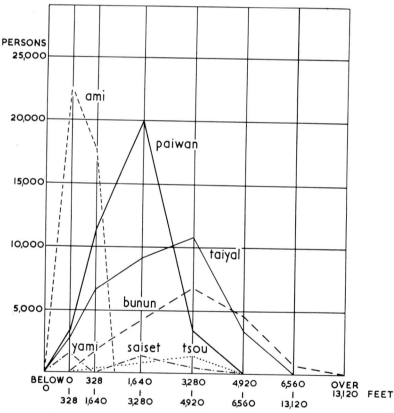

Figure 27.—The altitudinal distribution of seven tribes of aborigines in Taiwan (*After* TADAO KANO)

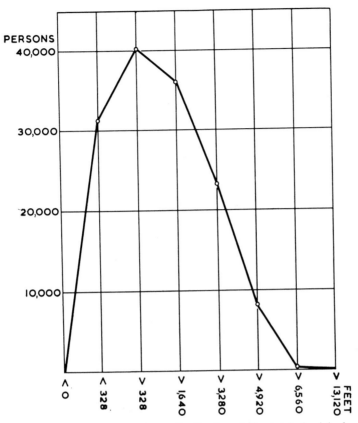

Figure 28.—The altitudinal distribution of the total aboriginal population of Taiwan (*After* Tadao Kano)

SOCIAL CUSTOMS AND ORGANIZATION

Various anthropologists from countries outside of Taiwan, such as William Kirk and Wirth Albrecht of the United States, Janet M. McGovern and George Leslie Mackay of Great Britain, and Neozo Utsurikawa, Tadao Kano, and Toichi Mabuchi of Japan, have reported on the social customs of Taiwan's aborigines, as observed during several years spent among the tribes at various periods of the 19th and 20th centuries.

Some of the earlier customs of the aborigines which have been abolished, still can be traced as a result of the recent field work conducted by the Institute of Ethnology, the Academia Sinica, and the Department of Anthropology of the National Taiwan University, under the leadership of Professors Shun-sheng Ling and Hwei-lin Wei. Some of their reports on the present and past customs are noted in the following sections.

TRIBAL ORGANIZATION

The aborigines in Taiwan are neither chiefless hordes nor citizens of constitutional states; they have tribal organization, which consists of two basic elements: the kinship group and the local unit.[19] The kinship group includes the clan, which can be subdivided into patrilineal and matrilineal descents. The Saiset, the Bunun, and the Tsou follow the patrilineal clan system; the Ami follow the matrilineal. However, the matriarchy stays within the limit of family life. For example, among the Ami, the family is ruled generally by women, and the clan by a maternal uncle; tribal affairs are managed by the eldest man.

The local unit refers to their residential systems, which take different forms, such as (a) the integrated or concentrated form, in which the population of one tribe is concentrated in one large village, with no segregation of tribes; the Ami and the Paiwan are examples of this form; (b) the scattered or segregated form, in which each tribe lives apart from the others in villages and hamlets; the Saiset and a part of the Taiyal follow this form; (c) the composite or nuclear form, in which one tribe always has a central village as the headquarters; some of the Bunun and the Tsou live in this way; (d) the federated or allied form, in which each tribe always forms an independent local unit, which is not strong enough for defense, so that a number of the neighbor tribes join a confederation to defend all; some of the Taiyal and the Saiset are good examples of the federated form. The two basic elements, the kinship group and the local unit, are parallel and preexistent in each tribal society, and they help to maintain the natural equilibrium of authority.

Besides the previously-mentioned natural elements of the tribal organization, there are functional elements, which include the hunting bands and the agricultural ritual group. The former is an economic organization, and the latter a religious one.

When the natural equilibrium breaks down, as a general rule the dual chieftainship and the equilibrium of the tribal authorities begin to be operative. Equilibrium between the peace chief and the war chief is the most usual feature.

According to the size of the family, Taiwan's aborigines may be divided into two groups: (1) the large-family group, which includes the Bunun, the Ami, the Tsou, and the Saiset, and (2) the small-family group, which includes the Paiwan, the Taiyal, and the Yami. The former have clan organization; the latter do not. The size of a family is affected by the age at marriage and the mode of residence. The Bunun have the largest families because of their early marriage. The Yami have the smallest families, for they practice neolocal residence. The form of marriage of Taiwan's aborigines, with no exception is monogamy.[20] Marriage by purchase (with betrothal presents) is seen among the Taiyal, the Saiset, the Bunun, and the Paiwan. Marriage by exchange, that is, when a man's sister is given to his wife's brother in return for the latter's sister, is found only among tribes that have clan organization, such as the Saiset, the Bunun, and the Tsou. Marriage by capture has not been noted, but some ceremonial pretense of capture to dramatize the transition to a new mode of life has been reported as customary among the Taiyal, the Bunun, and the Paiwan.

In earlier days, though customs varied in the different tribes, in general each tribal member considered the interests of the tribe and his own personal interests as one and inseparable. No noble class existed; rich and poor had equal standing. A chief was selected according to his maturity, his physical strength, his skill in hunting and fishing, and diligence in farming. Maturity was not judged by age, but by strength and bravery. After a man became chief, he still had to support himself by hunting, fishing, and farming. Tribal rules were enforced through public opinion.

TRIBAL CUSTOMS

The following were old customs of Taiwan's tribes:

HEAD-HUNTING.—Head-hunting was not merely a form of fighting enemies; heads were often offered by young men as initiation fees for admission into the adult community. A man was not allowed to marry until he had brought in a head; this rule was especially enforced in the Taiyal, Saiset, and Bunun tribes. When enemy heads became scarce, the chief sometimes granted a special dispensation to a man who had killed a deer or a wild boar.

TATTOOING.—To show that a boy or girl had reached the age of puberty, to beautify themselves, and to differentiate one tribe from another, the tribesmen used tattoo; this was especially true among the Taiyal and the Paiwan. When a young person had been tattooed, he was formally accepted as a member of the tribe, entitled to members' rights and privileges.

ROOTING OUT OF TEETH.—The most painful form of showing maturity was probably the knocking out of the two upper lateral incisor teeth. That puberty ceremony was performed upon both boys and girls when they reached the age of thirteen or fourteen years. The reason given for this custom was that as these youths were no longer children, they must cease to resemble monkeys and dogs, which, the aborigines said, have not the wisdom to remove their teeth. In the aboriginal society this operation served to show the sharp distinction between the mature and the immature.

THE BACHELOR-HOUSE SYSTEM.—Each tribe had and they still have, a public building called *Khuva*, which means "bachelors' dormitory." These dormitories are frequently elevated six feet or more above the ground; a notched pole serves as a ladder to afford entrance. At fifteen or sixteen years of age, a youth has to leave his parents' home and live in the bachelor's dormitory until he marries.

While in the *Khuva* the bachelors are assigned the duties of gathering wood for the fire, fetching water, and watching for the enemy in the night. The tribes enforce the bachelor-house system and explain that the bachelor house tends to develop courage and the fighting spirit and to train young men in warfare.

This building, which consists of one large room, is also used as a military barracks and town hall. It is furthermore open to visiting aborigines from the neighboring villages, and so functions as an official hotel.

It is reported that in the Tanan village in eastern Taiwan during recent years the aborigines have adopted many changes in their customs—in the garments they wear, the utensils they use, and the structure of their houses. One thing remains unchanged, however, and that is the bachelor house.[21]

133

POSITION OF WOMEN.—The woman's work in the aboriginal society was heavy. The aborigines allowed the woman to control the "hoe-culture" for the tribe and the raising of animals; the men controlled the hunting and fishing. The women did not plow in the field, but it was their duty to fashion a crude hoe to use in raising millet and sweet potatoes. Women had charge of the storehouses and distributed food to the senior woman of each family. They also made cloth.

Writing in 1896, Mackay described the hard work of the native woman:[22]

> The heaviest burdens rest upon her. All day long she toils in the fields, and at night carries home the fruit of her work. Then she goes out into the bush and gathers firewood, returning with a heavy load on her back. Exposure, drudgery, poor food, and all the other ills of her burdened life soon tell on her strength; the strong, healthy, finely developed girl is old before her time; and at an age when her civilized sister is in her prime, she is worn, haggard, and utterly repulsive in her decrepit ugliness.

Because the value of woman's labor was recognized, their position in tribal society was high. McGovern suggests that the women's control of growing the staple foods, of curing tobacco leaves, and of fermenting wine may account for the power that they exercised in the tribal affairs.[23]

The close cooperation between the sexes led to a stable and well-balanced society. Each able-bodied man brought in his share of meat, and every woman who was physically able cultivated the fields, harvested the crops, and stored the food.

PERSONAL PROPERTY.—Disputes over personal or communal property seldom arose; but when they did, they were usually settled by the chief. There were no serious punishments; the worst was the confiscation of personal belongings and the rationing of food. Throughout the native villages the principle of "from each according to his ability, to each according to his need" seems to have worked very well for centuries.

RELIGION.—The aborigines of Taiwan worshipped nature. They did not have any shrines and had no concept of a supreme God. Like other primitive people, the aborigines of Taiwan practiced a series of rituals before or after every important farming and hunting activity to express their gratitude to nature. The ceremony involved the gathering together of a group of households to join in a ritual. The ritual was observed communally on the same day throughout the ritual cycle of the year. Hunting rites were part of the cycle of agrarian rites. Since millet was the most highly valued food, the cycle of agrarian rites concentrated largely upon it. This was especially true in the Bunun tribe; with the Tsou, rice was ritually of next importance.[24] The aborigines in Taiwan did not know how to write and certainly published no books; they learned their religion from their parents orally.

HUNTING, FISHING, AND PRIMITIVE FARMING

Before the establishment of the Dutch, Chinese, and Japanese settlements, the aborigines of the island were the only Taiwanese. Their techniques for using the land were primitive, their desires were few, and their living standards low. A simple culture with few wants and ambitions made the life of the aborigines uncomplicated. They had a workable connection between their existence and the land; hunting, fishing, or farming provided a living.

Hunting

Hunting was the aborigines' basic occupation. With spears and bows and arrows they hunted the deer, bear, and boar. The deer, which were especially numerous, provided for basic needs—food, clothing, implements, and even medicine. The aborigines rarely used the tusk of the boar, the horn of the deer, the skeleton of the monkey, or the scales of the fish. After the outside settlers came, these articles were used by the tribesmen as trading materials. Hunting was a community business; it was practiced in large bands for the protection of the tribe from other tribes and the new settlers. Each tribe had its own hunting ground and allowed no trespassing. Revenge for trespassing was confiscation of the animals and hunting weapons and even of other property. Each tribe inherited its hunting ground from its ancestors. It could be rented; for example, the Saiset usually rented hunting ground to the Taiyal. The rent agreement was approved not by private individuals but by the council of each tribe.

Fishing

Fishing was also an important economic activity among the aborigines, especially for the Ami, Yami, and Paiwan, who lived along the seacoast or along rivers. Unlike hunting, fishing was considered not only a means of obtaining food, but also a kind of recreation. After the fish were caught, they were usually salted although salt was scarce.

Farming

Besides collecting forest products, the aborigines also practiced farming by shifting methods. They usually cleared new land for cultivation by burning off the grass, rather than re-using the already harvested land. Each tract was used from three to five years, according to its fertility, and rarely more than four years. Fertilizer was not used. However, the aborigines seemed to know about the rotation method in raising crops in order to maintain the soil's fertility.

Millet, sweet potatoes, and taro were the chief crops. Having no calendar, the aborigines took advantage of natural phenomena to remind them of the times for agricultural activities. For example, the blossoms of certain flowers were reminders to start cultivating the land, and the occurrence of snow on the high mountains called attention to the time for transplanting the corn.

Generally the tribes that dwelt in the temperate or subtemperate zone depended primarily on cereals and secondly on root crops. It was the reverse among those whose habitats were in the subtropical or tropical zone. However, some cultural factors seem to be involved. For instance, the Bunun in the Central Mountain region often cultivated their land up to the very limit of the time for the possible raising of various kinds of millet, seeming to disregard the wide areas of lower land, where the harvest of root crops was highly promising. On the other hand, the Paiwan in the south were inclined generally to raise crops in the lower valleys, notwithstanding the vast areas on the higher slopes of the mountains that might be used for raising millet.

With the arrival of the Dutch, Chinese, and Japanese, the aborigines retreated to the Central Mountains, where they faced a special handicap in agricultural activity, the steep slopes. They built primitive terraces on the slopes, which often inclined forty degrees and sometimes as much as sixty or seventy degrees. They built the terraces by piling weeds and stones onto a small ridge, so as to prevent soil and crops from washing away. The percentage of land cultivated by the early aborigines is shown in *Table 36.*

Table 36. Land Cultivated by Early Aborigines in Different Climatic Zones,[*]

Zone	Per cent of land cultivated						
	Taiyal	Saiset	Bunun	Tsou	Paiwan	Ami	Yami
Tropical	8	—	9	13	91	100	100
Subtropical	82	100	87	87	9	—	—
Temperate	10	—	4	—	—	—	—

* Adapted from KOKOCHI SEGAWI. "The means of subsistence among the Formosan aborigines," *Jap. J. Ethnol.* **XVIII** Nos. 1-2, 55, (1953). [In Japanese, with abstract in English].

In spite of all the disadvantages, such as the crudeness of the farming implements, the limited variety of possible crops, and the steep slopes of the farmland, the Central Mountains of Taiwan are said to have been (and they still are) one of the most highly cultivated mountainous areas in the world.[25]

SETTLEMENTS, HOUSE TYPES, AND TRANSPORTATION

Settlements

The modern aborigines live in hamlets and small villages, with an average population of from 100 to 150 persons. A population of 500 people is considered very large.

The aborigines' huts are separated from each other; they mark off the surface of the land so that it looks like a checkerboard. The huts form small villages, which are often set among meager patches of fields, on a small plain, or on a trail along a river.

The tribes sometimes select their village sites on the steep hillsides at high elevation. This is done so that they can watch for their enemies more easily and also so they can avoid malaria, which is prevalent in the swampy lowland. In this high mountain area, the wind is strong, and therefore the aborigines build their huts low and surround them with bamboo and other trees.

Scattered settlements are characteristic of the northern tribes; compact settlements are normal among the southern tribes. The northern tribes change their abode from generation to generation, and this results in scattered settlements. In the south, the tribes bury their dead beneath their houses and their residence is fixed; therefore their settlements are compact.

House types

Although the houses of the different tribes are not exactly alike, there is a general similarity among them. The shape of the aborigine's house is usually square or rectangular and the roof is mostly in flat form. Some of the roofs have long back eaves, but occasionally a roof is one sided. Cornerstones are not used to support the pillars. The beams and pillars are fastened by rattan; nails are not used.

According to structure, form, and material, the aborigines' houses can be classified in two major types; that used by the Taiyal, Ami, and Tsou; and that used by the Bunun, Paiwan, and Saiset.

TAIYAL, AMI, AND TSOU.—The Taiyal, Ami, and Tsou live in huts constructed of bamboo, straw, lumber, and reeds. The roof is heavily thatched with bamboo and rushes and its ends are inclined sharply. The roof of the Tsou's house usually slopes down on four sides. The walls may be built of bamboo latticework and the trunks of trees, as in the Taiyal's; or mainly of bamboo, as is the Ami's; or of rushes interlaced with grass, as is the Tsou's. The floor is of tamped earth. However, in the Ami's house the floor is comparatively high above the ground and it is covered with rattan matting. Because of the joint-family system, the houses are generally large; sometimes they accommodate fifty family members. They have no windows, and they are damp and dark. They are mere sleeping places, with bamboo benches for beds built along the sides of the walls. Only on rainy days is cooking or weaving done inside.

BUNUN, PAIWAN, AND SAISET.—The houses of the Bunun, Paiwan, and Saiset are much more substantial than the other types. These tribes dig a house rather than build one. A large excavation, or pit, is dug into the mountain slope. A strong back wall and supports are thus obtained. The pit is usually five feet deep, and its sides are lined with slabs of slate. These slate walls extend a little more than three feet above the surface of the earth. In the high mountain area the Bunun, Saiset, and Paiwan tribes keep themselves warm by digging their floor into the ground, and securing a wide space underground. The roof, of bamboo poles, with slabs of slate on top, gives the house a cavelike appearance. Steps also are built of slate. Some houses have human skulls hung as decorations.

YAMI.—A survey of house types of the aborigines would not be complete without mention of the Yami, who live on the island of Lanyu. Slate is not available on that island, and so the Yami use gravel stone in building their houses.

A Yami family has two kinds of house; one is called *bagai*, which is the living quarter, and the other is called *makarang*, where the family members work. Any family that owns one of the carefully constructed *bagai* also owns the less elaborate *makarang*, placed at right angles to the *bagai*.

The houses of the Yami are usually two stories high. One story is built half underground and is used in the winter. In warmer weather the family members live in the upper story, which is built about four feet above the ground, in order to avoid the heat and catch the cool breezes. The roof of the house is thatched with a strong dried grass, and a similar material is used on the outer walls. A room of the Yami's house is like a large flat box. The ceiling is so low that lying down one can almost touch it with uplifted hands. Since Yami people are short, the ceiling is high enough for them. Each house is surrounded by a high stone wall, designed to act as a windbreaker. These walls give the impression that the whole village is built on a series of artificial stone terraces.

Transportation

Transportation among the aborigines is rather primitive. Tribal traditions among all the aborigines reveal the fact that their ancestors were skillful navigators and that they understood the construction of boats capable of making long voyages. But deterioration among the aborigines in the craft of boatbuliding and in the understanding of navigation has taken place as a result of their being pushed back to the Central Mountains. The rafts used for fishing at the present time by the native tribes living on the southeast coast cannot be used for making even a short sea voyage.

It is not surprising that the tribes now living in the interior of the island should have lost the art of navigation. There are no navigable rivers there, and there is only one large lake, the beautiful Sun-Moon Lake. Members of the Taiyal and Tsou tribes who live near the lake paddle primitive dugout canoes. The dugouts, however, are of the most primitive type. They have open ends and are unfit for seafaring. Even a light storm on the lake sends the canoes hurrying to the shore.

The most skillful boatbuilders of the present aboriginal tribes are the Yami, on the island of Lanyu. Their boats, in both construction and ornamentation, resemble those of the Papuans of the Solomon Islands rather than those of any other tribe in Taiwan. This may be attributed to the Malayan influence. These boats are built from tree trunks, which are smoothed and trimmed by means of adzes and are lashed together along the seams with withes of rattan. The prow and stern are rounded in graceful curves. The boats present a picturesque and attractive appearance, but are of no use for long voyages. These boats, called *chinedkulan,* are not paddled, but rowed. The crew consists of ten oarmen and a steersman.

For transportation on land, most of the tribes of Taiwan do not use any sort of wheeled vehicle. They know nothing of using draft animals; they just go on foot, except the Ami tribe, who have a primitive two-wheeled cart, drawn by an ox. The Ami say that this cart was introduced by the "white fathers," evidently meaning the Dutch. (Oxen were introduced in Taiwan by the Dutch.)

For the aborigines of Taiwan, the vertical communication is more important than the horizontal. The natives of the Taiyal, Bunun, and Paiwan tribes have to cross deep canyons and torrential rivers in the interior of the island, especially in the mountainous areas, and they have developed a remarkable type of long suspension bridge. These bridges are made of bamboo, held together by deerhide thongs or flexible rattan. When the Japanese took over the island, they also built suspension bridges, but instead of bamboo, thongs, and rattan, the Japanese used galvanized iron wire.

REFERENCES

[1] Jose M. Alvarez, "The aboriginal inhabitants of Formosa," *Anthropos* **I–II,** 248 (1927).

[2] Robert von Heim-Geldern, "Urheimat und Früheste Wanderungen der Austronesier," *Anthropos* **XXVII,** 543 (1932).

[3] HUI-SIANG LIN, *The Primitive Aborigines of Formosa* (Monograph of the Institute of Social Sciences, Academia Sinica, Shanghai, 1930), No. 3.

[4] JOSHUA W. F. LIAO, "Formosa and its early inhabitants," *Far east. Rec.* **X**, 151 (1951).

[5] SHUN-SHENG LING, "Ancient Min-Yueh People of South China and the Formosan aborigines," *Acad. Quart.* **I**, No. 2 (1952). [In Chinese].

[6] TADAO KANO, "The Chinese mainland elements found among the stone implements and pottery in Formosa," In *Studies on the Ethnology and Prehistory of Southeast Asia* (Tokyo, 1948), **I**, pp. 255–268. [In Japanese].

[7] "Outline review of Taiwan's archeology and ethnology," (The Historical Research Commission of Taiwan Province, Taipei, 1955). [In Chinese].

[8] N. UTSUSHIKAWA, N. MIYANIOTO, T. MABUCHI, "Genealogical and classificatory studies on the Formosa aborigines," (Institute of Ethnology, Taihoku University of Formosa, 1935), **I**, pp. 104–108. [In Japanese].

[9] TADAO KANO, "On the remains of Megalithic Culture of the East Coast of Formosa," *J. anthrop. Soc. Tokyo* **7**, 9 (1930). [In Japanese].

[10] HWEI-LIN WEI. "Dual organization among the Formosa tribes," *Bull. Inst. Ethnol. Acad. Sinica (Taipei)* **2**, 1–30 (1956). [In Chinese with English summary].

[11] —, "Lineage system among the Formosa tribes," *Bull. Inst. Ethnol., Acad. Sinica (Taipei)* **5**, 1–44 (1958). [In Chinese with English abridgement].

[12] SHUN-SHENG LING, "Ancestor temple and earth altar among the Formosa aborigines," *Bull. Inst. Ethnol., Acad. Sinica (Taipei)* **6**, 1–46 (1958). [In Chinese with English summary].

[13] TANG MEI-CHUN, "A comparative study of bows and arrows of the Formosa aborigines," *Bull. Ethnological Soc. China (Taipei)* **I**, 139–170 (1955). [In Chinese with English summary].

[14] LI YIH-YUAN, "A study on the people of 'Teimo' in the western Paiwan tribe," *Bull. Inst. Ethnol., Acad. Sinica (Taipei)* **I**, 55 (1956). [In Chinese with English summary].

[15] KWANG-CHIH CHANG, "A brief survey of the archaeology of Formosa," *Sthwest. J. Anthrop.* **XII**, 371 (1956).

[16] *Ibid.*, p. 382.

[17] TADAO KANO, "Legends of the occupation of the Negritoes in Formosa," *J. anthrop. Soc. Tokyo* **XLVII**, 255 (1932).

[18] —, "An investigation on the distribution of population and altitude of habitation of the Formosan aborigines," *Geogr. Rev. Jap.* **XIV**, 649–668, 761–796 (1939). [In Japanese].

[19] HWEI-LIN WEI, "Tribal organization and dual chieftainship among the Formosa aborigines," *Bull. Ethnological Soc. China* **I**, 79 (1955). [In Chinese with English summary].

[20] CHEN CHI-LU, "Family and marriage of the Budai Rukai of Pintung, Taiwan," *Bull. Ethnological Soc. China* **I**, 103 (1955). [In Chinese with English summary].

[21] JEN SHEIN-MEN, "A study of men's house of the Tanan Rukai," *Bull. Inst. Ethnol., Acad. Sinica,* **1**, 141 (1956). [In Chinese with English summary].

[22] GEORGE LESLIE MACKAY, *From Far Formosa* (Fleming H. Revell Co., New York, 1896), p. 265.

[23] JANET B. M. MCGOVERN, *Among the Head-Hunters of Formosa* (T. Fisher Unwin, London, 1922), p. 125.

[24] TOICHI MABUCHI, "The social organization of central tribes of Formosa," *J. E. Asiatic Stud.* **I**, 43 (1951).

[25] K. TANAKA, "Type of land utilization of the Taiyal tribe in Taiwan," *Geogr. Rev. Jap.* **XIII**, 123 (1937).

ELEVEN

The Dutch Commercial Period

EUROPEAN RIVALRY IN TAIWAN

DURING THE SIXTEENTH AND SEVENTEENTH CENTURIES, European powers began to lay the foundations of their Asiatic colonial empires. The Portuguese acquired a base in China at Macao in 1557; Spain took over the Philippine Islands in 1571; and the Dutch colonized Java in 1595.

In 1590 Portuguese navigators came upon an island off the coast of China, about one hundred miles from their base at Macao. Because of the lush, subtropical beauty they called it *Formosa*, which means "beautiful," and under this name the island was introduced to the western world. After establishing a settlement in the northern part of the island the Portuguese left.

The next Europeans to occupy Taiwan were the Dutch. As early as 1600 the Netherlands government chartered the Dutch East India Company with a view to exploiting the Malay Peninsula and the Sunda Islands and in 1619 the company's head office was established in Batavia, Java. In 1622 the Dutch established a military base on the Penghu Islands. The next year they were forced by the Chinese to give up the Penghu Islands, and they then moved to the main island of Taiwan.

At the end of 1624 the Dutch landed on the southwestern coast of Taiwan and took territory from the tribe of aborigines living there. They at once started building "Fort Zeelandia" and also the town of Anping. In 1630 a number of Dutch merchants, technicians, and missionaries, as well as sailors, soldiers, and officials, settled on the island to expand their foreign trade, develop virgin land, encourage the planting of sugar cane, carry on the production of camphor, tax the people (many of whom were Chinese immigrants who had reached the islands before the arrival of the Dutch), and convert the natives to Christianity.

The news of the Dutch success in Taiwan so alarmed the Spaniards in the Philippines that they lost no time in sending a fleet from Manila to the northern part of Taiwan, which in 1626 was still not occupied by the Dutch. The Spaniards soon took the northeastern cape of the island, naming it Santiago. (Approximating the pronunciation of this word, the name of the cape is now San Tiao Ko.) Before long, however, they gave up this location and moved to a more desirable area, which they named Santissima Trinidad and which is known now as Keelung harbor. On an island in the harbor they built a fort and named it Fort San Salvador as the Spanish counterpart of the Dutch Fort Zeelandia. In the summer of 1629, they entered the harbor at a place they named Castillo, now Tamshui harbor, and on its hilltop built another fort—Fort Santo Domingo. At this fort they set up a government, appointed civil officials, and prepared to occupy the colony permanently.

Meanwhile, besides focusing efforts on colonial and commercial expansion, the Spaniards attempted to convert the natives to Christianity, and in the brief period between 1626 and 1642 they sent many Catholic missionaries of the Dominican order to this island. To facilitate their activities, Father Jacinto Esquival, a Spanish Dominican, in the year 1630 published at least two books—one on the language of the Taiwan natives and one on Christian doctrine. The missionaries' influence seems to have continued beyond Spanish rule in Taiwan, for as late as 1662, when the Italian Dominican Father Vittorio Ricci came to the island, he found a number of Catholics among the natives.[1]

The Dutch in southern Taiwan made many attempts to drive out the Spaniards. In 1630 and 1641 they assaulted Castillo and Fort Santo Domingo, but in vain. Finally, in the summer of 1642, when the Spaniards, menaced by native rebels in the Philippines, had to recall three-quarters of their garrisons from Taiwan, the Dutch invaders effected a landing at Castillo and conquered it.

From then on (for two decades) the whole island, under Dutch rule, experienced the great Chinese immigration to Taiwan. In 1650, in view of the growing prosperity of the new colony, the Dutch moved the capital from Fort Zeelandia to the newly completed Fort Providentia, called by the Chinese Hung Mao Chen or "Red Hair Castle" from a characteristic they ascribed to the Dutch. On the southwestern coast, where the city of Tainan is now located, the new fort accommodated as many as 600 Dutch officials and other civilians and a garrison of 2200. This settlement continued to be the main base of colonization throughout the Dutch period.

THE DUTCH RULE

After 1642 the Dutch, freed from all European competitors, began to strengthen their hold on Taiwan through the Dutch East India Company. The governor was appointed by the company and for thirty-eight years the company used the island as a trading center. The Dutch government gave the company full power to rule and taxed the aborigines and the Chinese on Taiwan. The number of Dutch civilians on the island was small, but there were many native aborigines, and as many Chinese who had migrated there before the Europeans arrived.

The company divided the aborigines' territory into seven districts, each of which was governed by an aborigine elder, chosen by his own people. The company gave badges of honor to the elders and established an advisory council made up of them. The council opened its season each year in March in the northern sector and in April in the southern. During the council's opening ceremony, each of the elders was invested with a silver-headed staff, ornamented with the company's coat of arms, as his insignia of authority. On this occasion new appointments were confirmed, orders given for the succeeding year, and gifts lavishly bestowed on the most worthy of the elders before they returned to their respective districts to carry out the company's orders.

In 1650 nearly 300 Chinese villages were under the direct jurisdiction of the Dutch East India Company. The Dutch recognized the value of the Chinese immigrants on account of their agricultural experience and organized them into farm groups. Each 50 households were placed under one head and every 30 or 40 heads elected a captain, who was responsible to the governor for local peace and order. The captains and heads were unpaid and their positions were honorary ones. This organization proved very efficient with regard to agricultural production and the area of cultivated land continued to increase.[2]

The Dutch rule in Taiwan (1624–62) may be discussed under the following headings: agriculture, trade, taxes, and missionary work.

AGRICULTURE

Since Taiwan is an agricultural island, the Dutch encouraged agricultural production and took steps to expand the area of cultivated land. Before the Dutch arrived, there were no cows and no horses in Taiwan and no agricultural implements with the exception of the plow. The plow consisted of a sharpened stone attached to a wooden handle about one foot long.[3] After the Dutch had been in Taiwan for about two decades, the company purchased more than 100 head of cattle in India and brought them to the island.[4]

Realizing the importance of the use of cattle in increasing the area of cultivation, the company appointed two officials to take the responsibility for raising cows in the northern and in the southern part of Taiwan.

With the animals and agricultural implements, Chinese tenants of the Dutch landowners cultivated the farms and raised rice, sugar cane, wheat, and tobacco.

Human labor was a very important element in increasing agricultural production. But most of the Dutch who came to Taiwan were merchants, teachers, missionaries, or soldiers; very few were farmers. There were some aborigines who could do farm work, but they needed much training before they could be put to work in the field. Fortunately for the Dutch landowners, many Chinese had settled on the island, and their number was increasing owing to the unstable political situation of their home mainland. It is reported that during the Dutch rule there were 25,000 Chinese families, including 100,000 persons.[5] The Chinese immigrants had come to Taiwan without any money or other belongings, but each brought agricultural technology, two hands, and a strong will to cultivate the land. With the encouragement of the Dutch, more Chinese continued to move to the island. The Dutch East India Company lent not only land and money to the Chinese tenants, but also the cattle they used in cultivating the land.

Land was alloted to each tenant according to his industry and ability. The land survey unit was called a *kah* from the Dutch word *akker*. (The term Dutch *kah* is still used in Taiwan; it equals about 2400 acres, or about 106,000 square feet. Five *kah* equal a Chinese *li* or a "plow.")

Before the Dutch arrived, the inhabitants of Taiwan did not know how to dig wells; they drank water from the rivers. The Dutch introduced well digging and throughout the western and southern plains they dug many wells. The largest and deepest well on the island, located in the present city of Chiayi, is believed to have been constructed by the early Dutch colonists. The Chinese call it the "red-hair well."

TRADE

Before the Dutch arrived on the island, the Chinese in Taiwan enjoyed free trade with the Japanese and there was no tax. The Dutch established a tax on exports, at that time mainly on deerskins and sugar. The annual deerskin export amounted to 40,000 or 50,000 pieces and the sugar export to 4665 or 5332 tons.[6] Because of the tax, the Japanese and Dutch quarreled and the relations between them became so poor that the trade was once discontinued.[7]

Taiwan, under Dutch control, was the center for exchange goods among a number of areas, such as Japan, China, and Batavia, as well as Holland. Taiwan's products exported to China included rice, sugar, rattan, deerskins, deerhorns, and drugs. The island's imports from China included raw silk and silk textiles, porcelain, and medicine. Some of the products after reaching Taiwan were again shipped either to Japan or to Batavia, or even to Holland. Imports to Taiwan from Batavia included spices, amber, tin, lead, cotton, and opium, and some of those were later traded to China. Taiwan was then a busy area, handling all these goods, and the Dutch East India Company, which carried on the business, made a large profit. The Dutch on the island also exchanged goods with the aborigines on the outskirts of their capital, Zeelandia. No money was involved in the exchanges—goods were traded for goods. In trade with China, the Dutch used silver as money; the Dutch received the silver from Japan where they sold Chinese goods.

The Dutch on Taiwan also carried on trade with Persia. The Taiwan products exported were rice, sugar, and camphor. Copper from Japan and ginseng from China were also sold to Persia by the Dutch, carrying those products by way of Taiwan.

Among the branches of the Dutch East India Company in the Far East, Taiwan stood high as a source of profit. In a typical year, 1649 for example, the branches in Ceylon and Siam did not make any profit, but those in Japan and Taiwan made large profits. In that year, 39 per cent of the Dutch East India Company's profit was made by its Japanese branch. The Taiwanese branch was second with 26 per cent.[8] Actually the profit made in Japan was mainly made on goods that the Dutch carried from China by way of Taiwan. It is clear that Taiwan's position in the Dutch East India Company was important.

During the Dutch period (1624–62), the East India Company's activities extended from Japan in the east to the Cape of Good Hope on the southern tip of Africa, covering the western Pacific Ocean and the Indian Ocean. Dominating the field of transportation with its ships, and receiving the quickest news of prices of different goods, the company controlled the market. It exchanged goods—shipped Japan's copper and Taiwan's camphor to Persia and India and carried Persia's rugs to Japan and China's gold to India. With such exchange of goods, the company made its tremendous profits.

TAXES

For making a profit from a colony, trade is quicker than agriculture, and taxation is even quicker. Making a profit from agriculture takes a long time and needs much labor. Making a profit from trade needs capital; it sometimes involves risk of loss. It also depends on market opportunities. But taxing the inhabitants of the colony involves little capital and no risk, and is rather safe. The Dutch East India Company recognized this fact and imposed heavy taxes on the people of Taiwan.

The Dutch first imposed a land tax. Farms were classified as upper, middle, and low grade, and different taxes were collected accordingly. The exact amount of the tax collected from farmers in Taiwan by the Dutch East India Company is difficult to trace, but it is known to have been very high. The Dutch added to the tax the interest on the company's land investment, and fees for protection from attack by the aborigines. During the period of rule of the Cheng Ch'eng-Kung family, the farm tax was the same as that imposed by the Dutch, even though Cheng's time saw improved methods of cultivation and increased production. The taxes imposed by the Cheng family were still considered too high by the Ch'ing Dynasty when it later took over the island.

Not only was each farm taxed by the company, but every inhabitant who had reached the age of seven years had to pay a poll tax. Between 1623 and 1644 the number of Chinese immigrants almost doubled and the poll tax collected from them amounted to an extremely large sum.[9] The aborigines also had to pay the poll tax; but they were permitted to pay in deerskins, instead of in money.

At that time deer hunting was a profitable occupation, not only for hunters, but also for the Dutch company, which received license fees from each hunter.[10] Other taxes were numerous; even fishermen were obliged to turn over a portion of their catch to the Dutch company and to pay fees on all shipments of fish out of Taiwan.

MISSIONARY WORK

The Dutch were interested in Taiwan not only as a colony or a commercial enterprise, but also as a field for missionary work. Protestant missionaries endeavored to Christianize the aborigines, establishing schools where the Dutch language as well as religion was taught. By 1650 the Dutch reported 5,900 converts.[11]

The first Dutch missionary, the Rev. Georgius Candidius, who went to Taiwan in 1627, wrote a work entitled *Short Account of the Island of*

Formosa, describing the manners, customs, and religion of the inhabitants, which was published in 1627 in Germany. In the first 16 months of his stay he instructed 120 natives in the Christian religion. So inspiring was his teaching that the other Dutch missionaries and the aboriginal converts gave his name to what is now Sun Moon Lake. Some maps in western countries still call it Lake Candidius.

Another missionary, the Rev. Robertus Junius, spent 13 years, from 1629 to 1641, on the island and converted as many as 5,900 aborigines. In 1636 he founded the first school in Taiwan, starting with a class of 70 boys. Primary schools were established in every aboriginal hamlet. In three years the schools had enrolled over 600 pupils. Each grade had 30 pupils, who were taught the Dutch language and literature, the Bible, writing, and arithmetic. In 1645, after his return to his native country, the Reverend Junius published in the Netherlands a catechism of the Formosan language.

After the Dutch had expelled the Spanish Catholic missionaries in 1642, a translation of the Gospels of Matthew and John into an aboriginal dialect by the Reverend Junius was used to spread Protestant Christianity among the aborigines. Likewise, the Rev. Gilbertus Happartius completed the compilation of his famous *Oriental Language Dictionary.* It is one of the oldest dictionaries including both an oriental and an occidental language.

The external effects on the aborigines of the Dutch religious and educational work were threefold—adoption of Dutch names (they kept the names long after they had forgotten where they came from), adoption of Dutch dress for Sundays, and use of the Dutch language. More significantly, when Father de Marilla, S.J., visited the island in 1715 he found several aborigines still able to speak and read Dutch and who had in their possession fragments of a Dutch Bible. Du Halde had a similar experience in the 1720's. As late as the close of the 19th century the English Presbyterian missionary, Dr. William Campbell, found in the hands of an illiterate vegetable gardener an old copy of that Bible. The man said it was an heirloom.[11]

To help in missionary work among the aborigines, which had been handicapped by the differences in languages, the Dutch sent young aborigines to Holland to learn about the Christian religion and returned them to Taiwan to help teach what they had learned. Since youngsters always learn languages faster than do adults, the Dutch also brought youngsters from Batavia to Taiwan to learn the aborigines' languages and hired them as interpreters and in other services.

THE DUTCH AND CHINESE CONFLICT

While the Dutch were colonizing Taiwan, China was going through a period of strife. In 1644 that country was invaded by the Manchus, who overthrew the Ming Dynasty in the north; the struggle continued for many years in the south, and the population suffered. In addition, Japanese pirates constantly ravaged Chinese coastal towns. Consequently thousands of people, especially from the coastal provinces of Fukien and Kwangtung, began to pour across the Taiwan Strait to the island. They found the soil of Taiwan much richer than that of the mainland, and crops twice as abundant. During the twenty years from 1624 to 1644, more than 25,000 Chinese households—some 100,000 persons—immigrated to Taiwan.

This mass migration to Taiwan changed the character of the island. At first the Dutch welcomed the new settlers warmly. They had found most of the land in Taiwan still covered with heavy growth and jungles and sparsely populated by aborigines, who were primitive in agricultural practice. Recognizing the urgent need for industrious farmers, the Dutch employed the Chinese immigrants, providing them with oxen, seeds, and agricultural implements on condition that the new settlers would at once start working on the farms. The Chinese immigrants were informed that the Dutch East India Company would bear all the expense for constructing irrigation canals and embanking rivers. Every new settler was promised an annual subsidy of cash and an ox. In the hands of the Chinese toilers, the farms of the island flourished and the Dutch collected rents and taxes from their new tenants.

The roots of the Chinese go deep into the earth. Agriculture has always been their chief means of life. To own their land has been their hope and ambition. However, the Dutch, as was mentioned before, did not allow farmers to own any real estate. All the land belonged to the Dutch East India Company. Time and again ambitious and prosperous Chinese settlers petitioned to be allowed to buy and own the land they were tilling so that they could pay taxes on it instead of rent, but the Dutch paid no attention to them.

These different attitudes toward the land brought about a conflict between the two groups of people, and it was intensified by the difference in agricultural interests. The Chinese were primarily interested in growing rice. The Dutch wanted more sugar cane produced for export; in 1650, however, the area of rice fields was three times that of sugar cane farms.

The friction mounted when the Dutch decided to collect a poll tax from every Chinese of more than six years of age. By means of this tax they expected to increase their annual revenue by a large sum. The differences between the Dutch and the Chinese became greater and greater, and the struggles that were to come between these two groups were inevitable.

The Chinese immigrants soon had an opportunity to end Dutch rule, for out of the struggle on the Chinese mainland between the Manchus and the Ming Dynasty came the military leader Cheng Ch'eng-Kung (Koxinga), a loyal supporter of the Ming Dynasty, who wanted to use Taiwan as a base from which to attack the Manchus. The Chinese settlers joined forces with him, and put an end to Dutch rule in Taiwan in 1661.

Within a few years after the Dutch left, the forts fell to ruin, and most of the aboriginal converts returned to their old beliefs.

The European settlement in Taiwan was temporary. The chief purpose of both the Dutch and the Spanish colonization had been trade; the Chinese settlers were looked upon only as a source of income. In addition, the smallness of the military forces stationed in the colonies and the great distance between bases prevented speedy reinforcement of the garrisons. All these conditions joined to bring about the failure of the Spaniards and the Dutch in Taiwan.

After the Spaniards had been driven out by the Dutch, a trace of their influence could be found in the ruins of Fort Santo Domingo. And even though the Dutch were expelled by the Chinese, vestiges of their culture withstood the challenge of wind and wave. The ruins of Fort Zeelandia and Fort Providentia have remained. Traces of other influence may be seen in the fallen ramparts, old wells, and irrigation canals, and the remains of a few churches. Even now, on the outskirts of many towns is a section called the "barbarian quarter," which was originally inhabited by aborigines or by descendants of the Dutch settlers, full-blooded or mixed. Also, sugar cane is still raised on Taiwan, and the linguistic influence of the Dutch can be traced in present-day Taiwan.[11]

SETTLEMENTS, BUILDINGS, AND TRANSPORTATION

Settlements

During the European period, especially under the Dutch administration of southern Taiwan (1624–1662), village communities were organized to facilitate cooperation among the tenants, most of whom were early Chinese immigrants. Hence compact settlements began to appear in southern Taiwan during the Dutch period; no such definite settlement pattern was developed in northern Taiwan.

Buildings

When the Spanish occupied the northern part of Taiwan and the Dutch the southern part, both built castles for defense; they also built churches.

Castles for defense were the outstanding buildings erected during the European period in the south. They were constructed by the Dutch at Anping, Tainan, and on the Penghu Islands, and by the Spanish in the north at Keelung and Tamshui. Some of these old castles or their remnants can still be seen in Taiwan today. They were generally built in typical European style, square in form with two concentric walls enclosing a fort. Within the outer wall were a church, dwellings, barracks, trading posts, and storehouses. The base of the wall was made of locally found stone; the wall itself was built of European bricks, which were usually larger than native bricks.

At Anping there are remnants of the Dutch-built Fort Zeelandia. Castle Providentia, built by the Dutch at Tainan and still remaining, has become the most interesting historical place in Taiwan, attracting many tourists every year.

The Spaniards' Castle Santo Domingo still stands, in Tamshui on the Tamshui River. Since 1861 the castle has been serving as a British consulate. San Salvador Castle, built in 1626 in the north by the Spaniards, lost three of its towers during the Dutch attack in 1642. Unfortunately most of the castles have been destroyed; only their ruins remain.

Both the Dutch and the Spaniards also built churches. The Dutch began building Protestant churches in 1626, and soon the influence of their missionaries had spread from south to north. Meanwhile the Spaniards in the north were building Catholic churches, the first of which was the

All Saints Church, built in 1626 on an offshore island near Keelung. In 1628, when the Spaniards moved to Tamshui, the missionaries built Our Lady of the Rosary Church.

During the rule of Cheng Ch'eng-Kung Christianity was outlawed, and this ban lasted until it was lifted by the Manchu emperor of China after he had conquered the Ming. Many of the churches now existing in Taiwan were built in the Chinese period after 1846. Remnants of the early seventeenth century churches can hardly be traced.

Transportation

During the European period, the only means of land transportation in Taiwan was the two-wheeled ox cart, which had solid wheels fixed on the axle. The axle turned with the revolution of the wheel emitting a strident squeak. These two-wheeled ox carts are still used in the sugar cane district of southern Taiwan and by the Ami tribe of the eastern coast.

REFERENCES

[1] JOSHUA LIAO, "Formosa under the Dutch," *Far East. Econ. Rev.* **X,** 184 (1951).

[2] S. W. CHOW, "The robber economy in Taiwan during the Dutch period," In *Taiwan's Economic History* (Provincial Bank of Taiwan, Taipei, 1956), Vol. 4, p. 55.

[3] G. CANDIDIUS, *Short History of the Island of Formosa* (1637).

[4] LUDWIG RIESS, *Geschichte der Insel Formosa* (1897), Chinese translation in *Taiwan's Economic History* (Provincial Bank of Taiwan, Taipei, 1956), Vol. 3.

[5] S. W. CHOW, "A general economic history of Taiwan," translated from Japanese in *Taiwan's Economic History* (Provincial Bank of Taiwan, Taipei, 1955), Vol. 2, p. 7.

[6] *Ibid.,* p. 8.

[7] LUDWIG RIESS, *Geschichte der Insel Formosa* (1897), Chinese translation in *Taiwan's Economic History* (Provincial Bank of Taiwan, Taipei, 1956), Vol. 3. pp. 14–16.

[8] S. W. CHOW, "The robber economy in Taiwan during the Dutch period," In *Taiwan's Economic History* (Provincial Bank of Taiwan, Taipei, 1956), Vol. 4, pp. 62–63.

[9] LUDWIG RIESS, *Geschichte der Insel Formosa* (1897), Chinese translation in *Taiwan's Economic History* (Provincial Bank of Taiwan, Taipei, 1956), Vol. 3.

[10] S. W. CHOW, "The robber economy in Taiwan during the Dutch period," In *Taiwan's Economic History* (Provincial Bank of Taiwan, Taipei, 1956), Vol. 4, p. 64.

[11] JOSHUA LIAO, "Formosa and its early inhabitants," *Far. East. Econ. Rev.* **X,** 152 (1951).

TWELVE

Period of the Chinese Agricultural Settlers

CHINESE IMMIGRATION AND CUSTOMS

Immigration

CHINESE SETTLEMENT IN Taiwan dates back as far as the 12th century A.D., but large-scale immigration did not begin until the 17th century during the period of Dutch administration. The flow of immigration increased after 1661, when the island was taken from the Dutch by Cheng Ch'eng-Kung, a loyal adherent of China's Ming Dynasty. For the next twenty years the island was ruled by Cheng and his descendants as independent sovereigns. In 1683 the island was incorporated into the Chinese Empire as a part of Fukien province. Meanwhile emigration from China to Taiwan continued.

The early Chinese immigrants came mostly from the provinces of Fukien and Kwangtung. Fukien province contributed most of them. In the early 19th century, 82 per cent (2,500,000) of the Chinese population on the island was Fukienese; the Cantonese constituted only 13 per cent (400,000), and about 150,000 persons were from other provinces of China.[1] The people from Fukien and those from Kwangtung had dialects and customs that were widely different, and they settled in different localities (*Figure 29*).

The Fukienese fall into four groups—Anchi, Tungan, Sanpa, and Changchow—according to their dialects and the districts of Fukien from which they came. They occupied most of the fertile western plain of Taiwan—the Anchi and Tungan people settled in the north, the Sanpa group on the coast, and those from Changchow in the south and the center.

The Cantonese included persons from Chaochow, Waichow, and Chaiying districts. The Chaochow group settled in central Taiwan, and the Waichow in the northwestern area. The Chaiying provincial groups were Hakkas, that is, Chinese who had moved to Kwantung from further north and so were not regarded as true Cantonese. They settled mostly in the foothills between the plains and mountains from the north to the central part of the island.

In China the Hakkas had travelled from place to place like gypsies and had possessed no land of their own. Since there was little to keep them in China, they came in great numbers, seeking a settled life in Taiwan. Their immigration increased rapidly and it is estimated that in a century one-third of the Hakkas of Kwangtung had migrated to Taiwan.[2]

Customs

The Chinese, like other settlers, brought with them their habits of life and their customs. Rice farms and tea plantations took the place of forest tangles and rude aborigine huts, and the "red hair" castles of the Dutch almost vanished. Villages and towns with their unmistakable marks

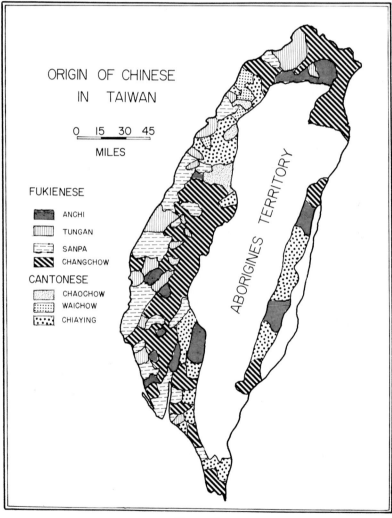

Figure 29

of the "Middle Kingdom" of China took their place; the island became Chinese in character.

Generally speaking, the Chinese, with the exception of the Christians, worshipped gods that were the deified spirits of the distinguished dead. But the worship of their gods was not the real religion of the Chinese; nor was the idol-shrine their most holy place. Their real religion was the worship of their ancestors; their real idols were the ancestral tablet and graves. The Chinese in Taiwan, as in China, considered their ancestors' graves so important that they devoted a large amount of land to them. Each grave was covered by a central dome-like mound of earth, with a stone tablet and various altar-like accessories at ground level before it—a typical scene in southern China. These countryside burial mounds in Taiwan took up a considerable area of fertile ground, and on the whole must represent a great acreage denied to cultivation. Here, as in southern China, a great problem in land utilization existed.

Among Chinese, the family is the most important social unit. The individual is subordinated to the group. In work, in financial affairs, in relation to the community and to society, the family group stands together. All this remains the same among the descendents of the Chinese immigrants to Taiwan. The food for the group is cooked in a common kitchen and eaten in a common dining room, but each generation lives in a separate part of the house, so that all the generations are together and yet apart. Most houses in Taiwan, therefore, are built with many rooms, following the architectural pattern of southern China.

Most Chinese immigrants were farmers. On the whole the farmer in Taiwan, as in China, was hard-working and honest. He brought his chief implements with him from the mainland. The livestock on the farm were water buffalo, hogs, and chickens. Almost every family had a hog or two and a few chickens. The hog was a favorite among the Chinese farmers, for pork was their principal meat.

TWO STAGES OF CHINESE RULE

The Chinese period was divided into two stages: (1) the rule of Cheng Ch'eng-Kung and his family, and (2) that of the Manchus or Ch'ing Dynasty. The Cheng family stage lasted from 1662 to 1683, only one-tenth of the time covered by the Ch'ing Dynasty, which lasted 212 years, from 1683 to 1895. During the Cheng period, Taiwan was an independent state; under the Ch'ing Dynasty Taiwan was part of one of the provinces of China.

CHENG PERIOD

When Cheng Ch'eng-Kung drove the Dutch out of Taiwan, he became its ruler. He instituted schools for the education of the young. He introduced Chinese laws and customs and the Chinese form of government and transplanted Chinese tradition to the island. He also built the first Confucian temple in Taiwan as a symbol of the introduction of Chinese culture.

Cheng, as supporter of the Ming Dynasty which had been driven out by the Manchus, drilled his soldiers intensively for a planned attack on the mainland, where the Manchus had established the Ch'ing Dynasty. He had strong fortifications erected on islands in the Taiwan Strait to bar the Manchus from crossing the Strait to Taiwan. The Manchu rulers feared him so much that they forced persons living within ten miles of the mainland coast to move further inland lest Cheng receive supplies and other assistance from them if he carried out his threat of returning to the mainland. As a result, many civilians fled to Taiwan to join Cheng's forces. During his rule, an unending stream of Chinese continued to pour into Taiwan and settlements sprang up in increasing numbers along the western coast.

In Cheng's time, agriculture was emphasized, but was limited to southern Taiwan. The farms were of three kinds: the official farm, the semi-official farm, and the military farm. The official farms were located on land confiscated from the Dutch. The semi-official farms were owned by Cheng's military or civilian officials and other loyal supporters. The owner paid the tax and the farming was done by tenants. Cheng Ch'eng-Kung designed a military camp farming system under which soldiers participated in farm work during their spare time in order to support themselves. Such military farms were established in about forty locations.

The land tax system was adapted from that used by the Ming Dynasty. The three kinds of farms paid different taxes. The soldiers cultivating a military farm did not need to pay any tax on it until it had been cultivated for three years. The rate of tax for an official farm was almost five times as great as that for a semi-official farm because the government supplied the official farm with seeds and agricultural tools; the semi-official farm did not receive any supplies, for it more or less belonged to the individual who invested his money and energy in the farm land.

A poll tax also was collected from every person who had reached the age of ten years. This applied not only to the Chinese, but also to the aborigines and deerskins were accepted from them instead of gold. Each year from 10,000 to 50,000 deerskins were collected.

During the Cheng family's rule, manufacturing was also promoted. Sugar refining was encouraged, and manufacture of tiles was started. The method of salt production was improved. Instead of the old baking method, the sun-drying method was used; this laid the foundation for a salt production industry on the island. Some shipbuilding was initiated.

Brisk trade was carried on with the neighboring areas, such as the Philippines, Japan, and Okinawa. Under Cheng's efficient administration, Taiwan's economy laid a foundation, and Cheng, the ambitious ruler, began to cast about for territorial expansion. He sent a Spanish Dominican friar, Riccio, to the Philippines demanding that the Spanish government pay him a yearly tribute. But Riccio's mission was a total failure, and many Chinese living in the Philippine capital were killed. Cheng then set about organizing an expedition to take the Philippines. At that time, however, he was attacked by a serious illness, and he died in 1662 at thirty-nine years of age. Possessed of extraordinary courage, enterprise, and ability, Cheng Ch'eng-Kung had created a kingdom for himself and had provided a safe refuge for loyal followers of the Ming Dynasty.

Cheng's son then became ruler. During his reign many departments of industry, education, and commerce made remarkable progress. Twenty years later he died, and his son was placed on the throne. The next year

China's Ch'ing Dynasty government attacked Taiwan and occupied Pen-ghu Island and at the end forced an unconditional surrender. Thus, after having been governed by Cheng's family for more than two decades, Taiwan passed under the Ch'ing Dynasty rule and became a part of the Chinese province of Fukien. It later became an independent province.

CH'ING DYNASTY

From 1683, when the grandson of Cheng Ch'eng-Kung surrendered Taiwan to the Ch'ing Dynasty, until 1895, when Taiwan was ceded to Japan, it remained under the Ch'ing Dynasty rule. Despite the attitude of some officials of the Ch'ing Dynasty who advocated the abandonment of Taiwan because of its wildness and unproductiveness, Taiwan developed under that rule. During that time the area of cultivated land on the island expanded northward. Previously it had been limited to the south (*Figure 30*).

The most noticeable characteristic of the land during the Ch'ing Dynasty period was that the official, semi-official, and military farms gave way to farms privately owned. The change took place for two reasons. First, the official farms were mostly located in the south around Tainan and did not have a chance for expansion, while the private farms extended to new territory without any limitation. Also, the owners of the official farms were dignitaries who enjoyed a luxurious life, unlike the private farmers who had the initiative and incentive to expand their farm land. All the official, semi-official, and military farms were abolished, and only the private farms remained.

At the beginning of the Ch'ing Dynasty, the poor pioneers with ambitions and energy received some farm land, either from the Manchu government or through negotiations with the aborigines, and they became the owners of the land. As the immigration from mainland China continued, the newly-arrived immigrants became tenants of the new farm owners who supplied them with agricultural tools and, in return, collected rents from them. Gradually, with more capital the owners obtained more land and their wealth increased. They then possessed several thousand acres of farm land and collected rents from several thousand farmers. So they gradually became a kind of lord in their districts. Compared with the conditions in Cheng Ch'eng-Kung's period, the relationship between tenant farmers and land owners was more nearly modern, but it was still feudal. Gradually, the landowner became like a king in his community; he received the rent from his tenants and lost direct relationship with his land. As time went on, the tenant farmer, by hard work and endurance, gradually became the owner of the farm, and he hired more recent arrivals to do his farm work. Conditions concerning the rent of the farms changed. In the beginning the amount of rent was based on the crop, but by 1843 it had to be paid in gold. As a result the land became a commodity and could be bought and sold.

Thus on the same farm land there were two kinds of rent; one large and the other small. Also there were three classes of farm people; owners of large tracts, tenants, and farmers. These three classes dominated Taiwan for a long time during the Ch'ing Dynasty period.

In the Ch'ing Dynasty period, rice was the dominating crop. In culti-vating this crop, the Ch'ing government emphasized irrigation and the employment of agricultural tools. The irrigation systems of the Ch'ing Dynasty were privately owned, in contrast to those during Cheng Ch'eng-Kung's rule, when the systems were owned by the government.

An important agricultural advance took place with the use of oxen. The ox was first imported from India by the Dutch. In the middle of the Manchu period, an ox market was set up, and oxen were extensively used.

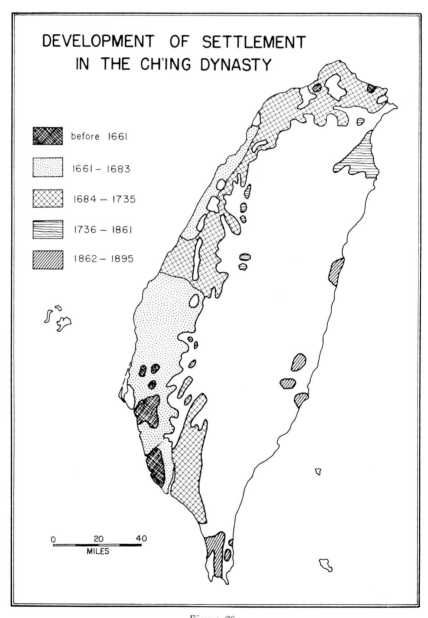

DEVELOPMENT OF SETTLEMENT IN THE CH'ING DYNASTY

before 1661

1661 – 1683

1684 – 1735

1736 – 1861

1862 – 1895

0   20   40
MILES

Figure 30

154

INDEPENDENT PROVINCE

In 1887 Taiwan became an independent province. Under an able governor, Liu Ming-chuan, postal service, telegraph lines, railroads, and sea ports were developed. The manufacture of camphor developed in close relation to military needs, for camphor wood was used in building ships. Mining of sulfur was begun; it was used in making munitions. Its production was controlled by the government, which permitted it to be exported. Coal mining in northern Taiwan and gold mining in the east were developed.

CAMPHOR, BAMBOO, RICE, AND TEA

After the Chinese settled on the island of Taiwan, camphor became a cause of conflict between them and the aborigines. Bamboo became a widely used item. Rice and tea, typical Chinese crops, were introduced on the island.

Camphor

Of all the products of Taiwan, none is of greater interest than camphor, which comes from a beautiful tree with a shapely trunk and widespreading branches. These trees grow wild in the mountain forests only in Taiwan, Indochina, Java, South China, and Japan. In 1858 an Englishman discovered how to manufacture celluloid from camphor and thereafter camphor was in demand not only as a drug, but as a raw material for making celluloid. Combs, tobacco pouches, billiard balls, knife and umbrella handles, and indeed everything that before had been made of ivory, coral, or tortoise-shell could then be made of celluloid.

The development of the camphor industry in Taiwan brought conflicts between the aborigines and the Chinese, for the aborigines lived in the mountain districts where the trees were found. Since the Chinese method of collecting camphor necessitated the destruction of the trees, the camphor workers had to go further and further inland, where they often encountered hostile natives, and bloody conflicts ensued. Although scarcely a month elapsed without an outbreak between the two groups, the Chinese were willing to risk their lives, for abundant profits could be obtained from the camphor trade. Although the camphor industry had been known in Taiwan since the late 19th century, successful production was not achieved until the beginning of the 20th century, when Hakka camphor workers forced the aborigines to retreat further into the mountains.

Bamboo

Taiwan abounds in many different species of bamboo. This fast-growing grass usually grows in thickets, with many slender stems surrounding the main stems, which are hollow. It is found around farmsteads, along the rivers, and in the foothills.

The Chinese in Taiwan made far more use of bamboo than had the aborigines or the Dutch, and still use it widely, as do the mainland Chinese. The tender bamboo shoots are used as a vegetable and are one of the most famous Chinese delicacies. The small stems are used for making paper, chopsticks, baskets, and light household utensils; the large stems are used for making furniture. Strips of bamboo are woven into mats to form the walls of buildings; plaited bamboo ropes are used to haul junks on the rivers. Bamboo is also used in building boats and bridges, and for numerous industrial purposes. It is estimated that the bamboo is used in more than 600 different ways. In Taiwan as in southern China, the people are truly in the "bamboo age."

Rice

When the Chinese settlers with their traditional technology of rice cultivation practiced rice cultivation year after year, they made the island the "rice bowl" of the Far East.

Whenever the Chinese settled in Taiwan, especially in the western plains, crops of rice grown in paddies replaced the shifting agricultural crops of the aborigines. As on the mainland, the rice farms on Taiwan were small, seldom covering more than five acres. They were divided into irregular plots, separated by low mounds of earth, to permit irrigation.

The Chinese brought with them the technical knowledge required for the irrigation of the rice paddies. Rice is a thirsty crop, and water is very important in its cultivation. Two methods were used by the Chinese to convey the water to where it was needed.

One of their devices was a treadmill used to raise the water from one field to another. It consisted of a box-trough in which a windlass was fixed. The lower end of the trough was placed in a stream; the upper end was operated by three or four men, who formed an endless chain of carriers, pumping the water up to the fields.

The other method was to dig a pond on the upland to store rain water for use in the dry season. These ponds were connected by a network of river tributaries, creeks, canals, and ditches to conduct the water from a pond to the farm. The pond or reservoir was exceedingly useful, not only for irrigation, but also as a bathing place for water buffaloes.

The Chinese also introduced the terrace method of cultivating rice. Rice cultivation needs flat landforms, and when the western plains were almost entirely occupied by paddy fields, rice farming was extended to the hills; the hillsides were cut into gigantic steps to provide flat land for paddy fields.

The farming tools used by the Chinese rice farmer included a broad hoe, a wooden plow with an iron share, a heavy wooden harrow, and a harvest sickle. For dry plowing the ox is used, but for growing rice, the water buffalo is indispensable.

The Chinese farmers possess a high degree of skill in cultivating rice. Not only do the irrigating, terracing, transplanting, and harvesting call for unending attention, but long experience is also necessary, and the process requires the cooperation and mobilization of the family or the whole village community. The cultivation of rice needs much labor. On the other hand, rice can support more people than any other crop.

Tea

Tea is another crop that was brought to Taiwan by Chinese. Although it can not be ascertained whether or not tea plants were ever found growing wild in Taiwan, the production of tea for use as a beverage began only with the arrival of large numbers of Chinese in the 17th century. It was completely unknown to the aborigines and to the early Dutch settlers.[3]

From time immemorial tea has been the favorite beverage of the Chinese. In Chinese society friendship is renewed and human warmth displayed over a cup of hot tea. Tea to Chinese is what coffee is to Europeans and Americans. For commercial use, tea is manufactured from the leaves of an evergreen shrub, known botanically as *Thea*, a name derived from the Fukienese dialect. In the 17th century many merchants from the Chinese city of Amoy brought Fukienese tea to Taiwan, but not until the early 19th century were large quantities of the tea plant itself brought to the island. Then the industry was established and operated mainly by the Fukienese.

According to native accounts, two tea plantations existed southeast of Taipei in early 1850. As the manufacture of tea spread, seeds, slips, and cuttings were brought over from China, and finally in 1865 the shrub itself was imported on a large scale. Between 1868 and 1878 a part of the forest east of Taipei was cleared to make way for a small plantation of tea, and within the same decade tea production jumped from a few thousand pounds to more than eight million pounds.[4]

Since the light sandy loam, the most suitable soil for raising tea, was found in hilly land, tea plantations spread to the hills close to the district inhabited by aborigines. The latter, however, were not inclined to give up their territory to the strange invader without a struggle. Thus the expansion of tea culture, like the cutting of camphor trees, had a bloody history.

The tea plantations in Taiwan, as in China, are usually small, from two to five acres, but despite their small size, each tea garden requires a great amount of labor in the picking season. Most of the tea pickers are teen-age girls. Besides the girl pickers, four or five thousand Chinese are brought over each season from Amoy and Foochow on the mainland to assist in preparing the tea for shipment.

Until 1854 Taiwan's tea was shipped chiefly from Tamshui to Amoy and Foochow on the mainland, where it was refined and transhipped to foreign countries. But from 1868 onward, all of Taiwan's tea for export was prepared on the island by skilled labor brought from Amoy and Foochow for shipment direct to foreign lands.

SETTLEMENT, HOUSE TYPES, AND TRANSPORTATION

Settlement

In the rural areas of Taiwan the farm settlements are predominantly in the Chinese style. Two contrasting types can be distinguished, the dispersed and the compact. The former is found in the northern part of the island, the latter in the southern; the dividing line is the Choshui River. Besides these two types of settlements, there is also the linear type, which is found along the Choshui River and in the Taipei area (*Figure 31*).

In the dispersed type each rural house is enclosed by a bamboo hedge; the houses are distributed among the paddy fields like so many floating islets. The means of communication between them is a narrow ridge between paddy fields.

South of the Choshui River the isolated farm houses become fewer and fewer, the dispersed type of settlement disappears, and the compact type is found. The compact villages in the south are distributed in the vast plains, roughly one half mile apart. The village is frequently enclosed by a bamboo hedge. In these villages are crowded hundreds of rural houses, all smaller in size than those of the north. Each house is fenced in and is inhabited by one, two, or three families. Stone-paved pathways provide a means of communication between adjoining houses.

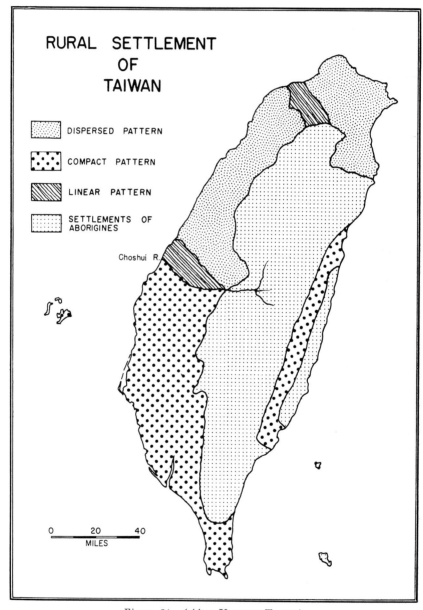

Figure 31.—(After YOSHIRO TOMITA)

The idea of compact villages was introduced from the mainland of southern China, where they are still seen. In the beginning the Chinese colonists lived for some time in scattered temporary cottages while they cultivated the land, and then they built their permanent compact settlements. The villages of the south probably did not develop as enlargements of the dispersed villages of the north, but rather seem to have been established from the first in the compact style.

Along the sides of canals and rivers, and on natural levees, rural houses are frequently joined to each other by hedges to form small groups or hamlets. When the houses are placed in orderly lines the settlements are said to be of the linear type. These groups of rural houses developed through repeated additions of houses as the population increased. Originally, the houses were distributed sporadically, and development of these linear groups was different from that of the compact type in the south.

Factors influencing settlement formation

Some factors that may have led to the formation of the dispersed and of the compact rural settlements are as follows:[5, 6]

DEFENSE AGAINST THE ABORIGINES.—In the 16th century, when the waves of Chinese immigrants were pushing the aborigines into the mountains, the tribes in the south often attacked the agriculturists on the plains; thus the settlers had to keep their dwellings close together in defendable clusters. In the north, on the other hand, there was no such necessity because the aboriginal population was very sparse. Therefore compact settlements tended to spring up in the south; scattered housing predominated in the north. Even so, in the foothill regions of the north the immigrants frequently settled in compact groups.

WATER SUPPLY.—Water supply for domestic use is generally less available in the south than in the north owing to the difference in the seasonal distribution of rainfall. The rainfall in the south is concentrated in the summer season and there is a drought in the winter. In the early days of settlement the habitations had to be situated around areas of water supply in order to cope with the lack of water during the winter months. It might have been for this reason that the rural settlements in the south were established in compact groups. In the north, however, the rainfall is rather evenly distributed throughout the year, and so the sites chosen for residence did not have to be near natural sources of water; thus they were often scattered.

MILITIA CAMPS.—During the regime of Cheng Ch'eng-Kung (1662–83) the militia were encamped chiefly in the region around Tainan in the south, and the names of the camping places still remain here and there. These camp systems might have been organized as a kind of village for the convenience of the tenants, and they may have promoted the development of compact settlements.

AGRICULTURAL MANAGEMENT.—In northern Taiwan at that time the farmers received extensive tracts of uncultivated land from the Cheng government. These tracts of land were operated by tenants who had come from southern Taiwan or southern China. The owner built a cottage for each tenant on his share of land for convenience in agricultural management.

Probably the present day form of dispersed rural settlements in the north resulted mainly from this agricultural plan.

NATURAL LANDSCAPES.—In the northern part of Taiwan there are dense forests or swamps, in the south there are sparse forests separated by heaths, and there has been a tendency to establish dispersed villages in the northern forest lands and compact villages in the south and elsewhere.

OTHER CAUSES.—Agriculturists in China have for a long time lived under the "extended family" system (*see* page **244**). These people naturally tend to form the compact type of settlement, which is commonly seen in the rural regions of southern China even today. It is quite natural therefore that in migrating to Taiwan they should begin their life there in the form familiar to them.

Sometimes there were struggles among the immigrants coming from different *hsiens* (counties) of their home provinces and these also necessitated community life.

House types

The Chinese buildings in Taiwan can be divided into two groups: those of the Fukien type and those of the Kwangtung design. Buildings of the Fukien type are more numerous than are those of the Kwangtung, since most of the settlers in Taiwan came from that region. Generally speaking, the Fukien type buildings are solidly built, with heavy lines and many curves; those of the Kwangtung type are graceful, with straight, trim lines. The pillars of the Fukien houses are rounded and made of wood or stone; the Kwangtung houses have stone pillars with angular lines. The Fukien-style roof is usually of red tiles; the Kwangtung style has roofs made of dark blue tiles. The Fukien house has more curvings than the Kwangtung.

With respect to the dwellings, we may differentiate between rural and urban types. A third type of structure is exemplified by the temples.

RURAL TYPES.—The Chinese rural houses are usually built of sun-dried bricks; they are roofed with tiles and floored with stones. Enclosed by walls, the rectangular unit in transverse positions has become very popular.

A rural house consists of three units; a main building and two side buildings, arranged around a central courtyard. The windows are narrow and the doors are hinged. Usually each unit is surrounded by a thick bamboo hedge. The main building stands on a higher foundation than do the others and is entered by going up stone steps.

URBAN TYPES.—An urban house is oblong in shape. All the houses are much alike, and they are close together. The average urban dwelling has two stories. It consists of a front building and one or two parallel additional buildings behind the front one, separated by a courtyard. Most buildings combine both residential and commercial functions; a shop usually occupies the front, and the family lives either in the back building or in the room over the shop.

The most conspicuous feature of an urban area in Taiwan is the arcade. The business streets are lined with these arcades, which shelter shoppers from the sun and rain and permit the display of goods. Many shops open upon the arcades. Above and in the rear of these shops are crowded dwell-ling places. Although the arcades darken the shops, their usefulness outweighs this disadvantage.

TEMPLES.—The Chinese also built many public buildings, including temples for Buddhist, Taoist, and Confucian ceremonies. Many are repositories for objects of reverence and many carry out definite rituals. Some of these temples are resorts.

Most of the temples were built in the foothills, somewhat out of the way. The approaches to the temples are often marked by altars, images, and rest pavilions. If a temple is very popular, small shops along the way offer tea, food, and souvenirs.

Several temples are located in cities and stand on street corners, where they are visible from several directions. Their location often causes streets to turn irregularly and this also interferes with communication.

GRAVES AND MEMORIALS.—Throughout the countryside old tombs belonging to fairly well-to-do families can be found. A structure found on many roads in Taiwan is the memorial arch, built by Chinese emperors to honor persons who showed special loyalty to their country or to their family.

Transportation

When the Chinese came to Taiwan, they brought with them bamboo rafts and sailboats for water transportation and sedan chairs for use on land. These are still used today.

RAFTS AND BOATS.—The rafts are more than eighteen feet long, and about six feet wide, and one foot thick. They are made by lashing together a number of bamboo poles three or four inches thick. Each raft is built like a platform. In the middle of it a square box-like arrangement is partly embedded, which is used for storing goods and as a seat. The box is out of reach of the waves, which at times almost entirely submerge the rest of the raft. It is safe when going with the tide. This type of raft is characteristically Taiwanese. Although there is a type of bamboo raft found in south China and along the Chinese coast, it is not nearly so large as the Taiwan raft, since the bamboo on the mainland cannot compare in size with that growing on the island.

Chinese boats are usually equipped with a sail, which greatly aids the oarsmen when going with the wind.

SEDAN CHAIRS.—During the Chinese settlement period Taiwan had few roads. Paths led from village to village; some country roads connected towns with the surrounding villages; and in some of the sugar districts were roads used by ox carts transporting sugar cane. But on the whole, travel was limited to walking and using the sedan chair.

REFERENCES

[1] J. W. DAVIDSON, The Island of Formosa, Past and Present (Macmillan and Company, London, 1933).
[2] FLOY, HURLBUT, The Fukienese—A Study in Human Geography (1939), p. 48.
[3] J. W. DAVIDSON, The Island of Formosa, Past and Present (Macmillan and Company, London, 1933).
[4] J. Y. YANG, "The tea of China and Formosa," Far East. Econ. Rev. XIV, 207 (1952).
[5] YOSHIRO TOMITA, "On the rural settlement forms in Taiwan (Formosa), Japan," In Proceedings of the Fifth Pacific Science Congress, Canada (University of Toronto Press, Toronto, 1933), Vol. II, p. 1391.
[6] —, "Characteristic features of the Formosan settlements in Taiwan, Japan," C. R. Congr. internat. geog., Amsterdam, 172 (1938).

THIRTEEN | # The Japanese Industrial Period

JAPANESE COLONIZATION—EARLY STAGE

CHINA CEDED Taiwan to Japan in 1895, at the end of a war between the Chinese and the Japanese. The Japanese colonization of Taiwan differed from that of the Dutch in a number of ways.

Differences from the Dutch period

First, unlike the Dutch, who in the 17th century colonized Taiwan for immediate commercial profit and considered political sovereignty second (saying, "the flag follows the trade"), the Japanese in the 20th century considered political control to be more important than commercialization (saying "trade follows the flag"). The Japanese exercised scientific management and long-range planning in their colonization methods. In a sense, the Japanese colonization of Taiwan was more efficient and penetrating than that of the British in India, or of the French in Indochina, or even the Dutch in East India, in what is now called Indonesia.

Second, during the Dutch period, the Protestant missionary priests were the main agents for the practice of Dutch rule. They organized the farmers, collected the poll tax, received the rent, and Christianized the aborigines. In the Japanese period, the policeman was the most important person in the exercise of colonial aims.

Third, during the Dutch rule, Taiwan's exports rather than her imports were emphasized. In the Japanese period however, Taiwan's trade was centered on imports of manufactured goods, and on the export of agricultural raw material.

Fourth, in the Japanese period the foreign trade was centered on "capitals" in contrast to the Dutch stage when the trade was mainly in "goods."

Pacification of the island

When Taiwan was ceded to Japan by the Ch'ing dynasty of China, an Independent Republic of Taiwan had been set up by the Chinese inhabitants. Even though the Independent Republic was soon eliminated by Japanese military power, the Chinese in Taiwan persisted for some years in uprisings against the new rulers, and the aborigines also fought them, as they had fought the Chinese. As a result the Japanese had to concentrate their efforts for some years on pacifying the island. The Chinese resistance fighters were largely subdued within a decade, the aborigines a decade and a half later.

Long-range goals of Japan

The Japanese worked toward carrying out a long-range plan, under which Taiwan was to serve three purposes: (1) to supply the Japanese Empire with agricultural products, (2) to serve as a market for Japan's industrial products, and (3) to provide living space for emigrants from overpopulated Japan. They succeeded in carrying out the first two parts of their plan. However, the third part was a failure, as will be shown later in this section.

Four stages, each covering approximately a decade, can be recognized in the Japanese occupation of Taiwan:

During the first stage the Japanese introduced strict police control, made a land survey, standardized the measurement and money systems, brought under government monopoly the manufacture and sale of a number of important products, began collecting census data, and made an ethnological study of the aborigines. In the second stage the chief accomplishment was an increase and improvement in transportation facilities. The third stage was characterized by the initiation of irrigation systems and intensification of agricultural production. The fourth and last stage, which extended into the World War II period, was centered on industrialization.

Police control

From the beginning of their rule the Japanese gave their police a great deal of power. The police were charged not only with keeping order, but with assigning permission to cultivate certain crops, arranging for use of irrigation facilities, recruiting soldiers, collecting taxes, conducting censuses, employing labor for roadbuilding, and supervising work. The Japanese kept nearly twice as many policemen in rural Taiwan as they did in industrial Japan. A fifteen-year record (1898–1912) shows that in Taiwan the Japanese government spent more than twice as much for police service as for civil service.[1] In the same year there was, in Japan, one policeman for every 1,052 persons, while in agricultural Taiwan there was one policeman for every 580 persons.[2] The police were cruel to the inhabitants, but they contributed greatly to Japan's success in controlling Taiwan.

Land ownership

An important step in the Japanese occupation of Taiwan during its first stage was to clarify land ownership throughout the island. Such a survey was needed in order that land taxes might be collected efficiently. During

163

233 years of Chinese rule the land ownership system had become extremely complicated. Early in the island's history a few Chinese pioneers had become big land owners, and they had rented land to later arrivals. As time went on the big land owners and their descendants discontinued active supervision of their properties and became absentee landlords. Some tenants gradually became owners of land and began to sublet to later arrivals, thus becoming landlords themselves. With property rights so indefinite, land taxes were difficult to collect.

The Japanese established a land survey bureau, which found that the amount of land cultivated on the island was almost twice the amount reported during the Chinese rule. This apparent increase did not represent an actual expansion of cultivated land; it merely pointed to the inaccuracy of the earlier report. After the land survey was completed the unit of land measurement was standardized, land ownership was clarified, and tax collection became efficient.

The survey was not limited to the agricultural land, but included also forested areas. After the survey both the agricultural land and the forests had definite property value, which they had not had under Chinese rule. As a result of the survey of the agricultural and forest lands the Japanese authorities gained definite data necessary for economic planning. They were enabled to modernize the management of the farm and forest lands. Usually the authorities did not confiscate the land, but paid large sums for it. By the end of the Japanese period nearly 80 per cent of the cultivated land and nearly 95 per cent of the forest land was in the hands of the Japanese government.

Population census

Not only did the Japanese government of the island need accurate and complete information about the land, but data about the inhabitants were also required. Therefore, the government established a carefully planned census which began in 1905. More than 7,000 persons were employed for the task, with the result that the demographic records for Taiwan were even better than those for Japan. The Japanese also launched a study of the aborigines, reporting on the number of tribes and their customs.

Standardization of measures and money

Another step taken during the first stage of the Japanese occupation was to standardize the measurement of commerical goods and to set up a money system that corresponded with that of Japan. During the Chinese period units of measurement had differed from place to place. In 1895 the Japanese system of measurement was introduced, and in 1911 the money system was made the same as Japan's.

Monopolies

During the first stage also the Japanese authorities acted to increase the revenues they gained from Taiwan. They monopolized the industries producing salt, camphor, opium, tobacco, and alcoholic beverages. These monopolies became responsible for bringing in two-thirds of the Japanese government's revenues from Taiwan sources.

SECOND STAGE

EXPANSION OF TRANSPORTATION

As an essential corollary to industrialization, the Japanese soon set out to increase Taiwan's transportation facilities by developing steamship lines, improving harbors, and building railroads and highways.

Steamship development

Early in the second stage of the Japanese occupation the government subsidized a steamship company operating a line running from Taiwan to Japan, and later operating additional lines to other parts of Asia. In 1926 the line had six steamers of 6,000–10,000 tons from Keelung to Kobe, in Japan. Each made two trips a month from each terminus. Later the company added more lines and soon another company entered the shipping business.

Harbor improvement

Recognizing the importance of harbors to Taiwan's economy, the Japanese immediately set to work improving them. In the modernization of the island's seventeen harbors, the largest of which are Keelung, Kaohsiung, and Hualien, new piers and other facilities were installed, and shallow harbors were dredged.

Railroad construction

Nearly a decade before the Japanese took over Taiwan, and at a time when most mainland Chinese were ignorant of the existence of railroads, the Chinese on the island, under the leadership of an able governor, built a railroad in the north 62 miles long. When the Japanese occupied Taiwan they were surprised to find that the Chinese had built a railroad there. The Japanese immediately reconstructed the old line to eliminate the numerous hairpin curves and steep gradients. They then built a new line, 250 miles long, connecting Keelung on the northern coast with Kaohsiung on the southwestern tip and passing through a number of other major cities. The building of the line and of others in Taiwan was very difficult, as the hills and rivers required that many tunnels and bridges be constructed.

Even before the government's Keelung–Kaohsuing line was completed some Japanese sugar manufacturers had begun building private lines to transport sugar cane (*Figure 32*). The lines were used for general traffic as well as for sugar-cane. Later many branches of the government railroad were constructed; these also carried passengers and freight.

At the end of the Japanese rule the private lines combined amounted to 1863 miles in length and the government ones accounted for 994 miles—a total of 2857 miles.

The mountain railroad on Ali Shan was a brilliant Japanese engineering feat, which took 12 years to accomplish. With this mountain line the Japanese began to conquer the steep slopes of the mountainous land and to tap its timber resources. Those resources had not been developed by the Chinese, who had made agriculture their main occupation. The railroad, which is still used, is 45 miles long and has a 30 mile branch. It is a narrow-

Figure 32.—Many private railroad lines were constructed by the Japanese to transport sugar cane (AID/JCRR photo)

gauge railroad, only 30 inches in width. The railroad was designed for the transportation of lumber (*Figure 33*), but now the public is permitted to travel on it.

As the train crawls up Mount Ali Shan, which rises more than 9800 feet above sea level, it goes through many tunnels and across many bridges. The difficulties that were met in building this mountain railroad are well known in the railroad-construction history of the world.

PUSH-CARS.—An important form of transportation in Taiwan was the *daisha*, or push-car, which was brought to the island by the Japanese and helped to develop the mountain land. The *daisha*, which is still used, is a little flatcar for passengers or freight, which travels on a narrow-gauge track and is pushed by two laborers from behind. The seats are just large enough to accommodate two passengers, and there is a small platform where the two pushers can stand and ride when the route is downhill. They make about 5.5 miles an hour on level ground, much less uphill, and about 10 miles an hour downhill. In 1938 the aggregate mileage of the push-car line was 586 miles with about 4,000 *daishas* carrying 3,000,000 passengers and 553,300,000 tons of freight for the year.

166

Figure 33.—The brilliant Japanese engineering feat of building a mountain railroad on Ali Shan allowed its vast timber resources to be tapped for the first time (AID/JCRR photo)

Highway development

The highways in Taiwan were begun by a Japanese expeditionary army. The first highway was completed in 1913, and thereafter highway building proceeded rapidly. Various companies were organized for the highway transportation of passengers and freight. The companies prospered, and they expanded so much that at one time the profits of the railroads were affected. To prevent competition with the railroads the Japanese government took over the management of the 1242-mile main highway. The branch lines were left to the companies. At the end of the Japanese period Taiwan had about 2500 miles of highway. This does not include suburban roads.

Ricksha and bicycle

In the urban areas the ricksha and the bicycle began to be used widely in the Japanese period, rather than the sedan chain which had been in vogue during the Chinese period.

167

THIRD STAGE

NEW IRRIGATION SYSTEM

In the development of Taiwan's agriculture the key to overcoming the handicap of uneven rainfall is irrigation, and the Japanese provided that key when they learned to use cement for building dams. Previously, in the Chinese period, irrigation systems were used, but they were on a small scale and were built of bamboo, wood, earth, and rock. At that time the irrigation systems were privately owned; under the Japanese they were government owned.

In 1904 books on cement construction were published in the United States, and Japanese engineers in Taiwan were well acquainted with these books. At first the Japanese used cement to construct buildings; it was not until 1907 that they began to use it in irrigation systems. They used it first on Ilan plain in the northeast.

Then, realizing the importance of irrigation to their own plans for Taiwan's agriculture, they began to build the great Chianan irrigation system, which was so important during the Japanese occupance stage that it deserves a detailed description.

Chianan irrigation system

On the west coast of Taiwan, between the Choshui River in the north and the Tsengwen River in the south, lies the extensive plain called Chianan. It is about 1930 squares miles in area and it constitutes about 60 per cent of the total plains area of the island. It includes Chiayi and Tainan counties, and its name, *Chianan*, is composed of the first part of *Chiayi* and the last of *Tainan*.

Flat land is a rarity on the island, and ordinarily a plain would be an important agricultural region. This one, however, had not been, for its rainfall is very unevenly distributed over the seasons. The months from May to September are rainy; more than 80 per cent of the annual rainfall is concentrated in those months. On the other hand, from October to April the plain receives very little rain; several months pass without a drop. In the rainy season the intense rains, together with the torrential rivers from the eastern foothills, often flood Chianan plain. In the dry season the strong wind makes the region dusty and dry, and in the past it was difficult to cultivate any crop. With this alternate superfluity and scarcity of water, the farmers could not fully utilize the land. In addition, the salt in the soils along the coastal strip and the sand in those of the middle part of the plain increased the cultivation difficulties.

The Japanese started to build the Chianan irrigation system in 1920, and completed it in 1930. This irrigation system has converted 67,050 acres of poor land, which previously had suffered from flood and drought, into the most fertile farmland of the island. It has made the extensive Chianan plain the granary and has made it possible for many prosperous villages to be located there. A diagram of the canal system is shown in *Figure 34*.

The Chianan irrigation system conducts the water of the Tsengwen River through an aqueduct 10,168 feet long into an artificial reservoir. The reservoir is created by a dam 4260 feet long and 184 feet high. It looks like coral, and is called Coral Reservoir, or in Chinese, *Sanhutan*. With a depth of 525 feet, the reservoir is sufficient to irrigate about 457,000 acres of land. It is one of the largest reservoirs in the Far East. The water is conducted to the farms by many rivers and their tributaries, as well as by irrigation canals; the canals total 10,868 miles in length. The rivers and their tributaries and the canals not only are used for irrigation purposes, but also, during the rainy season serve as drainage routes transporting extra water to the ocean.

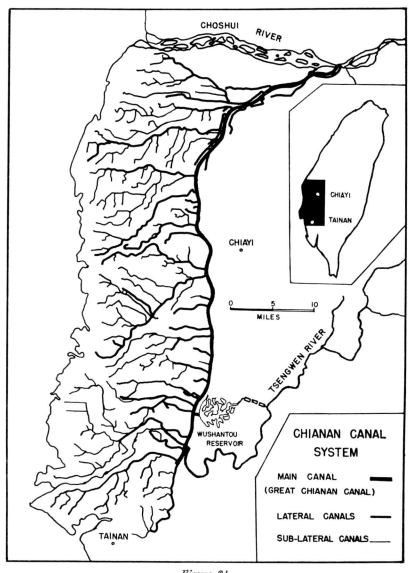

Figure 34

169

How is the Chianan irrigation system maintained and managed? In this region there are 190,000 families, comprising one and a half million people, of whom more than 150,000 are employed directly on the irrigation system. Irrigation associations have been organized whose members include landlords, tenants, and employees. Membership fees are collected for each unit of land. One hundred and forty-two supervising irrigation stations and 55 water route stations have been set up.

The Chianan irrigation system is characterized by extensive farmlands and a limited reservoir area for water storage. Distribution of the limited reservoir water to the whole area is a difficult problem. However, a three year rotation method has been designed, which makes the irrigation system function more efficiently (*Figure 35*).

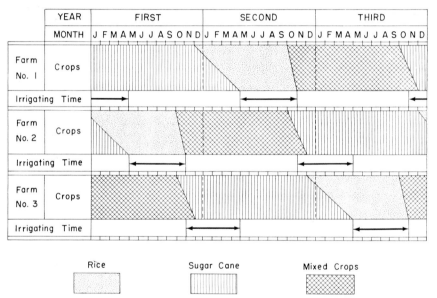

Figure 35.—A three-year crop rotation method allows the Chianan irrigation system to function efficiently

Through use of the Chianan irrigation system, many dry farm areas, wastelands, and fishing ponds have been converted into fertile farm lands. The irrigated region has suffered neither flood nor drought.

After the system went into operation the land used for growing rice increased by more than 74 per cent and the sugar-cane land by 30 per cent, at a time when the total area of cultivated land decreased by 12 per cent. The increases took place at the expense of the mixed-crop lands, which decreased by more than half.[3] With the irrigation, the production of rice per unit area nearly doubled, and the total rice production increased nearly eight times.

Similar increase took place with regard to sugar cane. The value of the sugar cane production per unit area increased nearly three times and the value of its total production rose more than four times. The value of the total production of the irrigated area—all crops—increased about eight times, and the value of that area about five times. The success of the irrigation system intensified Taiwan's agriculture.

INTENSIFICATION OF AGRICULTURE

During the Japanese rule, Taiwan's agricultural production was of vital importance to Japan for Japan imported from Taiwan about 60 per cent of the rice the Empire used and nearly 90 per cent of the sugar. The intensification of Taiwan's agriculture may be illustrated by taking as an example the most important crops of Taiwan: rice, sugar cane, and fruit.

Rice

Even before the Chianan irrigation system was begun in the years from 1901 to 1920 Taiwan's area of rice cultivation was expanding, though slowly, under the Japanese program which included not only irrigation, but also establishment of new agricultural experiment stations and payment of small subsidies to new rice producers.

Total production of rice was also increasing, but that increase was slow, and the yield per acre showed no increase. But between 1920 and 1935 the area devoted to rice cultivation increased by more than one-third. The yield per acre also increased one-third, and the amount of rice produced doubled (*Figure 36*), partly due to the introduction of the

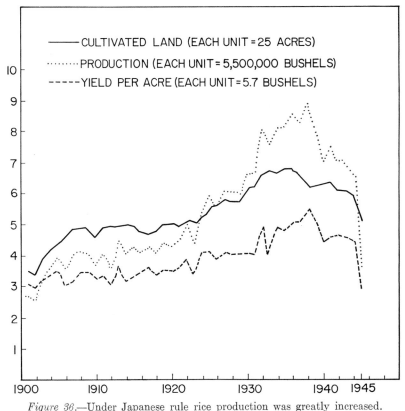

Figure 36.—Under Japanese rule rice production was greatly increased.

171

Chianan irrigation system and partly to the fact that in 1922 the Japanese had introduced into Taiwan a kind of rice with a higher yield than that of the Taiwan variety. The new kind of rice was called *Ponlai* by the Taiwanese and *Horai* by the Japanese. It is a round-grain type; in contrast with the long-grain type of Taiwan rice.

Between 1922 and 1935 the amount of land devoted to Ponlai rice rose from zero to 731,120 acres; the native rice area dropped from 1,012,580 to 629,850 acres. In the same period the amount of Ponlai rice produced jumped nearly five-fold; the amount of native rice dropped by nearly one-fourth as can be seen in *Figure 37*.

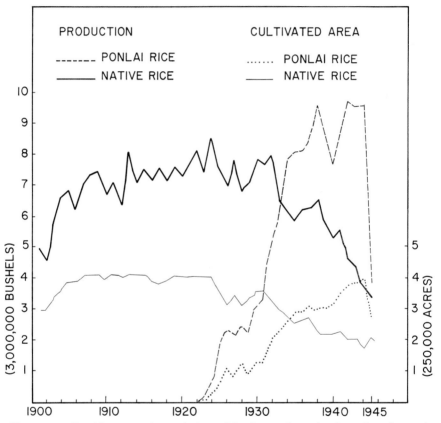

Figure 37.—Graphic comparison of the cultivation and production of native and Ponlai rice under Japanese rule

Owing to the large export of rice to Japan, its consumption by the Taiwan population decreased. After the exporting began, the annual per capita consumption of rice in Taiwan fell by two-thirds.

On the basis of the increase both in acreage and production, one might conclude that the Taiwan farmers were much better off than they had been before. It would seem that their profits had increased and that they would be able to purchase Japanese manufactured goods and also to increase their own consumption of rice. However, the true picture reveals

172

an opposite condition. As Gradjdanzev points out, although Ponlai rice has a greater yield per acre, the actual cost of production is more than one-third higher.[4] It requires the use of commercial fertilizers, which have to be purchased by the farmer. The farmer did not receive as much profit from Ponlai, but he was compelled to plant it because he could not sell his own kind of rice in the Japanese market. The expansion of the area producing Ponlai was therefore not a sign of prosperity. The farmer increasingly needed money to pay taxes and to defray the cost of irrigation and of fertilizer.

During the Japanese period the average per capita consumption of rice in Japan was 31 per cent higher than it was in Taiwan, though the Japanese consumed in addition considerable amounts of wheat, barley, and other cereals, which were almost entirely absent in Taiwan.

Sugar

The great increase in the production of sugar cane and the development of the sugar industry are considered two of the most spectacular achievements of the Japanese occupation of Taiwan. Prior to that occupation the value of Japan's imports of sugar amounted to about 10 per cent of the value of her total imports. The Japanese worked toward improvement of Taiwan's sugar-cane plantations and sugar industry. As early as 1896 the Japanese imported seedlings of improved types of sugar cane from the Hawaiian Islands to Taiwan. An investigation of the future prospects for the cultivation of sugar cane in Taiwan was made. The report of the investigation made recommendations for the following measures: introduction of superior varieties of sugar cane, improved cultivation and fertilization, more effective irrigation, improvements in crushing machinery and methods of manufacture, opening of new land for cane cultivation, and replacement of rice fields by cane plantations.

As a result a special sugar bureau was established in 1902 and at the same time a sugar industry encouragement ordinance was promulgated. The Japanese government granted subsidies to encourage the industry.

For the purpose of obtaining the varieties of cane best suited to the climate, the Japanese government imported various cane cuttings and seedlings from Java, Cuba, Louisiana, and Australia, as well as from Hawaii. *Lahaina* and *Rose Bamboo*, the varieties obtained from Hawaii, were most successful; they were found to yield a harvest two or three times as great as did the indigenous varieties. With the government distribution of seedlings from the Hawaiian varieties of sugar cane the area used for cultivation and production of sugar cane in Taiwan increased, as is seen in *Figure 38*. The only disadvantage that the Hawaiian varieties had was their low resistance to wind.

Within 30 years (1905–35) the sugar-cane producing area increased almost five times, the total production thirteen times, and the yield per acre two and four-tenths times.

In 1939 The Japanese Empire took seventh place among producers of sugar; most of the Empire's sugar production came from Taiwan. The first six producers in order of importance were Cuba, India, U.S.S.R., Germany, the United States, and Java.

During the Japanese period the development of Taiwan's sugar-cane cultivation was not smooth and uninterrupted. The curves at both the amounts produced and of the area of cultivated land are erratic. This indicates that the industry passed through booms, crises, and depressions, as revealed in *Figure 38*. In 1902 there were 61,750 acres of sugar cane under cultivation, but by 1910 the area had doubled. During the period of World War I, to meet the wartime increase in the demand for sugar, the Japanese expanded the area of cultivation of sugar cane in Taiwan to more than six times the 1902 area. In 1933 and 1934 the amount of land used for cultivation of sugar decreased, but in 1940 it increased again, to 417,430 acres.

Sugar-cane production in Taiwan amounted to only about 19 million bushels in 1902, but by 1910 it had reached three times that total. By 1917 the production had increased seven fold over the 1902 production. By 1938 production was at its height, 358 million bushels. In *Figure 38* noticeable depressions in sugar production can be seen. In 1913, as a result

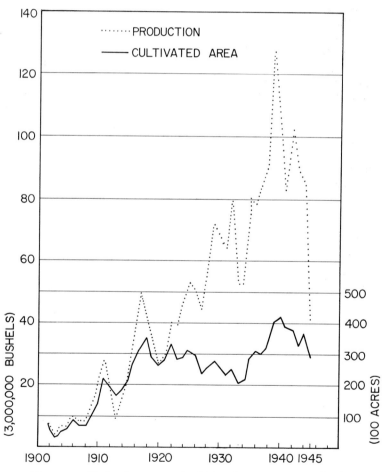

Figure 38.—Under Japanese rule, Taiwan's sugar cane production was also greatly increased

174

of infestation, production was reduced to 25 million bushels and another reduction occurred in 1933–34 due to typhoons.

These fluctuations were influenced by several other factors. Conflicts between farmers and manufacturers took place because of changes in price. Before the Japanese occupation, sugar production was carried on by small Chinese cooperative enterprises. From 1895 on this old type of enterprise disappeared with the advent of the Japanese form of enterprise. In 1905 only 9 per cent of the sugar was produced in modern mills; in 1937 such mills produced 98 per cent of the total. Production of sugar in modern mills was concentrated in nine Japanese corporations, and of these, six produced 95 per cent of all the sugar produced in Taiwan.

In addition, there was competition between sugar cane and rice because in many areas of the island it is possible to plant both. This competition and the rotation with other crops led to the acreage devoted to a given crop being varied from year to year. Besides, farmers were disposed to plant rice rather than sugar cane, partly because their families wanted rice and partly because it can be stored, whereas sugar cane cannot.

Any increase in sugar production depends not only on the expansion of the land cultivated for that purpose, but also on the increase of sugar content in the juice of the sugar cane. In this respect, little improvement occurred until 1922. In that year the sugar content was 9.5 per cent; in 1935 it rose to 13.2 per cent. In 1935 the sugar content was considerably higher in Taiwan's cane than in Java's or Cuba's which had 12.3 and 11.6 per cent sugar content respectively. Increase in sugar content results from better seeds and more fertilization.

As for Taiwan's per capita consumption of sugar during the Japanese occupation, almost 95 per cent of the sugar produced in Taiwan was exported and in 1938 Japan's consumption was 43 per cent higher than that in Taiwan.

Fruit

In addition to the cultivation of rice and sugar, which was increased in both acreage and production during the Japanese occupation of the island, the raising of bananas and pineapples was also increased during that period.

The banana tree is indigenous to Taiwan, but only after the Japanese rule began did bananas become an important export item. Between 1910 and 1940 the production of bananas rose by about 86 per cent a year. A considerable number of bananas are consumed in Taiwan, about 24 pounds per person per year, an amount that may be partially explained by the perishability of the fruit.

Pineapples were cultivated in Taiwan before the occupation of the island by the Japanese, but only after the Japanese introduced canning processes (about 1923) did the industry begin to expand. Through the canning techniques introduced by the Japanese, the pineapples were preserved and exported; thus they could be profitably grown in large quantities. In addition, the fruit is grown on hill slopes and thus did not compete with cereals or sugar cane. The expansion of pineapple raising is illustrated in *Figure 39*.

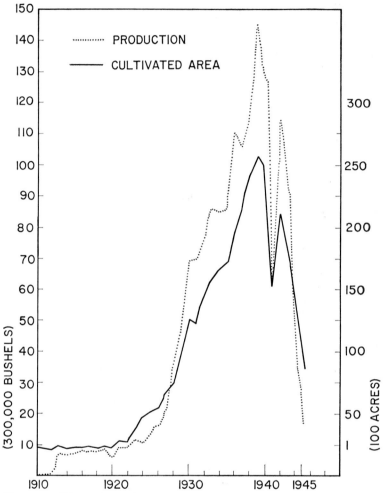

Figure 39.—Pineapple production was greatly expanded by the Japanese

FOURTH STAGE

INDUSTRIAL DEVELOPMENT

Under the Japanese policy of "An agricultural Taiwan and an industrial Japan," the Empire at first did not intend to develop Taiwan's industry to a high degree. For a decade after the Japanese rule began, agricultural production continued to constitute about 80 per cent of the island's total production, just as under Chinese rule.

But after 1907, when sugar refining had advanced noticeably, industrial production began showing an increase, and by 1939, industry and agriculture were about equal, with industry slightly ahead.[5]

176

The change in the island's economic basis is shown in the changes in the proportions of the population employed in agriculture and in industry. Between 1905 and 1930 the number of those working in agriculture dropped from 71 per cent to 70 per cent; the number of those working in industry rose from 6 per cent to 9 per cent.[6]

Increase in number of factories

The increase took place in the number of factories on the island because of the rise in industry. At the beginning of the Japanese period only 24 factories existed in Taiwan; 30 years later the number had risen more than fifty-fold. In the next decade that figure nearly tripled. The factories, however, were in general small. Even as late as 1935, 95 per cent of Taiwan's factories had fewer than 30 workers each.

Not until World War II necessities pressured the Japanese to develop the chemical, metal, and other strategic industries did Taiwan's industries reach a high level. Between 1921 and 1942, the year after World War II began, the chemical and metal industries doubled their percentages of the island's total industrial production. First place among the industries was still held by food processing, but between 1921 and 1942 its proportion dropped by more than one-fifth—from 74 per cent to 59 per cent.

The factory workers were few at first, but their number increased rapidly. Between 1920 and 1941 the number rose three-fold. The number of workers in the metal industry increased the most—eleven times; in the textile and the forestry industries the number increased six-fold and five-fold respectively; in machinery and printing, five-fold and three-fold respectively. The number of workers doubled in both the chemical and food-processing industries.[7]

There were fifteen times as many Chinese factory workers as there were Japanese. The Japanese were for the most part technicians; the Chinese, laborers.

Development of hydroelectric power

Long before World War II began the Japanese realized that the key to the island's industrial development was cheap hydroelectric power.

At first the development of such power was slow. In fact, after World War I the total capacity of Taiwan's power plants was only 10,000 kilowatts. But physical conditions on the island—heavy rainfall and swift mountain streams—permit establishment of large hydroelectric plants. Under those favorable conditions a project was worked out in 1931 for the utilization of Sun Moon Lake and the Choshui River, which drains it, to generate power.

Sun Moon Lake is a small lake, located in the center of the island. It is more than 2300 feet above sea level and is surrounded by mountains.

With the completion of that project and another one at the same lake, the power generated, totaling 180,000 kilowatts, was distributed throughout the west coast region to the industrial cities. Thus the Japanese laid the foundation for further industrialization of the island.

The Sun Moon power plant stands out as the greatest achievement of the Japanese period in Taiwan. In engineering importance it parallels the Chianan irrigation system and the railroad that climbs Mount Ali.

It is now considered the TVA of the Far East. Through this power project, it was possible for the island to support aluminum, chemical, and steel alloy plants.

FOREIGN TRADE

Economic dependence on Japan

The most effective way for Japan to exercise political power over Taiwan and to make Taiwan a supplier of raw material and also a market for Japanese goods was to cut Taiwan's trade relations with other countries, especially with the mainland of China. The most convenient means to this end was the increasing of the customs tax on Taiwan's trade with other countries. After careful planning, in 1910 the Japanese abolished the customs barrier between Japan and Taiwan and raised the customs tax on Taiwan's trade with other countries. As a result of this customs policy, the economic life of the Taiwanese increasingly depended upon Japan.

From 1903 to 1935, while the economic dependence of Taiwan on other countries in general increased from 26 per cent to 44 per cent, its dependence upon Japan increased even more, from 13 per cent to 37 per cent.[8]

The years of more import than export occurred in the early days; after 1914 there was always more export than import. A further look into the import and export situation of Taiwan during the Japanese period is warranted. Between 1897 and 1944, there were only 12 years in which there was more import than export; there were 36 years in which there was more export than import. Not only were the export periods much longer than the import ones, but the value of the exports was also much higher than that of the imports. Between 1897 and 1944 the export value increased more than twenty-fold. During the same period the value of imports increased about ten-fold.

Of course, imports from Japan were handled by the Japanese, but exports from Taiwan to Japan were also monopolized by the Japanese, who collected raw material from local Taiwanese salesmen and exported it to Japan. Thus the native inhabitants really had no foreign trade, but simply trade within the island.

Characteristics of Taiwan's foreign trade

The characteristics of foreign trade in Taiwan during the Japanese period have been summarized as follows by Chow and are illustrated in *Figures 40* and *41*.

(1) Ninety per cent of Taiwan's foreign trade was with Japan.

(2) Since exports from Taiwan to Japan were all agricultural products, while imports from Japan to Taiwan included various kinds of manufactured goods, the subordinate position of Taiwan's economy to that of Japan is clearly indicated.

(3) If a trade involved the same kind of goods, the best quality was exported from Taiwan to Japan and the worst was imported to Taiwan from Japan. For example, Taiwan exported Ponlai rice to Japan and

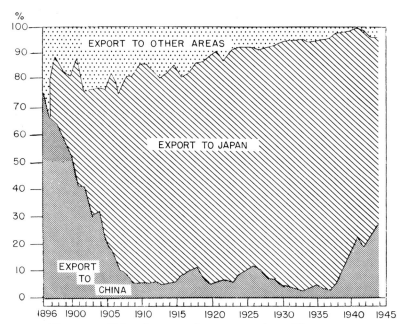

Figure 40.—Taiwan's export (in percentage) to different areas
between 1896 and 1945 (after H. W. Chow)

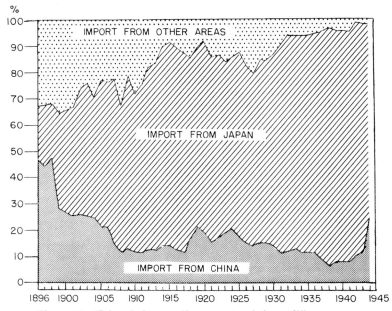

Figure 41.—Taiwan's import (in percentage) from different areas
between 1896 and 1945 (after H. W. Chow)

179

imported lower-quality rice from other areas to supply the local inhabitant's needs. Taiwan also exported good Chinese juniper trees to Japan and imported poor pine and fir trees from Japan.

(4) The Japanese promoted Taiwan's trade with themselves by political force. First they monopolized camphor, opium, tobacco and alcoholic beverages, and secondly they set up a customs system that diverted the whole foreign trade from the island to Japan.

(5) Export goods from Taiwan had two characteristics; first, they were the raw materials that Japan needed greatly, and secondly, they were mass-produced. Eight items of export—sugar, rice, tea, bananas, canned pineapple, camphor, alcohol, and coal—accounted for more than 80 per cent of Taiwan's total export.

(6) The value of exports from Taiwan went up and down before 1931, but after that year it was continuously high until 1939, when the peak of export was reached. After that year exports declined, evidently influenced by the Pacific phase of World War II.

(7) The importance of Taiwan's exports to Japan can be seen in the following figures: In 1897 the export from Taiwan to Japan amounted to only 14 per cent of the island's total export; in 1944 it reached 69 per cent. During those 48 years (1897–1944) there were 8 years in which Taiwan's exports to Japan accounted for more than 90 per cent of the total; 15 years, for 80–90 per cent; 13 years, for 70–80 per cent; and 4 years for 50–70 per cent. In other words, within those 48 years there were 40 years in which Taiwan's export to Japan amounted to over 50 per cent of its total and only eight years in which it was less than 50 per cent.

(8) On the other hand, export from Taiwan to mainland China declined. In 1897 that export amounted to 66 per cent of the island's total export; in 1933 it was only 3 per cent; in 1944 it was 27 per cent. Between 1897 and 1944 there were only two years (1897 and 1898) when Taiwan's export to mainland China accounted for more than 60 per cent of its total export. For 26 years that export was less than 10 per cent, and for the other 20 years it was between 10 and 60 per cent.

(9) The imports to Taiwan had two characteristics. First, they comprised manufactured goods produced in Japan, and secondly they included a great variety of goods—wheat flour, fishery products, dairy goods, canned goods, textile products, soap, matches, clothes, shoes, paper, printing machines, bicycles, electrical equipment, iron, railroad cars, fertilizers, wood, and soy beans. Those items together accounted for 50 per cent of the total import from Japan.

(10) In 1897 the value of Taiwan's imports from Japan was only 23 per cent of the total imports; by 1944 it had increased to 74 per cent. During 48 years there were 12 years in which the value of imports from Japan was more than 80 per cent of the total, 8 in which it was more than 70 per cent, 15 in which it was more than 60 per cent, 6 in which it was more than 50 per cent, 3 in which it was more than 40 per cent, 2 in which it was more than 30 per cent, and 2 in which it was more than 20 per cent.

(11) At the same time, the imports from China decreased. In 1897 imports from China amounted to 45 per cent of Taiwan's total imports, but by 1944 they had decreased to 24 per cent, and in 1938 they amounted to only 8 per cent. During the 48 year period there were three years,

1896–98, in which the island's imports from China amounted to more than 40 per cent of the total; 11 in which they were between 20 and 30 per cent; 30 in which they were between 10 and 20 per cent; and 5 in which they were less than 10 per cent.

JAPANESE OCCUPATIONS IN TAIWAN

Immigration to the island

When Taiwan was ceded to Japan in 1895 at the close of the Sino-Japanese War, the Japanese hoped to japanize the island population. Therefore, the government offered subsidies to Japanese subjects if they would emigrate to Taiwan. Also, they forbade further Chinese emigration to the island and permitted only slightly more than 10,000 seasonal workers from China to enter Taiwan each year.

The first seven years of the subsidy program, however, brought disappointment. From 1898 to 1900 the number of Japanese arriving at Taiwan jumped from 13,000 to 21,000. Many of these people were attracted by the prospect of government jobs in the new colony. Once these jobs were filled the number of arrivals decreased and the average annual net Japanese immigration after 1900 never exceeded 4,000 persons.

The Japanese government continued its efforts to persuade Japanese people to move to Taiwan. In 1907 a plan was devised to encourage the emigration of farmers to Taiwan. Some 94,000 acres of land were divided into thirty-eight prospective settlements. However, only eight settlements were actually made and even those ended in failure. Fishermen were then sought; in 1909 the Japanese government promised subsidies and other advantages to fishermen if they would emigrate to Taiwan. Those who answered the call, however, preferred to take up other occupations there.

In 1910 another attempt was made to lure Japanese farmers to settle in Taiwan, this time in the Taitung area. The government offered to pay for houses, roads, schools, hospitals, and irrigation works on condition that the immigrants would repay all advances in 10 years. Only less than 4,000 persons took advantage of the offer; they settled in three different villages. Twenty-five years later, these villages instead of increasing in population had decreased.

In 1915 the Taito Sugar Company, with the support of the Japanese government, set up a program to attract Japanese colonists to engage in the production of sugar cane. By 1936 only 78 families had come for that purpose and had remained on the land.

Thus the Japanese never constituted a large proportion of the island's population. In spite of Japanese rule, the island remained overwhelmingly Chinese. Between 1905 and 1940, the proportion of Japanese in the population increased only from 2 to 5 per cent.

Natural increase in population

One reason why the Chinese in Taiwan continued to outnumber the Japanese by a wide margin was that natural increase in population was much smaller among the Japanese than among the Chinese. The natural increase of the Chinese rose from 16,000 in 1906 to 130,000 in 1945, while the Japanese natural increase was from 490 in 1906 to 8,000 in 1942. Thus the Chinese increase was 16 times as great.

Japanese occupational categories

As to the occupations of the Japanese in Taiwan, as shown in data collected on October 1, 1930 (no other figures concerning their occupations are available, but the data reveal the general situations in 1930, and no great changes took place between that year and the end of the Japanese rule in Taiwan), nearly twenty times as many Japanese as Chinese were occupied in public service and the professions. They formed the backbone of the administrative services of the island. Also more than twice as many Japanese as Chinese were in industry. The same proportion held true in trade and in communications. Only 5 per cent of the Japanese were engaged in agriculture, as compared with 71 per cent of the Chinese.[9]

In short, the Chinese in Taiwan were mostly farmers, while the Japanese were chiefly in public service, trade, and industry. Since more of the Japanese in Taiwan were in public service than in any other occupation, it is only natural that they were concentrated in Taipei, the capital of the island, where the Japanese population numbered 41 per cent of the total.

JAPANESE SETTLEMENT AND HOUSE TYPES

Settlement

The Japanese immigrants to Taiwan were under their government sponsorship and they settled at assigned places. Nearly half of the Japanese population was concentrated in the island's nine cities—especially, as was mentioned above, in Taipei, the capital of the island.

The Japanese influence over the rural settlements of Taiwan was very slight and the present features of rural settlements show only the Chinese influence. The small towns also remained Chinese.

Only in the urban areas did a Japanese settlement pattern superimpose itself upon the Chinese type. During the Japanese period the defense features of settlement, such as walls, became unnecessary. The Japanese gradually remodeled the cities to make them more modern. They took away the Chinese city walls, but preserved the gates as historical and decorative monuments. The sites of the walls were turned into esplanades and driving roads.

The urban tentacles radiated through the old Chinese gates to the suburbs. The result was a quadrilateral or circular arrangement of streets in the "old town" or core area and a very irregular pattern of streets and alleys outside. Thus the rural and urban compound settlement was formed.

House types

The Japanese houses were built in their homeland style of architecture, admirably suited to the subtropical climate of Taiwan. Those we see today are unsubstantial in appearance and meager in color.

Unlike the Chinese house, which is made of brick, clay, and stone, the Japanese house is made of wood, grass, and paper, and is fragile, simple, and inexpensive. There are no attic, no cellar, no chimney, no permanently-enclosed rooms, no beds, and no chairs.

The form of the Japanese house is rectilinear; usually it has one story, but sometimes two. A three-room structure is most common, although four and five-room houses are also numerous.

Despite frequent and disastrous fires the Japanese built their homes of wood. In Taiwan this was attributable not only to the easy availability of timber, but to the artistic preference of the Japanese for wood.

Wooden posts resting upon stones serve as the underpinnings of the house, and the structure is anchored to the ground by the weight of its heavy thatch or tile roof. This makes the Japanese house top heavy, but enables it to withstand strong winds.

The floor of the first story is raised about three feet from the ground. This stilt arrangement is suggestive of the tropical house. In the immediate vicinity of flooded paddy fields the elevation is desirable for it permits free passage of air beneath and prevents excessive dampness.

Since Taiwan, like Japan, is in the zone of frequent earthquakes, the introduction of the fragile wooden Japanese house reduced loss of life and property from earthquakes.

The Japanese added Shinto shrines to Taiwan's Chinese-built temples. The shrines were built on the outskirts of towns. The main building of a shrine, and its subsidiary structures, were constructed of plain, unpainted wood and were roofed with copper or thatch. The *torii*, or gate of the shrine, was made of unpainted wood. The shrine grounds were covered with thick trees and some contained a pond. Construction of the main shrine and its *torii* began in 1926.

The Japanese also constructed public buildings such as government offices, schools, and railroad stations. These public buildings were usually built of concrete, brick, and stones to withstand seismic vibration, and they are fire resistant.

The Japanese houses have since 1945 gradually changed from their original appearance into Chinese styles.

REFERENCES

[1] H. W. Chow, *The Economic History of Taiwan During the Japanese Rule* (Bank of Taiwan, Taipei, 1958), Vol. I, pp. 3-4. [In Chinese].

[2] A. J. Grajdanzev, "Formosa under Japanese rule," *Pacif. Affrs.* **XV**, 323 (1942).

[3] T. T. Sun, "A preliminary study of the Chianan irrigation system in Taiwan," *Quart., Bank of Taiwan* **8**, 4, (1956).

[4] A. J. Grajdanzev, *Formosa Today* (Institute of Pacific Relations, New York, 1942), pp. 54-56.

[5] *Taiwan Agricultural Yearbook, 1950* (Taiwan Provincial Government Taipei, 1950), pp. 30-31.

[6] H. W. Chow, *The Economic History of Taiwan During the Japanese Rule* (Bank of Taiwan, Taipei, 1958), Vol. I, p. 14. [In Chinese].

[7] —, *Ibid.*, p. 68.

[8] H. Y. Chang, "The changes of Taiwan's economy during the Japanese rule," *Quart., Bank of Taiwan* **IX**, No. 4, 60 (1951).

[9] *Fifty-one Years of Statistical Abstracts of Taiwan*, (Taiwan Governor General's Office, Taipei, 1946), p. 139.

FOURTEEN	The Return
	to China

CHANGES IN TAIWAN'S ECONOMY

As a result of World War II, Taiwan was returned to China by Japan. The island then entered a new stage in sequent occupance.

The shift in control from Japan to China brought changes in the island's economy. Instead of serving as a colony, supplying rice and sugar to Japan, the island became one of the thirty-five provinces of the Republic of China. Practically all the exportable surpluses now went to China, and Chinese government control replaced that of the Japanese.

ECONOMIC DIFFICULTIES

The island's economy met difficulties, for which three interrelated factors were responsible: the damage to the island resulting from World War II; the disruption of imports, especially fertilizers; and the rapid increase in population.

Bombings during the war had greatly damaged metallurgical plants, oil refineries, the hydroelectric system, and factory machinery.

The decrease in fertilizer imports from Japan resulted in a large drop in the production of sugar and rice, the two chief cash crops.

The rapid increase in the population further complicated the island's economy. Early in 1949 the Nationalist government authorities, driven from the mainland by the Communists, moved to Taiwan's capital, Taipei, along with large numbers of officials and other civilians, as well as soldiers. Thus the island's population increased from 6,807,601 to 7,555,588 in 1950, besides 600,000 military personnel.[1]

The 400,000 Japanese repatriates who left Taiwan early in 1946 were partly offset in the population by 100,000 Taiwanese repatriates from Japan. As immigration from mainland China continued, the cities swelled, and the island's export capacity was further limited by the increasing domestic consumption. The population influx brought a change in Taiwan's social structure. Most of the mainland people crowded into the cities. Thus more houses of mainland style were built, and the number of automobiles increased in urban areas.

Communist supremacy in mainland China meant the loss of the mainland as an export market. Thus Taiwan, which had lived under a colonial-type economy, had to adjust to the world market.

COMPARISON OF CHINESE RULING PERIODS

Comparing the present stage of Chinese rule in Taiwan with the early stage about 300 years ago, we note that both stages resulted from a political upheaval that caused a spectacular migration from the Chinese mainland to the island.

In the middle 17th century—1661 to be specific—a migration was spurred by a loyalist of the Ming Dynasty named Cheng Ch'eng-Kung, who had been driven out of China by the Manchus. Cheng made Taiwan a refuge for persons resisting the Manchus, who had conquered the mainland.

The second major migration started in 1945, when Taiwan was restored to China by Japan, and lasted through 1949, when the Chinese Communist party conquered the mainland. This migration was led by the Chinese Nationalist leader Chiang Kai-shek, who repatriated many Japanese and made the island a stronghold against Chinese Communists.

In the early migration the estimated 100,000 persons who moved to Taiwan came largely from the two Chinese coastal provinces nearest to Taiwan, Fukien and Kwangtung. The second migration drew an estimated million or more persons from all the provinces of China, though mostly from the coastal provinces of Fukien, Kwangtung, Chekiang, Kiangsu, Shangtung, and Topei.

Of the early immigrants the majority were farmers and other rural residents. Their main contribution to Taiwan was their pioneering labor in agriculture. The people who came in the second stage, unlike the early immigrants, were city dwellers; very few were farmers. They were government employees and intellectuals. Their major contribution has been development of the island's manufacturing and its commercial activities, including foreign trade.

PRESENT CHINESE ACCOMPLISHMENTS

The later Chinese rule has tried to achieve three major engineering feats: the cross-island highway, the Shihmen Reservoir project, and the new beach land on the western coast. These three efforts parallel the great Japanese achievements: the hydroelectric power plant at Sun-Moon Lake, the irrigation system at Chianan, and the mountain railroad.

185

THE CROSS-ISLAND HIGHWAY

The high, rugged Central Mountain Range, which divides Taiwan into two parts, was an obstacle to transportation between the east and the west before the east–west highway was completed at the end of 1960.

Before that, to go from one side of Taiwan to the other, one had to travel by way of either the northern or the southern tip of the island. In order to go from Taichung in West Taiwan to Hualien in the east, one first had to go to Taipei in the north, a distance of more than 124 miles, and then travel southeast for another 124 miles. The trip took at least 12 hours, and the final 75 miles had to be traveled on a one-way coastal road that during severe typhoons or earthquakes was closed by landslides. When the cross-island road was completed, the distance from Taichung to Hualien was reduced to 205 miles—an easy seven-hour drive.

The products of Kaohsiung, the leading industrial city of Taiwan, are now transported to all parts of the island. Before direct highway transportation between Kaohsiung and Hualien was possible, motor vehicles carrying goods from Kaohsiung had to travel to Taitung, a distance of nearly 124 miles, and then transfer the products to a railroad flatcar for the final 109-mile trip to Hualien. The trip took eleven hours if train connections were on time. On the new east–west highway motor vehicles can travel from Kaohsiung directly to Hualien by way of Taichung. Although this route is longer, it can be covered in less time and without difficulty.

The need to build a cross-island highway on Taiwan in the middle zone had long been apparent, and such a highway, linking the scenic east with the populous west had long been just a dream. To carve this east–west cross-island highway through the sheer eastern cliffs, which in several places are more than 11,500 feet above sea level, was a daring engineering feat. The Japanese had tried it during World War II. They were constructing the highway from both ends, boring tunnels, when they abandoned the task as economically impracticable. With recent economic developments the need for direct communication between the east and west became more pronounced and, undoubtedly, the road will be of tremendous and far-reaching political, military, and economic value.

Actual construction of the road began in July 1956. One-third was completed by the end of 1957, and the whole by the end of 1960. The cross-island highway runs through some of the most beautiful and rugged terrain in the world. It is a hiker's paradise, but it was a nightmare for the roadbuilders. Mountains tower along the route and rivers flow between sheer cliffs in their rush to the sea. In one spot the land drops suddenly from an altitude of 5000 feet to 1380 feet. Although the eastern section constitutes only one-third of the whole highway, it includes 95 per cent of the tunnels and about 70 per cent of the bridges.

The entire length of the main road is 117 miles; it has a branch road 71 miles long. In addition to the main and the branch road there is a 27-mile supply road connecting the main highway.

About 5,000 retired soldiers from the Nationalist armed forces were engaged to work on the construction of the road. The existence of this labor force, as a matter of fact, gave the final impetus to the long-heralded project. A program for removing men ineffective in combat from the armed forces was undertaken by the Nationalist authorities, and these retired service men had to be placed in a productive civilian life. Since the plains of Taiwan were already overcrowded with a growing population, eyes turned to the lofty mountains, where a few tribes of aborigines supported themselves with primitive farming and hunting. Survey reports indicated that in the many upland areas that would be opened for cultivation by the new highway upward of 5,000 veterans could build their homes and find new occupations.

Now that the east–west highway has been constructed, the Central Mountain Range promises development in several fields.

One such field is power generation. According to an initial survey, the hydraulic power of three rivers flowing through the highway area can be harnessed to generate 800,000 kilowatts of electricity a year. Another field is gold mining, for gold deposits in the area are estimated at 200 million United States dollars. Logging is another possibility, for the Central Mountains are thickly wooded. Then there is the possibility of creating a national mountain park in the area. The scenery along the highway is the most magnificent in the Far East.

In spite of the advantages of the cross-island highway, maintenance of traffic on it will remain a problem. Strong winds during the typhoon season, snow accumulation in the winter, rapid rivers along steep slopes beside it, are all problems that have to be overcome.

Contributions to Taiwan's economy

In summary, the cross-island highway is a proud accomplishment of the Nationalist government. The highway is of vital importance to Taiwan; its contributions to the island's economy can be enumerated as follows.

(1) The highway will integrate into a single compact unit the two parts of the island previously separated by the high Central Mountains.

(2) The highway will relieve population pressure in the western plains and develop the eastern part of the island, which previously has been mostly inaccessible. The population density in the west is about 115 persons per square mile; in the east, it is only about 23. The highway will especially improve communication between west and east.

(3) Not only has the highway created job opportunities for retired soldiers; it is also providing a settlement along its route.

(4) Now that the cross-island highway is completed, many resources of the Central Mountains can be developed.

THE SHIHMEN RESERVOIR PROJECT

The development of agriculture in Taiwan is dependent on the utilization of water, such as the Chianan irrigation system. However, in recent years, the island's water resources have been gradually exhausted in meeting the needs of agricultural and industrial expansion, especially in two areas in the northern part of the island. Those two areas, the Taipei basin and the Taoyuan tableland, differ in surface structure, but they are closely related as the only broad, flat regions suitable for agricultural and industrial development in north Taiwan. The two areas suffer from different aspects of the water problem: the former is plagued by flooding, the latter by drought.

Taipei basin

Taipei basin is a triangular, swampy depression, with the highest part less than 200 feet in elevation and the lowest practically level with the flood tide. The Tamshui River enters the basin from the southeast and meets Hsientien Creek before it reaches the city of Taipei. From Taipei the river turns northwest, receives the southern branch of the Keelung River, and finally flows through mountains into the sea at Tamsui.

Taipei is the political, cultural, and economic center of Taiwan, with a population of one million persons. It is situated on the east bank of the Tamshui River, at the confluence of Hsientien Creek and the Keelung River, and it is easily overrun by floods. The possibility of damage grows with the continual increase in cultivation and population. Agriculturally, as a swampy basin, Taipei could easily divert water and produce bumper harvests. Development of irrigation systems for cultivation of paddy fields started as early as 200 years ago, and the canals diverting water from the Tamshui River serve an area of about 12,350 acres. Even though there are flood walls and levees around Taipei, the city is not wholly free from flood menace, for there are lower lands adjacent to it. Efforts to prevent floods in this low basin have been the most important phase of hydraulic engineering work near the capital.

Taoyuan tableland

One region subject to drought is the Taoyuan tableland. It is about 820 feet high, dipping down to sea level on an average grade of about 1 to 100. It is 232 square miles in area, and it is divided into five terraces with heights of 100–165 feet. Studded with mounds and ridges, the terraces are suitable for providing farm ponds. There are more than 800 ponds, occupying a total area of 19,300 acres; they look like pockmarks when seen from the air. The tableland is not without rivers, but either they are located so high that no water can be diverted from them or they are torrential and their water supply is insufficient.

The Taoyuan Canal has changed the tableland from a poor and barren region into a fruitful one: The canal diverts water from Takekan Creek at Shihmen and irrigates an area of 56,800 acres. Many check dams have been built on small creeks to divert rainfall and return the flow into the ponds in order to maintain a sufficient irrigational margin.

The city of Hsinchu in this region still suffers from water shortage. In a long period of drought, when the ponds and canals are dried up, there is even a shortage of drinking water.

Need for regulation of water resources

In north Taiwan, a project of dam reservoirs is needed to regulate the water resources so as to avoid flooding and drought. Since 1924, numerous persons and agencies have made studies of such a project. After the completion of the Taoyuan Canal irrigation system in 1924, a Japanese engineer made the first study on the Shihmen Reservoir Project. He formulated a general plan with the aim of extending irrigation to the high lands southeast of the Taoyuan Canal. The plan emphasized irrigation and gave some consideration to flood control.

After the restoration of the island to the Chinese in 1949, rehabilitation was the major work, and no attention was given to large engineering projects until 1954, when the Shihmen Planning Commission was established. The key structure of the project is the reservoir formed by the Shihmen dam. When it is completed, it will be the largest hydraulic dam in the Far East. The project is the island's first attempt to plan a multiple-purpose water-resource program on a major scale, with concentration of funds and personnel. It is known as Taiwan's TVA (*Figure 42*).

Figure 42.—Construction of the Shihmen reservoir (AID/JCRR photo)

Aims of the development program

This multiple-purpose, water-resource development program has four principal aims.[2]

(1) To eliminate or lessen flood damage to lowland along the Tamshui River, including the capital city of Taipei.

(2) To furnish domestic and industrial water supplies for the people living on the Taoyuan tableland.

(3) To irrigate 134,700 acres, including two crop rice fields, on the Taoyuan tableland and in areas along the Tamshui River, bringing an annual increase of 76,000 tons of rice.

(4) To equip a 120,000 kilowatt hydroelectric plant, having an annual energy output of 221,280 kilowatt-hours.

189

Incidental benefits from the plant include the controlling of sediment loads, creation of a navigation route in the reservoir, and provision of recreation grounds for a population of more than two million persons. The first stage of construction included completion of the reservoir, the main dam, the afterbay weir, the powerhouse, and the irrigation system; also installation of a 40,000-kilowatt generator, together with a transmission system and a central plant for water purification, with main pipe lines.

FLOOD CONTROL.—This is the first concern of the Shihmen Reservoir Project. The Tamshui River, Hsientien Creek, and the Keelung River meet west of Taipei and these three valleys are often visited by typhoons. Because the land surface favors concentration of runoff, flows usually arrive at Taipei simultaneously and cause inundation, with resulting damage to the alluvial plain. Levees and flood walls have been built and maintained at Taipei, but lowlands along the river still lack protection. Even in the city, owing to difficulty of drainage part of the land is still subject to inundation. The drainage area controlled by the Shihmen Reservoir is 295 square miles, or 30 per cent of the area drowned by the Tamshui River. Flood peaks will be lowered and retarded by the storage action of the reservoir. The chances of a simultaneous conflux of flood peaks from all tributaries at Taipei will be greatly lessened. The reduction of the flood stage of the Tamshui River will at the same time lower the water level to the point where the backwater of the Tamshui is affected. The protection will be especially effective for lands along the two banks below the reservoir. A highly protective system can be realized if it is coordinated with the improvement of the existing levees.

PUBLIC WATER SUPPLY.—The second purpose of the Shihmen Reservoir Project is to provide a public water supply. All drinking water in the project area is supplied by dug wells except a small amount supplied by a small water plant in the town of Taoyuan. Industrial plants use water from their own wells. Water for other purposes is taken from irrigation canals and farm ponds. After a prolonged drought, the water table in all of these wells is lowered to such an extent that pumping is greatly restricted and the irrigation canals and ponds dry up. For example, in the autumn of 1954 one had to fetch water many miles. As the population increases, the seriousness of the water shortage will increase unless the problem of a public water supply is solved. It is certainly uneconomic to obtain water by manual pumping as at present, and the water, unless treated, is unhygienic for domestic purposes. Thus the need for a public water supply to purification plants for towns and cities and to canals and ponds for scattered villages, which at present are often afraid of drying up.

IRRIGATION.—Irrigation is also an important purpose of the project. The rapid population growth in Taiwan necessitates an increase in food production. On the west bank of Takekan Creek more than 20 per cent of the arable land on the Taoyuan tableland has not been irrigated. The land already irrigated, except for a small portion, also experiences frequent water shortages. The region irrigated by the Taoyuan and Kuangfu Canals is particularly well watered, with farm ponds meeting urgent requirements.

The first crop of rice in the irrigation area is transplanted in February and March, just at the time when the natural flow of water might be sufficient, and during the growing season the water requirement can be supplemented by farm ponds to ensure a harvest. The water requirement of the second crop frequently exceeds the available flow from natural streams and the capacity of the farm ponds. The rainfall of late summer and early autumn is very irregular, and at the same time the higher temperatures cause an increased loss of soil moisture owing to evaporation. Thus, as failure of the rain supply often converts paddy rice land to dry land and even prevents crops along river banks from growing, the loss of the harvest is always to be feared.

It has been estimated that only about 10 per cent of the land in the project region—13,234 acres—has a sufficient water supply. The double-crop area, which has an occasional insufficiency of water, comprises 57,277 acres or 43 per cent of the region; the area with a frequent deficiency of water includes 37,396 acres or 28 per cent; and the single-crop area includes 7947 acres or 6 per cent. These three all need to be supplied with a supplementary source of water to bring them to full production. There is also an area of 18,266 acres or 14 per cent of dry farming land in the region that can be changed into two-crop rice fields.

Under present conditions about 160,000 tons of brown rice can be produced yearly in this region. If there were sufficient water supply, 90 per cent of the region could increase its present rice production by 69,000 tons annually.

The small creeks in the project region, other than the Takekan, are too small to be worth regulating. The Takekan is the only stream that can be developed to augment the low water flow by storage in the Shihmen Reservoir. Its regulation will relieve the water shortage in time of drought and provide water for converting one-crop and dry farming land to two-crop farms.

HYDROELECTRIC POWER.—The increase in hydroelectric power is another benefit of the project. Up to the end of 1954, the power system of Taiwan had a total installed capacity of 392,000 kilowatts, with a peak load of 314,000 kilowatts and a total energy output of 1,800 million kilowatt-hours. In order to meet the rapid growth of the demand for power for industrial and public use, additional power resources must be developed. The Taiwan Power Company is continually establishing hydroelectric and steam plants to keep up with the expansion of economic reconstruction. The Shihmen Reservoir has a large storage capacity to regulate the flow and can develop power through the head created by the dam. Owing to the proximity of the reservoir to the power plant, the reservoir can be operated to supply the system's increasing requirements.

Other functions of the reservoir

Effects of the operation of the reservoir are not limited to flood control, public water supply, irrigation, and increasing hydroelectric power, as mentioned above. It has other functions, such as increasing the facilities for hunting, fishing, and other outdoor recreation.

Takekan Creek is not navigable. Backwater above the dam will extend upstream for some twelve miles. The flow of the Takekan is torrential above Shihmen and is interrupted by irrigation during low-water seasons. Thus there is no prospect for the culture of fish in the area, but the building of a reservoir will provide a breeding pond for fish and a refuge for wild life. The volume of fishing and hunting will be greatly increased. The crowded cities of northern Taiwan are urgently in need of recreation facilities. The Shihmen Reservoir is in a scenic region—a two-hour drive from the large cities of the north. The beautiful recreation grounds around the reservoir will be appreciated on weekend and holiday trips.

DEVELOPMENT OF NEW BEACH LAND

On the western coast of the island, there has appeared new beach land that is covered by the sea at high tide and is dry at low tide. If this beach land were enclosed by dikes to prevent the tide from coming in, it could be used for crop cultivation.

Two conditions have led to the appearance of this new beach land: First, a long period of rising of the western coast—an estimated rise of 0.7 inch per 100 years. Secondly, deposit of sand, clay, and other debris from the rivers flowing from the Central Mountains westward to the coast. There are 13 such rivers, the Choshui River being the largest. The rivers first deposit their debris at their mouths. Later, the debris is gradually transported south by the northeastern monsoon. These factors have enlarged the beach land year after year.

From Taoyuan in the north and to Pingtung in the south, the coastal beach land is 170 miles long and 7.5 miles across at its widest point. The total beach land amounts to 163,000 acres. Dikes, drainage canals, roads, houses, and forests for preventing wind damage occupy about 30 per cent of the total beach land. Thus, about 114,000 acres will be left for agricultural purposes.

Benefits from new land

ECONOMIC IMPROVEMENT.—Development of the beach land will greatly improve the island's economy. First, cultivating the beach land can increase food production. At present, the island's population exceeds 11 million persons, with an annual increase rate of about 3.7 per cent. Thus 400,000 persons are being added every year, and each year they consume at least 57,000 tons of food. In order to meet this additional food requirement, the island must not only raise its production per unit area, but also increase the area of its cultivated land. The coastal plains have been tilled intensively and have little room for further cultivation. From 1947 to 1956 the amount of cultivated land on the island increased only 5 per cent, and in recent years it has not increased at all. There are only two areas of Taiwan where cultivation can expand. One is the marginal foothill land between the coastal plains and the Central Mountains; the other is the newly-elevated beach land. The former is used only for growing tea and fruit and for pasturing animals. It has little prospect for other production, and so the importance of the beach land for growing more food is clear.

EMPLOYMENT OPPORTUNITIES.—Secondly, the development of the beach land will create employment opportunity. At present, with the rapid increase of population and the continued unavailability of jobs, more unemployment on the island can be expected. During the development of the beach land 10,000 persons can be employed each year. Retired soldiers especially can be employed to do the pioneering work on the beach and later can settle there permanently.

192

RELIEF OF OVERPOPULATION.—Thirdly, the development of the beach land will relieve to some extent the overpopulation problem. If 110,000 acres of the beach land are developed within fifteen years, 150,000 families can by that time be housed. If each family includes six persons, the land can accommodate about 900,000 persons.

RICE AND FISH.—The most important products of the beach land will be rice and fish. It is estimated that each year about 22,000 pounds of fish can be produced. If the rest of the new land is used for two crops a year of paddy rice, it will produce annually about 170,000 tons of rice.

Problems in development

Even though the new beach land offers a rosy future, its development is by no means an easy job. A few problems these new lands are facing are as follows:

(1) The soil of the new beach land contains too much salt, and it is almost impossible to cultivate the land without first washing much of the salt away. The soil is also lacking in organic matter, and fertilizer has to be used.

(2) There is the problem of material for building dikes for holding back the sea. At present there is disagreement as to what materials should be used. Some specialists insist that cement would be best; others prefer bricks and clay. Generally speaking, the nature of the sea waves' erosion differs from that of the rivers. If there is a rock on the beach, we can see that the sea water rises and falls with the tide and each time deposits some sand under the rock. On the other hand, if the rock is located in a river bed, the lower part of the rock is always deeply eroded. Thus if bricks and clay are used for a dike, it may move up and down with the slight movement of the tides. If the dike material is cement, erosion will take place at the bottom of the dike, and the cement will gradually be eroded away and the cement dike will topple over. This has actually happened. In other words, bricks and clay may be stronger for the dikes than cement. Also, bricks and clay are much cheaper. Another thing that has to be considered is that after the sea retreats further from the coast, removal of a cement dike will take more labor than removal of one made of bricks and clay.

(3) The third problem is man-made. When the Nationalist government first began its plans to develop the beach land it did not have a definite program concerning the ownership of the new land. Before it issued the regulations concerning application for ownership of the land, many individuals had already built private dikes along the beach and had constructed buildings. Also, the government did not widely publicize its policy, and many complaints have been made about the situation. Many local farmers and fishermen were not aware that they could register for ownership of the new land; on the other hand, many city dwellers and government employees registered early for such ownership.

Steps in development program

As a whole, development of the new beach land must include four steps. The first will be the research work and planning; the second, the engineering work; the third will concentrate on procedures to enable everyone who would like to settle in these coastal areas to have a fair chance to do so: the fourth and last step will concern increasing the area's production.

Development of the new beach land is closely coordinated with other projects on the island, such as improvement of the rivers, salt-soil management, establishment of fishing ports, and the national defense project, as well as water supply, drainage, and raising trees for protection from the wind.

At present some pioneering work has been started along the beach land, concentrated in the Hsinchu and Yunlin areas. Most of it has been carried on by retired soldiers. In the Yunlin areas about 1,400 retired soldiers have been employed, and 278 acres are being cultivated. With the washing away of the salt and the adding of fertilizer, the yield of crops in the new land has increased considerably. This is a good sign for future development.

REFERENCES

[1] T. H. SHEN, "Food production and administration in Taiwan," *Sci. Mon., N. Y.* **LXXIV,** 257 (1950).

[2] *Definite Plan Report on Shihmen Reservoir Project* (Shihmen Planning Commission, Taipei, 1955).

FIFTEEN

Place Names

THE PLACE NAMES of Taiwan are a good index for tracing of the sequent occupance of the different cultural groups which have occupied the island.

The difficulties in interpreting place names have long been recognized by geographers. Underlying this problem is the fact that early place names become fossil names which are often unfamiliar to modern ears. Also certain names that have their origin in the language of one cultural group are frequently unintelligible to another.

Place names of aboriginal origin

Many place names in Taiwan that were written in Chinese words do not convey any meaning. When the aborigines settled the island, they named places in their own language. When the Chinese moved to the island they kept the pronunciation of the native word, but the transformation obscured the meaning of the word. The following place names are examples: *Pa-yao-wan* and *Lang-wei-chi* in Pingtung; *Ta-ma-li* or *Chia-lu-lan* and *Chia-li-meng Kai* in Taitung; *Siu-ku-luan* or *T'ai-lu-ku* in Hwalien; *Ma-lin* and *Li-tze-chien* in Ilan.

During the aboriginal period the vegetation was luxurious, and the wild animals were numerous. Many place names referred either to the natural vegetation of the region or the animals found in it.

Since rattan was very important to the aborigines, they named many places after this cane: for instance, *Teng-peng*, which means "plain of the rattan," and *Teng-hu*, which indicates "lake of the rattan", and so on.

Among the animals that the tribes hunted, deer were the most numerous. At the present time in the western plain there still exist many place names which bear the name of *Lu*, which means "deer." For example, *Lu-ch'ang*, which indicates "deer valley," *Lu-liao*, which means "small house for storing the hunted deer," and *Lu-man-shan*, which indicates "the hill where the deer are plentiful."

Other place names are associated with the monkey or *hou*, such as *Cho-hou*, which means "eminent monkey," and *Hou-hou-tien-liao*, which indicates "the small house for the monkey."

Place names of European origin

Many place names of Taiwan were given by the Europeans, such as the Portuguese, Spanish, English and Dutch. Some were brought to Taiwan directly from Europe, and some were influenced by the colonization.

The migration of place names.—During the 16th century the Portuguese and the Spanish named their settlements after their home towns. For example, on the northern part of the east coast of Taiwan near Hualien, there is a place named *Rio Quero*, which means "Gold River." This name was brought from Portugal, where there is a river of the same name.

The Spanish gave many names to places in the northern part of the island, such as *Santiago* (St. James), *San Salvador* (Savior), and *Santo Domingo* (Holy Sunday). At present, *Santiago* is spelled *Shan-tiao-ko*, but keeps approximately its old pronunciation. These place names were brought over from the West Indies to Taiwan.

Other place names were designed to honor some prominent European missionaries. For example, Dutch missionaries and aboriginal converts named the present Sun-Moon Lake as *Lake Candidius* after the Rev. Georgius Candidius. Maps of Taiwan which are printed in English still call it Lake Candidius.

The Penghu Islands, located in the Taiwan Strait, were called *pescadores* by the Spanish, meaning "fishermen."

The influence of colonization.—During the Dutch period, all the land of Taiwan belonged to the Dutch East Indies Company, and was called *Wang-t'ien*, or "the Empire farm land." At present there are many places still called *Wang-t'ien*.

Also under Dutch rule, the unit for measuring land in Taiwan was called *kah*, a linguistic vestige of the Dutch *Akker*. The present *kah* equals 105,624 square feet, or about 2,377 English acres. When the Chinese and the Japanese came to the island, they tried to change the term for land unit from *kah* to the Chinese *mu* and to the Japanese *cho*. But as the *kah* system had been used for a long time, it was difficult for the people to change it. This measuring unit gradually came to be used in place names. For example, near Taipei many common place names such as *Shih-erh-chia*, which means "12 kah," *Chiu-chia* or "9 kah," *Liu-chia*, or "6 kah," *Wu-shih-erh-chia*, or "52 kah," and *I-pai-chia*, or "100 kah" are encountered.

In the Dutch land surveying system, five *kah* was called a *li*, which means "plow." Gradually this land surveying unit became popular for place names. For instance: in Changhua *Shih-wu-chang-li*, meaning "15 pieces of li" in Taipei *San-chang-li* or "3 pieces of li," and *Lu-chang-li* or "6 pieces of li." In other localities *Erh-chang-li* or "2 pieces of li," *Wu-chang-li* or "5 pieces of li," *Erh-shih-chang-li*, or "20 pieces of li," and *San-shih-chang-li*, or "30 pieces of li" are encountered.

In agricultural colonies, several families would join together to operate a farm, especially in the Ilan plain where ten or more pioneering families united to form a unit. This unit was called a *chieh*. In the beginning the unit represented the cooperation among the pioneers and gradually it was used in place names. At present, many places are found called *I-chieh*, or "one unit," *Erh-chieh*, or "2 units," *Wu-chieh*, or "5 units," and *Shih-lu-chieh*, or "16 units."

In the early agricultural colonization period, the ox was the necessary animal to help farmers in the field. In the Dutch period, the oxen were used not only for cultivation, but also for transportation. During Cheng Ch'eng-Kung's rule, oxen were used more widely. Many place names in Taiwan are associated with the ox. For example, *Nu-chou* means "many oxen." *Nu-lan* indicates "ox enclosure," and *Nu-pu* means "ox port."

Place names of the Chinese period

Modification of place names by the early Chinese settlers.—When the Chinese came to Taiwan, they adopted many of the aboriginal place names, but gave them new meanings. Three examples are cited here: *Miaoli* was originally the name of a village of aborigines and means literally "the place of the cat"; For the tribes of Ami and Paiwan, the sound of *Lootung* meant "monkey." Now the word has been changed to mean "the east of Loo"; At the northern tip of Taiwan is an important port named *Keelung*. The name originally belonged to a village named for the Kietangaran (Pepowhan) tribe which lived there. Over a period of time, the middle syllables were dropped. This *Kietangaran* was changed to *Kieran*, then gradually it became *Keelung* which means "the prosperous base."

Migrated place names from the mainland of China.—The habits, customs, and farming calendar in Taiwan are almost the same as those of southern China. Also there are many place names that are the same. These names were originally used in the southeastern coast of China; very few are from the interior provinces. Also these Chinese place names appeared mainly in western Taiwan; a few were brought into the east.

During the wave of the Chinese migration, when many migrants came from Fukien province, they named places in Taiwan after places in that province. For example: in Chuanchow, *T'ungan*; in Changchow, *Lungch'i*, *Chaoan*, *Pingho*, *Changpu*, *Nanch'ing*, *Changtai*, and *Hai-ch'eng*; in Ting-chow, *Yungting*; in Hsinghwa, *Hsien-yu*.

The Chinese migrants who came from Kwangtung province named many places in Taiwan after places in that province. For example: in Waichow, *Haifeng*, *Luifeng*, *Yungting*, *Hopin*, *Ho yüan*, *Changning*, *Polo*, *Lungchuan*; in Chaochow, *Chaoyang*, *Taipu*, *Haiyang*, *Jaoping*, *Fengsheng*, *Hweilai*, *Chihyang*, *Tenghai*; in Kaying, *Chengping*, *Hsinging*, *Changlo*.

Some of the Chinese who migrated to Taiwan came from the Ryukyu Islands. They also named their settlements after their towns. For example, *Hou-shao-tao*, an island off the southeast coast of Taiwan, literally means "the burning island," and was the name of an island in Ryukyu.

The immigrants usually liked to name the beautiful places of their new settlements after their homeland. *Tzu-shan-yen* is one example. This place name was adopted from *Changchow* in Fukien. The city of *Anping* near Tainan was named after the native town in Fukien province of the hero Cheng Ch'eng-Kung.

197

Place names associated with fortification.—At present, many place names in the foothills between the mountains and the plains are reminiscent of the early conflict between the aborigines and Chinese, and many military terms are found in use in the foothills.

Three hundred years ago, people from Changchow in Fukien, who migrated to the south coast of Taiwan near Hengchen built a city and surrounded it with a wall of firewood in order to defend themselves against the native tribes. Thus the city was named *Ch'ai-ch'eng,* which means "firewood city."

In some places the Chinese immigrants built their city wall of earth, and many places are called *Tu-ch'eng,* or "earth city." Some towns were surrounded by walls built of bricks, and so the towns are called *Tu-wei,* or "earth enclosure." Others are called *Tu,* or "fort," such as *Ting-tu,* or "first fort," *Erh-tu,* or "second fort," *San-tu,* or "third fort," *Szu-tu,* or "fourth fort," all in Ilan; and *Wu-tu,* or "fifth fort," and *Pa-tu,* or "eighth fort" in Taipei. These forts were outposts of the immigrants' settlements.

Tu-niu, is very popular for place names in Taiwan. It was adopted for villages that built walls with earth and brick to keep out the aborigines. Since the bricks are red in color, they are usually called *Tu-niu-hung Hsien,* which indicates that they look like a solid red line from far away. Many settlements came to use these names.

Other place names are derived from the fact that the Chinese had to defend themselves from the natives. For example: *Mu-shan,* or "wood fence," *T'ung-Kuei,* or "mortar gun case," *Yi-kou,* or "strategic pass," *Yi-liao,* or "the small house at the pass."

Place names associated with the Chinese family system.—As the Chinese family system keeps the members of the family together whenever possible, it is natural that in most cases all the residents of a village who migrated to Taiwan were related, and in some cases have the same surname. This is especially true of the compact rural settlements in southern Taiwan. This kind of settlement is called *Sippendorf* by the Dutch. Thus family surnames enter into the names of a great many towns. *Lin-chia-chuang* and *Cheng-chia-t'sun* are "Sippendorf" towns.

Numerous villages in Taiwan definitely indicate that they originated from surnames by the use of the second characters *T'so* and *Liao,* which mean "homeland," and "small house" or "small village" respectively. Thus, *Wu-liao* means "homeland of Wu." *Lin-Ts'o* means "Lin village." *Young-Ts'o-liao,* means "home village of Young." There is a village named *Hsieh-Ts'o-Liao,* meaning "the village of Hsieh." About 48 per cent of the residents in this village have the last name of Hsieh[2] (the same surname as that of the author, although he comes from Chekiang Province in mainland China).

Place names associated with Chinese aspirations.—In the pioneering days of the Chinese colonists, the land was divided into certain "parts" (*Ku*) or certain "divisions" (*F'en*). Thus, the certain "parts" or "divisions" became the place names, such as *Liu-ku,* meaning "6 parts," and *Shih-san-fen,* meaning "13 divisions." These place names are found in Hsinchu.

In Cheng Ch'eng-Kung's reign, the Chinese changed the land system of *Wangt'ien,* ("Empire farm land") into *Kuan-t'ien,* ("government land") or *Ying-t'ien* ("military camp land").

Because of the steep slopes and torrential nature of streams in Taiwan, irrigation is necessary for cultivation of the land. The water is stored in ponds which are called *pei*, and it is distributed through canals called *Hsun*. These ponds and canals also gave their names to some places. The following are examples: *Lao-pei*, or "old pond," *Hau-pei*, or "behind pond," *T'ien-sung-pei* or "God-sent pond," *San-t'iao-Hsun* or "three canals."

Many of the names, when formalized, were given new characters, signifying happy portent, prophetic hope, and esthetic value.

Under the Ch'ing Dynasty there were rebellions on the island. After the rebellions were over, the Chinese Empire usually gave the towns names of new hope. Examples of this are *Chia-yi*, where *Chia* means "good," and *yi* means "fitting or proper." Originally the city was called *Ju-lo-shan*, which is the pronunciation of an aborigine's village which the Dutch called *Tilaossen*. Other examples include *Pao-chung-miao*, meaning "the temple of loyalty," and *Chung-yi-ting*, which means "the pavilion of loyalty and prosperity."

The Ch'ing Empire also attempted to extend its influence by renaming villages, and the names praised the regime. *Chang-hua* originally was called *Pan-Hsien*, which meant "half line" and was the aboriginal name. After the place became a *Hsien* or county, the Ching Empire renamed it *Chang-hua* which means "manifest the influence of the Empire," and this is what it is called today. *Kan-en* originally was called *Nin-ma-she* by the aborigines, but it became *Kan-en*, which means "thanks for the mercy."

Many place names were designated by the government to praise the Ch'ing Empire, *Yung-nin*, meaning "peaceful forever," *Kwei-jen*, meaning "return to the benevolent," and *Yen-ch'ang*, which means "prosperous forever," are all cases in point.

Some unpleasant place names were replaced by new ones. *Ch'ou-shui*, meaning "scent creek," was changed to *Shiu-shui*, which means "beautiful creek."

Place names of the Japanese period

The Japanese immigrants in Taiwan who were city dwellers, changed few place names in the rural areas. There are only four country villages named by the Japanese. These are *Yoshino-mura*, *Shikano-mura*, *Sayama-mura*, and *Je-ch'u Hinode-mura*. However, the Japanese added some place names in the urban areas. For example, *Kai*, for "street" or "market towns;" *Chuang*, for "towns;" *T'ing*, meaning "unit," for certain sections in the city; and *Ting-mu*, for "lanes."

Place names associated with environment and resources

Many place names in Taiwan may be rooted in natural environment as well as in cultural or man-made phenomena. The island itself was called *Taiwan* by both the Chinese and the Japanese. This literally means "big bay."

Some place names originated from the landforms, such as *Kau-chai*, which means "the foot of the cliff;" *Hou-pu*, meaning "the back of an uncultivated flatland;" *Hai-kang*, which means "sea edge;" and *Chi-kang*, which means "creek edge."

On the southwestern coast there were many sand bars and lagoons. So many places are named *Chou*, meaning "sand bar." As the lagoons became smaller, they were usually used as ponds for raising fish and some places were thus called *Yü-wen*, meaning "fish ponds." Many places in the Penghu Islands were named after *Ao*, which means "along the water."

Along the western coast, many rivers of the island empty into the sea and form alluvial plains. At the mouth of these rivers, ports were developed. In the 16th century, the ports were the main entrances of the immigrants. The Chinese immigrants entered through these ports and settled along the rivers. They gradually moved toward the interior into the area of the plains. Thus in the western plains, many places were named *Kong*, which means "port." However, because of the changing of the river courses and the extension of the coastal plains, the old ports may have been left far inland. Yet, the name *Kong* is still used inland. At the same time new ports along the extended coast appeared. Thus we find *Chiu-kong*, meaning "old port" and *Hsin-kong*, meaning "new port"—the former name is found inland and the latter name is found along the extended coast.

Many place names in Taiwan referred either to vegetation of the area or to the animals found in the area. For example, *Ch'ieh-tung Creek* means "creek of *Bischoffia Javanica*." In other parts of the island we find: *Ch'ieh-tung Lake*, indicating "lake of tropical tree"; *Ch'ieh-tung-chiao*, which means "foot of tropical tree," and *Ch'ieh-tung-lin*, which means "forest of tropical tree." Another tree which was associated with many places was the maple, or *Feng*. Names using this word are: *Feng-kong*, indicating "port of maple;" *Feng-shu-chiao*, which is translated as "bridge of the maple tree," and *Feng-shu-kong*, which represents "pit of the maple tree."

Other places were associated with wild cats and mosquitoes. There are names such as *Ta-mao*, which indicates "beat the cats," and *Wen-li-shan-ting*, which means "the mountain summit of mosquitoes."

Some places names along the seacoast were named after the oyster, such as *Kokoukong*, which means "port of the oyster shell" and *Koliao*, which represents "the small house of the oyster."

Some place names are related to mineral resources found in the area. For example: *Hsian-tie'n*, meaning "salt field" and *Hwang-shan*, which refers to a "mountain of sulfur."

REFERENCES

[1] ABE AKIYOSHI, *A Study of Place Names in Taiwan* (Taiwan Chimei Kenkyn, Taihoku, 1938). [In Japanese].

[2] SIH-FUH YANG, "Gazeteer geography of Taiwan," *Wen-Hsien* **1**, No. 4, 10 (1950). [In Chinese].

PART THREE

THE **PRESENT**

| Present Status
of Taiwan

No LONGER A COLONY, Taiwan now stands as an entity, the home of the Republic of China, and the last repository of Chinese culture. It is prosperous and its social conditions are improving.

However, in 1949 when the Communists seized control of mainland China and the Nationalist government moved to Taiwan, the island's prospects were grim. The Communist regime on the mainland warned the world that it was about to "liberate" the island. The United States government, though providing economic assistance at that time, found no relation between Taiwan's status and American security, and, therefore did not offer military aid or advice. Later, in 1950, after the North Korean army, supported by Soviet and Chinese Communists, attacked the Republic of Korea forces, the President of the United States stated that the occupation of Taiwan by Communist forces would directly threaten the Pacific area and the United States forces there, and he ordered the United States Seventh Fleet to prevent any attack on the island.[1]

It will be remembered that during World War II the Nationalist government moved to the Chinese interior province of Szechuan as a defensive base against which the strong Japanese navy could do little harm. Once again the Nationalists, under the leadership of Chiang Kai-shek, have been fortunate in relocating their defensive base. Having the Nationalist base of resistance on Taiwan presents a major difficulty to the Communists, for to attack the island successfully the Communists would need a strong navy, which is still one of their unattained goals.[2]

An important reason for Taiwan's changed position is the remarkable Nationalist record of achievement and regeneration in the period following 1949. The years of 1951 and 1952 were years of reorganization of the government with United States protection and support. Then followed a four-year period (1953–1956) of adjustment and planning. In 1957 and 1958 the cumulative effect of domestic reforms and United States aid brought a great improvement in economic and cultural fields.

203

Six areas of major achievement in Taiwan deserve special mention[3]:

(1) The land reform program, internationally acclaimed as a model.

(2) Improved living conditions, which give Taiwan one of the highest standards of living in southeast Asia, indicating the success of the work of the Chinese-American Joint Commission of Rural Reconstruction.

(3) The development of industry, with new types of export products, such as bicycles, plate glass, electric fans, plastics, aviation gasoline, and even jeeps, which previously had been unknown in Taiwan.

(4) The development of democratic, responsible local government, with free election of officials.

(5) The expansion of public education and cultural activities, with a large number of enrollments in public schools and with the issuance of a large number of publications.

(6) The building of an efficient military force, which makes a substantial contribution to free-world defenses in Asia.

The above record has received too little attention, because of world interest in and concern over developments on the mainland under the Communist rule, and partly because of the tendency to assume weakness on the part of the Nationalists on the basis of their poor performance in the years immediately following World War II.

However, Taiwan is not without weaknesses. Noticeable ones include the pressure of increasing population on limited land resources; the burden of large military expenditure, which could swallow up a sizable share of the national products; the lack of harmony between the Chinese newly arrived from the mainland and the descendants of the early Chinese settlers, although relations have improved recently; the shortages in employment opportunities for college graduates, and in other incentives.

Despite such weaknesses, Nationalist achievements tip the balance in their favor. In their years of exile they have done much to keep up their energy and have conquered seemingly insuperable difficulties. They have shown a truly indomitable faith in their cause and their culture. With the concerted efforts of Taiwan's people and government and the generous flow of economic assistance from the United States, it has been demonstrated that a satisfactory rate of economic growth can be achieved in a free society without collectivist regimentation, even on so congested an island as Taiwan. Reform may be too slow to satisfy outside critics, but without Taiwan the hope for a free China and for Chinese civilization would have been extinguished long ago.

In this situation there is a great need for more adequate study and more generally available information concerning the achievements as well as the problems of Taiwan. *Part Three* of this book analyzes Taiwan's current population conditions; changing patterns of settlement and means of transportation; the outlook for agriculture, livestock raising, fishing, and forestry; and the development of industry.

REFERENCES

[1] Memorandum by the Department of State on the Authority of the President, July 3, 1950.

[2] HAN LIH-WU, *Taiwan Today* (Hwa Kuo Publishing Company, Taipei, 1956), p. 11.

[3] RICHARD L. WALKER, "Taiwan's development as free China," *Ann. Amer. Acad. Polit. Soc. Sci.* **CCCXXI**, 122 (1959).

SEVENTEEN

Population

THE NATURE OF POPULATION DATA

No ONE KNOWS how long Taiwan has been inhabited. Nor is there any record to show the original number of the native aborigines. Although the first large number of Chinese who settled on the island arrived during the 17th century, no census of the island was taken until the Japanese occupation, which lasted from 1895 to 1945.

In order to control the island effectively and to develop its resources as a support for Japan, it was essential for the Japanese to have accurate and complete information concerning the island's population, extending even to details about each family. Hence the Japanese government put great emphasis on the recording of each year's births and deaths and on each census enumeration, both of which they carried out with careful planning.

As a result, while under Japanese control the island had an outstanding set of demographic records, even better than those of Japan itself. The data on the population of Taiwan were the most complete and accurate in the Far East and surpassed even the data collected in most European countries.

Two kinds of data were collected in Taiwan. One, concerning a person's status, such as birth, death, marriage, divorce, and migration, was obtained in Taiwan through a system of household registration that the Japanese developed. The household information, compiled and published at the end of each year in a comprehensive statistical report, became the principal source of information for use in routine local government activities and for assembling vital statistics. The second type of data was obtained through a population census. To be useful, a census must follow a predetermined pattern and must be conducted regularly at some specific time. For most demographic records, this type of enumeration is generally

205

considered the most dependable and effective method for obtaining accurate figures. The Japanese in Taiwan used the census as a check on the accuracy of the household registration (*Table 37*).

During the Japanese occupation seven population censuses were conducted. The first one was taken in 1905 and the second in 1915; after that, one was taken every five years (each conducted on October 1); the last was taken in 1940. From 1920 to 1940 each census emphasized certain population features. For example, the census of 1920 concentrated attention on occupation, that of 1925 on the age composition, and that of 1935 on the marital status. Because of the war, the census of 1940 was not published. Only recently, through the financial assistance of the Chinese-American Joint Commission on Rural Reconstruction, the Taiwan Provincial Government's Bureau of Statistics published the chief tables of the 1940 census, with an explanation of the procedure employed (*Table 38*).

Table 37. Household Registration Data on the Growth of Population
(specified years, 1905–1960)*

Year	All groups; total population	Taiwanese	Main-landers	Aborigines	Japanese	Korean	Other foreigners
1905	3,123,302	2,942,266	8,223	113,195	59,618	—	—
1910	3,299,493	3,064,499	14,840	122,106	98,048	—	—
1915	3,569,842	3,282,109	18,225	132,279	137,229	—	—
1920	3,757,838	3,436,071	24,836	130,310	166,621	—	—
1925	4,147,462	3,787,868	33,258	136,706	189,630	—	—
1930	4,679,066	4,259,523	46,691	140,553	232,299	—	—
1935	5,315,642	4,839,629	53,900	150,502	269,798	1,604	209
1940	6,077,478	5,523,910	46,190	158,321	346,663	2,299	93
1945	6,559,014	5,984,032	47,551	167,561	355,596	3,982	292
1950	7,555,588	6,861,155	524,940	168,304	376	—	813
1955	9,080,474	8,039,691	852,688	185,264	534	—	1,297
1960	11,002,903	9,512,776	1,279,426	210,701	—	—	—
1963	11,883,523	10,349,254	1,534,269	—	—	—	—

*The data for years before 1940 are based on *Fifty-one Years of Statistical Abstracts in Taiwan*, Table 49, pp. 76–77; aborigine figures from Table 53, pp. 94–95; Taiwanese figures from Table 49–Table 53. Since 1949, the Aborigines are included in Taiwanese. Since 1945, Koreans are included in other foreigners.

Table 38. Taiwan's Census Data on the Growth of Population (all groups)

Year	Total population	Index	Annual rate of growth per 1,000	Number of families	Number of persons per family	Sex ratio (males per 100 females)	Population density (per square mile)
1905	3,039,751	100	—	487,353	6.2	112.7	220
1915	3,479,922	114	13.62	555,366	6.3	108.8	252
1920	3,655,308	120	9.88	596,208	6.1	107.5	265
1925	3,993,408	131	17.85	726,526	5.5	105.8	293
1930	4,592,537	151	23.35	805,797	5.7	105.1	333
1935	5,212,426	171	25.65	897,565	5.8	104.2	378
1940	5,872,084	193	24.12	979,447	6.0	102.4	426

Thus for thirty-five years Taiwan's population conditions were reported completely and accurately. Data from the household registration and census are summarized in *Tables 37* and *38*.

Since 1945 the Chinese government of Taiwan has employed the household registration system as did the Japanese, but the work is treated as a minor activity only.

POPULATION DISTRIBUTION AND DENSITY

Taiwan is one of the most densely populated regions in the world. More than 11 million people live on its 13,884 square miles. Although the population density (840 persons per square mile) is lower than that of the Netherlands (894 per square mile), it is higher than that of Belgium (768), of Japan (659), of South Korea (601), and even of Puerto Rico (676). Taiwan's population density is greater than that of any province of China except Kiangsu, which has 867 persons per square mile.

The average figure, however, does not tell the whole story. There are wide variations in the population among Taiwan's sixteen counties, or *hsiens*, as *Table 39* indicates.

Table 39. The Distribution of Population in Political Units of 1962*

County	Total area (square miles)	Total population	Density (per square mile)	Birth rate (per 1,000)	Death rate (per 1,000)
Changhua	409	919,066	2247	39.7	9.2
Penghu	48	103,030	2146	46.7	10.9
Yunglin	497	705,516	1420	40.7	9.2
Taoyuan	471	530,164	1126	41.3	8.1
Taipei	825	915,272	1109	41.9	9.1
Tainan	773	826,893	1070	43.2	8.3
Chiayi	753	746,790	992	42.9	8.4
Hsinchu	590	489,474	830	39.0	8.0
Taichung	791	637,292	806	40.5	9.1
Miaoli	702	455,120	648	40.7	8.7
Pingtung	1071	685,143	640	43.2	9.6
Kaohsiung	1093	657,927	602	43.3	8.1
Ilan	824	357,928	434	39.4	9.8
Nantou	1584	435,191	275	42.9	9.2
Hualien	1786	370,337	270	44.1	10.5
Taitung	1354	230,443	170	48.6	10.9
Municipalities					
Taipei	25	979,081	39,163	37.0	5.7
Kaohsiung	44	515,153	11,708	43.5	6.8
Tainan	67	362,668	5,413	39.1	6.4
Taichung	62	320,158	5,164	39.0	7.8
Keelung	50	248,799	4,976	43.4	7.6
Yang ming Shan	45	120,283	2,673	40.7	6.9

* Based on *China's Year Book* (China Year Book Society Taipei, Taiwan, 1963), pp. 55–6, and data from the Taiwan Provincial Government.

207

From the table it is evident that among the sixteen counties Changhua, on the west coast, and Penghu, on the Penghu Islands in the Taiwan Strait, have the highest population density, 2247 and 2146 persons per square mile respectively; while Hualien and Taitung, on the east coast, have the lowest, only 270 and 170. Most of the rest have between 500 and 1300 persons per square mile.

The uneven distribution of the population in Taiwan is closely related to the physical conditions of the island. Comparison of *Figure 43* with *Figure 10* showing rainfall reveals an inverse relation between the two. The heavy rainfall regions in the central part of the island are the

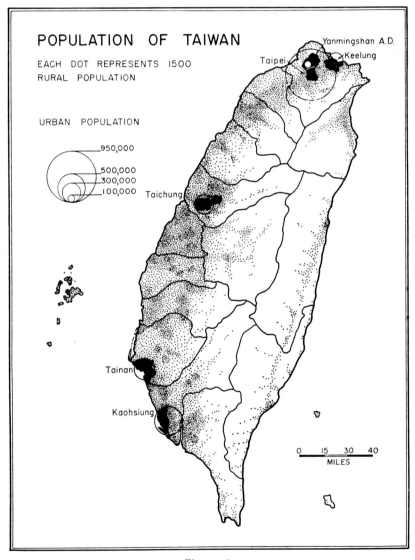

Figure 43

most lightly populated areas. Areas with an annual rainfall of 75 inches or more have a population density of fewer than 65 persons per square mile. On the other hand, densely populated areas in the western coastal region have an annual rainfall of less than 75 inches. It is clear that a dense population is not necessarily associated with a heavy rainfall; the density rather depends on how the rain is used. On the west coast, even though the precipitation is less than 75 inches, efficient utilization of the rainfall and careful irrigation of the land have made this region the most important agriculturally in Taiwan and the most populous. If a population map (*Figure 43*) is compared with landform (*Figure 9*), a close relationship between surface configuration and population density is seen. The plains are crowded, the mountain regions are inhabited by only a few people, while the western coastal plains have an average population of more than 2000 persons per square mile and comprise the most highly populated part of the island. They are an ideal place for paddy rice fields, and therefore, this area has attracted most of the population. The area of Taiwan's western coastal plain totals about 3000 square miles, about 22 per cent of the total area of the island; the population of the plain amounts to 7,200,000 persons, or 66 per cent of the total population of Taiwan. The only other heavily populated region is the Taitung rift valley in the east, which has a population density of 518 persons per square mile because of its valley-type landform.

In the central and eastern parts of the island, the mountains, unfit for agriculture, make all the difference. In the hilly areas the population density varies from 648 to 1300 persons per square mile; and in the higher mountains, where the heavy rainfall has not been well managed, the density decreases to 130 persons per square mile, and in some places even to less than 65. Thus, the mountainous counties have the lowest population density—only one-seventh of that of the counties located on the western coastal plains. Also, the distribution of the population on the western coastal plains is more even than that of the eastern areas where the people are concentrated either along transportation lines or in valleys and basins.

It is evident that the landforms have imposed limits on population distribution in Taiwan, but the distribution also depends on the occupations of the people, or the degree to which advancement in their technology has helped to settle the island.

For example, the physical environment of Hainan, the only other large island off the coast of China—size, climate, landforms, native vegetation, and soil—is not radically different from that of Taiwan; and about fifty years ago the two islands had the same population, approximately two and a half million persons. Today Taiwan's population is more than eleven million, while Hainan's has remained at two and a half million. Furthermore, Hainan has even more flat land than Taiwan; more than half of Hainan is less than 170 feet in elevation and the area higher than 1700 feet comprises less than one-tenth of the total. Hainan has a population density of about 181 persons per square mile, only one-fifth that of Taiwan.

What has caused this difference between the two islands? The answer lies in artificial irrigation. In the last fifty years more than twelve million acres of Taiwan's land have come under irrigation. This has both increased the area suitable for rice paddy fields and extended the time of harvest. Originally, Taiwan had only one crop of rice a year. But now a field, properly irrigated, may be cropped twice a year; Taiwan has thus been able to support more people, and its population has increased. Hainan, on the other hand, has very little irrigation.

The distribution of the population in Taiwan varies not only with the different types of landforms and with such factors as irrigation, but also with time. In half a century, as we have seen, the population density of the island as a whole has more than tripled: from 220 persons per square mile in 1905, to 265 in 1920, to 425 in 1940, 783 in 1960, and 840 in 1962. This great increase was accompanied by shifts in distribution, as is seen in *Table 40.*

Table 40. The Change of the Area of the Different Population Densities,
1920–1956*

Population density	1920		1940		1956	
	Area (sq. miles)	Area (percentage)	Area (sq. miles)	Area (percentage)	Area (sq. miles)	Area (percentage)
More than 1,000	8.07	0.5	13.67	1.4	22.99	3.8
500–1,000	15.50	1.7	24.85	4.6	36.66	9.8
100–500	6.21	33.7	71.45	36.9	68.35	33.9
Less than 100	95.69	64.1	88.85	57.1	85.12	52.5
Total	*125.47*	*100.0*	*198.82*	*100.0*	*213.12*	*100.0*

* Based on CHEN, C. S., *A Geography of Taiwan* (Fu-min Geographical Institute, Taipei, Taiwan, 1959), p. 210. [In Chinese].

Table 40 divides the nearly 14,000 square miles of land into four groups according to population density and shows the percentage of land that was characterized by each of the four densities in different years. In the two areas of the highest density, there was a marked increase between 1920 and 1956. The area of lowest density experienced a decrease.

In Taiwan a population density of more than 5000 persons per square mile is found, of course, only in cities (in 1920 only one city, Taipei, had a density as high as that) ; but by 1940 the populations of three additional cities—Keelung, Taichung, and Kaohsiung—had so increased that they moved into the over-5000 category. In 1962, the populations of four more cities—Tainan, Chiayi, Hsinchu, and Lutung—rose to that density.

The different rates of population increase among counties are closely related to the stage of development of each county. Generally speaking, an area where cultivation was begun early has, usually, a low rate of increase; whereas the higher rates of increase are enjoyed by areas with late development of cultivation. For example, Hualien and Taitung in the eastern part of Taiwan have the latest development in Taiwan's history of cultivation and have the highest rate of increase in population. On the other hand, Penghu Island, the earliest part of Taiwan to be developed for cultivation, has the lowest increase in rate of population growth. It is natural that the newly developed areas more easily attract new settlers than the areas which have had an early development.

Changes in the distribution of population from 1920 to 1940 took place in eight areas, four showing an increase and four a decrease.

The first of the areas showing an increase is the Taitung rift valley, together with the nearby southwestern part of the Ilan plain. In that area the growth was mainly due to an increase in cultivatable land. The second area that increased its population is the western coastal plain, where development of irrigation increased the amount of cultivatable land and thus caused the plain to attract more people. The third area consists of cities in which industrialization advanced, and to which rural people were attracted by opportunities for employment. The fourth area of increase is the northeastern part of the island. In one locality in that area, increase of population was due to a rise in mining activity; in another, to the establishment of a fishing port.

Of the four areas showing a decrease in population, one is located in the northeastern mountain area. This region, limited in natural resources and poor in productivity, lost a large part of its population to the surrounding mining and fishing communities which offered better economic opportunities. The second region to decline is the Penghu Islands. There the dry climate, with strong winds and salty soils, forced many people to look elsewhere for a living, and Kaohsiung port provided a place for them (at present, about one-fifth of the inhabitants of Kaohsiung have come from the Penghu Islands). In the Central Mountain area, the third region to show a decrease in population, the loss was due to the building of the Sun-Moon Lake electrical engineering project, which drowned part of the land and caused the inhabitants to move away. A local flood in 1919 caused the total depopulation of another area of the western coastal plain.

From 1950 to 1962, while Taiwan was increasing its population by more than three million persons, the distribution pattern of the increase rate remained similar to that of the years between 1920 and 1940. However, the areas of high increase were concentrated in the suburbs of Taipei, Keelung, Kaohsiung, and in the Taitung rift valley. The increasing population of the suburbs is due to industrialization and urbanization, which attracted much of the rural population. The growth of population in the Taitung rift valley is due to settlement by retired soldiers and a movement of the aborigines downward from the Central Mountain regions.

GROWTH OF THE POPULATION

The growth of Taiwan's population has been very rapid. The total population of the island in 1800 was estimated as 2 million persons; in 1905, 3 million; in 1925, 4 million; in 1940, 6 million; in 1950, 9 million; and in 1962, more than 11 million.

There are no records to show the number of Chinese who moved to the island before 1895. Such figures would be very important in showing the composition of Taiwan's population, as the Chinese are the basic race on the island. It is the descendants of the early Chinese immigrants who came to be called Taiwanese and who now constitute the majority.

The first reliable figure representing the total population is that for 1905, when, under Japanese rule, the first census was taken. The data for a number of years are shown in *Table 41*.

211

The table shows that if we represent the 1905 total population as 100, then in 1915 it was 114; in 1920, 120; in 1925, 131; in 1930, 151; in 1935, 171; and in 1940, 193. In other words, during this span of 35 years, the total population of the island almost doubled. A similar rate of growth occurred among the native Taiwanese.

In the same table we notice that the annual geometric rates of growth increased at each intercensal stage. The figures are significant because they show acceleration in growth, the rate of which increased along with an increase in the total number of people. During the period 1905–1915, the rate of growth was 13.6 per thousand a year; but in 1935–1940 the rate increased to 24.1 per thousand a year, averaging 19.1 per thousand annually. The rate of growth among the native Taiwanese was 11.2 per thousand a year during the period 1905–1915; it reached about 25 per thousand a year in the period 1940–1943, averaging 17.6 per thousand a year. The only setback in the rate of growth both for the whole population and for the Taiwanese came in the period 1915–1920, when the rates were 9.9 and 8.3 per thousand respectively. These low rates were due to three near-epidemic attacks of disease suffered on the island.

Table 41. Growth of Population in Taiwan, Specified Years, 1905–1943*

Year	Total population, all groups	Index	Annual rate of growth per 1,000 (geometric)	Native Taiwanese	Index	Annual rate of growth per 1,000 (geometric)
1905	3,039,751	100	—	2,973,280	100	
1915	3,479,922	114	13.6	3,325,733	111	11.2
1920	3,655,308	120	9.9	3,466,507	113	8.3
1925	3,993,408	131	17.9	3,775,288	126	17.1
1930	4,492,537	151	23.4	4,313,681	145	22.2
1935	5,212,426	171	25.7	4,882,945	160	24.8
1940	5,872,084	193	24.1	5,510,259	188	24.2
1943	—	—	—	5,962,000	200	24.2

* Data from *51 Years of Statistical Abstracts of Taiwan* (Taiwan Governor General's Office, Taipei, 1946), Table 62, and GEORGE W. BARCLAY, *Colonial Development of Population in Taiwan.* (Princeton University Press, Princeton, New Jersey, 1954) p. 13, Table 2.

In 1945, when Japan restored the island to China and many Japanese were repatriated from Taiwan, the total population of the island of course decreased. The total population on October 1, 1945, was estimated at 6,560,000 persons; by the end of 1946 it had decreased to 6,100,000. However, after 1949, when the Communist Party took control of the mainland, many Chinese migrated to Taiwan as refugees and increased the total population of the island to 9,000,000, three times the 1905 population. A comparison of population in age and sex composition between 1949 and 1962 in Taiwan can be seen in *Figure 44*.

Comparison with other parts of the world shows that the population of Britain doubled during the first half of the 19th century, and the population of Japan nearly doubled during the 64 years between 1879 and 1935.

In other words, it took half a century for Britain to double its population and more than 60 years for Japan to do so; but it took only 38 years for Taiwan. However, the Japanese growth took place a number of years ago, and the British, a century ago. Another comparison of population growth between Taiwan and a number of countries during the period from 1920 to 1940 shows that during this period only four areas of the world had a higher rate of population growth than Taiwan. However, those areas owe their growth chiefly to high rates of immigration; in each area, the rate of natural increase in 1940 was lower than that in Taiwan. For example, Malaya's rate of natural increase in 1940 was 20.6 per thousand; Honduras' 21.0; and Palestine's 20.2. Taiwan's was 24.0 per thousand. Therefore, during 1920–1940, as far as natural increase is concerned, the population growth of Taiwan seems to have been the highest in the world.[1]

POPULATION OF TAIWAN

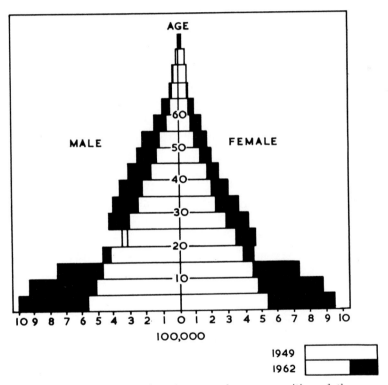

Figure 44.—A comparison in age and sex composition of the population in 1949 and 1962

The population growth of any region can only stem from the following conditions: (*a*) an excess of the number of persons entering the region over the number of those leaving it, and (*b*) the natural increase, the excess of the number of births over the number of deaths.

In Taiwan's history there were two spectacular periods of immigration, each caused by significant political events, which brought a sudden growth

213

of population. The first occurred in the 17th century, when about 100,000 Chinese migrated to Taiwan and formed the basis of today's population. The migration began in 1661, inspired by the celebrated Chinese hero, Chen Ch'eng-Kung, who drove the Dutch out of Taiwan.

The second migration started in 1945, when Taiwan was restored to China by Japan, and ended in 1949, when the Chinese Communist Party took control of the mainland. This immigration was lead by the Chinese Nationalist leader Chiang Kai-shek, who repatriated many Japanese and also made the island a refuge from Chinese communism.

Except for those two major movements caused by important political events, Taiwan's population has been little affected by immigration. The Japanese, during their rule, banned Chinese immigration, and the total increase through immigration between 1906 and 1943 (38 years) was less than 200,000 persons, only 6 per cent of Taiwan's total increase from all causes in those years. This figure is tiny compared with the total increase in population of more than three million during that period. Examining this matter further, we find that during the ten-year period 1906–1915 the total increase in population was 400,000, of which immigration accounted for 80,055, or 19 per cent. From 1916 to 1925, immigrants numbered about 17,000, or only 3 per cent of the total increase of 550,000. Again, from 1926 to 1935, the 4700 immigrants accounted for only 4 per cent of the total population increase of 1,000,000. In the eight years from 1936 to 1943 the population increase through immigration was 47,000, only 4 per cent of the total increase during that period, as shown in *Table 42*. Obviously, in the first ten-year period mentioned, the population increase through immigration was a much more significant part of the total increase than it was in later years when it accounted for very little of the total population increase.

Table 42. Total Migration in Taiwan During Japanese Rule (1906–1943)*

Year	Total			Chinese			Japanese			Korean		
	Immigration (A)	Emmigration (B)	Increase or Decrease (A − B)	Immigration (A)	Emmigration (B)	Increase or Decrease (A − B)	Immigration (A)	Emmigration (B)	Increase or decrease (A − B)	Immigration (A)	Emmigration (B)	Increase or decrease (A − B)
1906–1915	243,102	163,047	+80,055	48,659	37,194	+11,465	194,416	125,831	+68,585	27	22	+5
1916–1925	256,772	239,440	+17,332	57,942	44,232	+13,710	198,177	194,752	+3,425	653	456	+197
1926–1935	280,846	234,076	+46,770	76,776	65,047	+11,729	201,297	167,444	+33,853	2,773	1,585	+1,188
1936–1943	231,887	184,969	+46,918	23,771	33,185	−9,414	204,148	148,749	+55,399	3,968	3,035	+933
Total 1906–1943	1,012,607	821,532	+191,075	207,148	179,658	+27,490	798,038	636,776	+161,262	7,421	5,098	+2,323

* Based on *Fifty-one Years of Statistical Abstracts of Taiwan* (Governor General's Office, Taipei, 1946).

Since the growth of population in Taiwan was not due to immigration, it must have been due to natural increase. What accounts for Taiwan's natural increase? Between 1906 and 1943, the annual number of deaths in Taiwan did not show any remarkable change, but remained around 100,000. But the number of births doubled—it rose from 120,000 a year in 1906 to 240,000 in 1943. This accounts for the growth in Taiwan's population during that period.

One of the main causes of the low death rate is the availability of health and medical facilities in Taiwan which are better than those of most Far Eastern countries. There are a large number of trained doctors on the island, and effective new drugs have been introduced.

Between 1906 and 1943, the annual number of deaths remained the same, which, in view of the increasing population, meant that the death rate sharply declined. It stood at 34 per thousand in 1906 and had dropped to 18 by 1943, and to less than 8 by 1960. The result is clearly shown in *Figures 45* and *46*. The space between the lines for number of births and number of deaths in *Figure 45* represents the amount of natural increase, and the space between the lines for birth rate and death rate in *Figure 46* represents the rate of natural increase. Thus, the decline of the death rate was the key factor in Taiwan's population growth.

The trend of Taiwan's birth and death rates can be shown in four periods which are related to social change[2]. Each period has its characteristic type of average birth rate, average death rate, and average rate of natural increase. These four periods are indicated in *Table 43*.

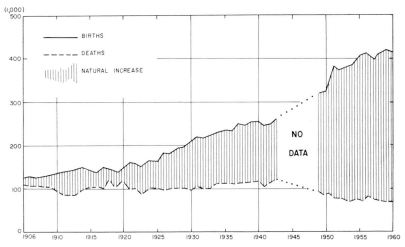

Figure 45.—The number of births and deaths per 1000 population between 1906 and 1960

Table 43. *Average Annual Birth Rate, Death Rate, and Rate of Natural Increase, Taiwan, Four Specified Periods**

(*per 1,000 persons*)	*1906–09*	*1910–25*	*1926–40*	*1941–43*
Average birth rate	40	42	45	41
Average death rate	33	28	22	18
Average rate of natural increase	7	14	23	23

* Modified from CHENG SHAO-HSING, "Population growth and social change in Taiwan," *Bull. Arch. Anthrop., Taiwan Univ.* **5**, 80, (1955).

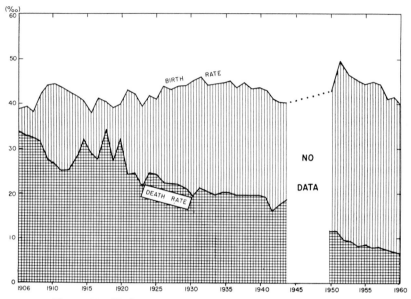

Figure 46.—Birth rate and death rate between 1906 and 1960

FIRST PERIOD.—In the pre-industrial society that existed before 1909 in Taiwan, widespread epidemics and occurrences of malaria, as well as frequent revolts of the Taiwanese against the Japanese, characterized the unstable period between 1906 and 1909. The birth rate was high, and the death rate also high. Thus, the rate of natural increase was low. This is the pattern of population change that characterizes many underdeveloped areas.

SECOND PERIOD.—In the first half of this sixteen-year period (1910–1925), fluctuation of both the birth and death rates was remarkable and frequent. But by the end of the period epidemic disease had been wiped out and a program for the prevention of malaria had been begun. The uprisings of the Taiwanese were suppressed by the Japanese about 1915, and the revolts of the aborigines had greatly diminished by 1920 so that comparative social stability was obtained. The latter half of the period became a preparation for the following period of expansion. Transportation was improved, agriculture intensified, industry initiated, and primary education extended. This era saw vigorous cultural growth and extensive social improvements. The Taiwanese had gradually changed their attitude toward the Japanese from open military revolt to a movement for political reform. In the meantime, the Japanese colonial policy had also improved somewhat. During this stage the birth rate showed a slight increase, and the death rate had dropped below the rate for the first period. Natural

216

increase during that time was twice that of the previous period. Many countries that are beginning to become industrialized and modernized have this kind of pattern of population change.

THIRD PERIOD.—During the fifteen-year period from 1926 to 1940, the industrialization of the island and its agricultural production reached their peak. The hydroelectric plant at Sun-Moon Lake was completed in 1934, enhancing industrial development. Prevention of malaria was successful to a great extent; infant mortality began to decline, and the birth rate rose to a new peak. The death rate declined again, and fluctuations in the birth and death rates became smaller and less frequent. The rate of natural increase rose to a new height. The age composition of the population changed; the proportion of infants and older children increased markedly.

FOURTH PERIOD.—During the three-year period from 1941 to 1943, the value of industrial products began to exceed that of agricultural products, and the tempo of urbanization quickened. The death rate continued its decline; the birth rate, however, also began to decline; thus the rate of natural increase decreased slightly. At the end of the Japanese rule, when industrialization and urbanization had been most highly developed, the pattern of population change was characterized by a decline in the birth rate, the most important factor, and a slight reduction in the death rate. This led to an eventual stabilization of the population figures. This type of stationary figure is exemplified in many industrialized European countries, especially France.

In Taiwan, though the rate of natural increase declined between 1906 and 1943, the average life expectancy increased; it was 13 years longer for males in 1943 than it had been in 1906, and 16.7 years longer for females.

With the increase in the proportion of old people, the death rate would naturally rise. As a result, there would be no growth in population and it would even decrease. Fortunately, after 1945, when the island was restored to China, a large number of Chinese immigrants poured into the island, totally changing the pattern of Taiwan's population growth.

COMPOSITION OF THE POPULATION

The most characteristic feature of the age composition of Taiwan's population is its youth. More than two-fifths of the population consists of children and adolescents; a somewhat similar proportion of young adults; more than one-tenth of somewhat older adults; and about one-third of adults in the oldest age group. A look at data compiled at intervals from 1905 to 1960 reveals that the number of persons of less than 15 years of age increased from 34 per cent of the population in 1905 to 45 per cent in 1960; the number between 15 and 44 years in age decreased from 50 per cent to 42 per cent; the number between 45 and 64 years in age decreased from 13 per cent to 11 per cent; and the number of persons of more than sixty-five years of age remained at 3 per cent. In other words, throughout more than half a century nearly 85 per cent of the total population was less than forty-five years old (*Figure 47*).

The explanation of this youthful age structure of Taiwan's population lies in the island's pattern of natural increase. In its early years, Taiwan

217

had a high birth rate and a high death rate; thus children made up a large proportion of the total population. Not many people survived long after childhood, and so older people could never constitute a large part of the total. With social betterment and improvement in health conditions, people of all ages had a chance to live longer. But despite this, the emphasis remained on youth. Not only did old people live longer, but potential parents did too, and thus were able to bear additional children. Births became more numerous, and as the children reached maturity the process repeated itself. With more children being born each year, young people constituted a still greater part of the total population.[3]

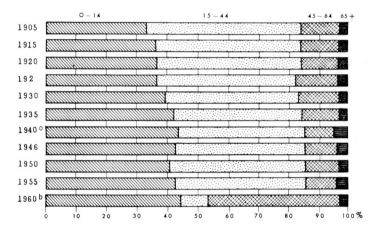

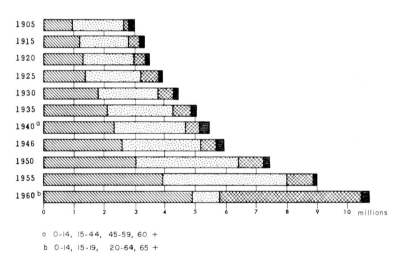

a 0-14, 15-44, 45-59, 60 +

b 0-14, 15-19, 20-64, 65 +

Figure 47.—A comparison of the population by age group between 1905 and 1960; (*at top*) in percentages, (*at bottom*) in millions

218

A comparison of the age structure of Taiwan's population in recent years with that of the populations of the United States, Japan, and France suggests close correlation between social conditions and age composition of the population.

Table 44 shows that in 1962 in Taiwan, the children in the age group between birth and fourteen years constituted 45 per cent of the total population. In Japan, which not long before had nearly the same age structure as Taiwan, the number in the age group between birth and fourteen years had declined to only 34 per cent and in France it had dropped to only 24 per cent, in comparison with a 31 per cent drop in the United States.

Table 44. A Comparison of Age Composition between Taiwan, Japan, the U. S. A., and France (in percentage)*

Age composition (years)	Taiwan	Japan	U.S.A.	France
0–14	44.5	33.6	30.5	24.4
15–44	41.7	45.6	40.7	39.1
45–64	11.3	15.6	20.2	24.5
Over 65	2.5	5.2	8.6	12.0

* Taiwan's data from Taiwan Provincial Government. Data of other countries computed from *United Nations Demographic Yearbook*, Ninth Issue, New York (1957), pp. 138, 142, 145.

In the percentage of its population of ages between fifteen and forty-five years, Japan ranked above Taiwan; the figures were 46 per cent and 42 per cent respectively. The United States was third with 40 per cent, and France fourth with 39 per cent.

On the other hand, in Taiwan, the age group between 45 to 64 years constituted only 11 per cent of the total population in 1962; in Japan it made up 16 per cent; in the United States, 20 per cent; and in France, 25 per cent.

It is more surprising to find that persons of more than 65 years of age totaled only 3 per cent of Taiwan's population; in Japan they accounted for 5 per cent; in the United States, 9 per cent, or three times the figure of Taiwan; and in France, 12 per cent, four times that of Taiwan.

These comparisons show that Taiwan has a young population, and that the island's aged have not been living longer as have those in the three other countries, France, Japan, and the United States.

In countries in which industrialization and urbanization have developed, the fertility rate declines and the proportion of children in the population drops sharply. At the same time, as sanitation and drugs are improved, and social security for the aged instituted, the proportion of aged people increases. In 1940, the ratio of the number of persons more than 60 years old to those under 20 (which is called the old age ratio) was as follows: among Taiwanese, 9 to 100; among Japanese, 17 to 100; among Americans, 30 to 100: and among the French in 1936 it was 45 to 100 and in 1950, 57 to 100. This is more than six times the aged among the Taiwanese. France's population is indeed old, while Taiwan's is rather young.

The emphasis on youth in Taiwan's population structure proves costly from the economic point of view, since most people of less than 20 years in age are too young to work or lack training and the burden of their support must be carried by others. In 1940 every 100 persons in Taiwan between the ages of 15 and 60 years had to support 88 persons, few of whom had any full-time employment. In 1952, this ratio was reduced to 78 per 100. The corresponding ratio for Japan in 1950 was 68 to 100; for the United States, 55 to 100; for Sweden, 36 to 100; and for France, 50 to 100.[3]

As for sex ratio, every year more boys than girls are born, 104 to 110 males for each 100 females. However, the death rate for boys is usually higher in infancy, and also during childhood because boys are usually more active and adventurous than girls. This progressively diminishes the difference in the numbers of the sexes, and helps the numbers to reach a state of equality in the adult period. After the age of 45 years, females, because of a longer life expectancy, begin to outnumber the males. This is the general pattern of the sex ratio of any society, but it can be influenced by many social factors.

In Taiwan there have always been more males than females. The explanation is to be found in the historical development of the island. Taiwan was an adventurer's frontier for the Chinese and a colony for the Japanese. Both Chinese and Japanese came to the island without bringing any members of their families. The resulting differences in the number of males and females became more marked with changing political circumstances. In 1661, when the Chinese Cheng Ch'eng-Kung ruled Taiwan, establishing a base for defense against the Manchu government of China, that government prohibited the inhabitants of the mainland from making contact with the Taiwanese and even encouraged the coastal mainlanders to move inland. In 1684, the year after Cheng's descendants surrendered to the Manchu emperor, the prohibition was lifted, but persons who left China for Taiwan were not permitted to take their families. Under those circumstances few children, aged persons, or women lived on the island; the population was chiefly composed of males—youths and adults, who were refugees and adventurers from China's mainland. The composition of the population was abnormal, and the family ties binding husbands, wives, parents, and children—the old and the young—were missing. It was not until 1760 that the settlers on Taiwan were allowed to bring their families from the mainland. This obviously eased the shortage of women, and the island's population composition gradually became more normal.

At the beginning of the 20th century, the sex ratio and the age distribution of the Chinese-born in Taiwan were both peculiar. In 1905, the first census counted 9,086 mainlander Chinese, of whom 8,644 were males and only 442 were females. The number of males in this section of the population was thus 19 times the number of females. The number of males between the ages of 20 and 39 years was 6,019, or 66 per cent of the total number of Chinese. With the passage of time the number of males and females was gradually equalized. In 1915 males were five times as numerous as females; in 1935, the ratio was about 2 to 1; in 1949 it was 151.1 males to 100 females.

Also among the Japanese in Taiwan there were more males than females, but the imbalance was less extreme. For example, in 1905 the sex ratio among Japanese on the island was 152 males to 100 females. But the ratio decreased with time; in 1920 it was 127; in 1935, 111; and in 1943, 109.

Of the sixteen counties in Taiwan, Penghu has the lowest ratio of males to females, 95.89 males for each 100 females, and Tainan the second lowest, 99.85. Penghu and Tainan were the first locations to be settled by the Chinese. Historically, men continue to seek new frontiers; and those two counties have been the first in Taiwan to be abandoned by the men.

The highest ratio of males to females occurs on the east coast in the counties of Taitung and Hualien, 109.15 and 109.07 respectively. Those two counties, which are the pioneering regions of modern times, obviously have attracted more males than females.

Concerning occupational structure in Taiwan's population, the agricultural and fishing group has always been the largest, but has been decreasing in percentage through the years. In 1905 agricultural workers constituted 74 per cent of all the workers on the island, but they decreased to 73.5 per cent in 1915. It was 71 per cent in 1920; 69 per cent in 1939; 64 per cent in 1940; 63 per cent in 1950; and 57 per cent in 1960 (*Figure 48*).

The manufacturing and mining workers constitute another group that has held an important position in Taiwan's occupational structure. The percentage of all workers who were employed in manufacturing and mining rose from 6 per cent in 1905 to 11 per cent in 1958. In contrast to the agriculture and fishing group, the percentage in manufacturing and mining

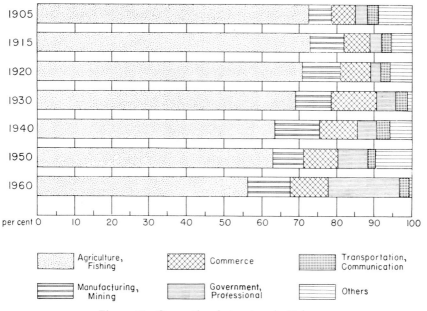

Figure 48.—Occupational structure in Taiwan

221

increased with the years, but not so steadily as the percentage of agriculturalist decreased. For example, in 1940, the culminating year of Taiwan's industrial development, the manufacturing and mining group increased to 12 per cent of the total working population, but it dropped in 1950 to 8 per cent.

The commerce group, the third most important group in Taiwan's working population, accounted for 7 per cent in 1905 and 9 per cent in 1960.

The transportation and communication group has always represented less than 3 per cent of the working population.

The government and professional group has shown much growth through the years. It stood at 2 per cent in 1905, 1915, and 1920, and then increased to 5 per cent in 1930 and 1940, to 7 per cent in 1950, and to 18 per cent in 1960.

In western industrial nations, employment generally comes later in life and the period of youth is more likely to be devoted to acquiring general and specialized knowledge and skill in preparation for future careers. In Taiwan these early years are spent at work by many who must make an early start. Hence, although a young labor force is a potential advantage in Taiwan, a large part of this advantage is nullified by the high cost of technical training and by the lack of opportunity for the Taiwanese to put such training to later use.

BIRTH RATE

Aside from migration, change in the number of persons living in any region is, as has been said, determined by two factors, birth rate and death rate. According to the variation of these factors a rise or fall in the population can be any of four types.

(1) In a primitive society, both birth and death rates are very high, and the rate of natural increase is low. In times of epidemics and other calamities, the population even decreases.

(2) At the start of industrialization, the birth rate remains high while the death rate is lowered. Thus the population will grow until the highest rate of natural increase is attained.

(3) When industrialization and urbanization develop more fully, the birth rate begins to decline, while the death rate becomes stationary. The natural increase begins to decline and eventually ceases altogether, and the population becomes stationary.

(4) When the society progresses even further, the birth rate will continue to drop to a point at which the population is not reproducing itself. In the meantime, with the change in age composition (the proportional increase of old people) the death rate becomes higher. Then there is no population growth; but rather a decrease.

To determine which type of change the population of the island has undergone, more detailed figures on birth and death rates are needed, such as those given in *Table 45*.

In more than 50 years the lowest birth rate was that of 1916—38.09 births per 1000 persons—and the highest, that of 1951—49.97. In most years the birth rates range from 40 to 45 per thousand population.

Compared with birth rates in other countries, Taiwan's has been rather high. For example, in 1950 Japan's birth rate was 28.8 and India's 26.4. In 1952 the United States' birth rate was 24.5; that of the Netherlands, 22.3; and that of France, 19.2. Except in South America, where the birth rate in certain countries equals or even exceeds Taiwan's (Chile's was 33.6 in 1952), most countries have a lower birth rate. Also the birth rates in many countries show a general tendency to decline. This is especially true of the countries in western Europe and North America and in Australia. Even though their birth rates did increase somewhat immediately after World War II, it is believed that this is a temporary phenomenon and that the rate will eventually resume its decline. In any case, Taiwan's birth rate is one of the highest in the world. Taiwan's birth rate not only fluctuates with the years, but also varies with different counties. Generally, it is higher in the southern and eastern parts than in the north or west.

Table 45. *Average Annual Birth Rate and Death Rate**

Period	Birth rate (per 1,000)	Death rate (per 1,000)
1906–10	40.27	31.89
1911–15	41.73	27.51
1916–20	39.91	30.26
1921–25	41.64	23.99
1926–30	44.23	21.65
1931–35	44.96	20.44
1936–40	43.75	19.73
1941–43	40.19	17.55
1947–50	40.73	14.27
1951–55	46.34	9.52
1956–60	41.48	7.71

* The data for the years from 1906 to 1943 are based on *51 Years of Statistical Abstracts of Taiwan* (Governor General's Office, Taipei, 1946). The data from 1947 to 1960 are from the Taiwan Provincial Government.

The number of births varies with the seasons. Generally speaking, there are more births in Taiwan in November, December, and January than in May, June, and July. More Taiwanese marry in January and February than in any other month. After March the number of marriages gradually decreases, and it reaches its low point in July and August. With September the number of marriages again increases.

There are practical reasons for holding marriages in the winter months. In January and February, the climate is cool and pleasant and there are no mosquitos; but the most important reason is that those two months mark the farmer's leisure period. Since January is the peak month for marriages, the number of births naturally begins to reach its maximum in October. *Figure 49* provides a comparison between the monthly distribution of births and the seasonal figures for marriages.

The increase in population is closely related to the birth rate, but the increase can be better understood through study of the fertility rate. The fertility rate is found by dividing the number of children under five years of age in the population by the number of women between the ages of 15 and 44 years, and multiplying the result by a thousand. Such data can show clearly the trend of its population increase. The fertility rate in Taiwan is very high in comparison to that in other countries. It is higher than that in most European countries by three to five times, and even higher than that of Negroes in the United States, whose rate in 1940 was 368 per thousand. The fertility rate in Taiwan in 1920 was 654, and it increased to 999 in 1935. This means that for every woman between 14 and 44 years of age, there was a baby born some time in each five year period between 1920 and 1935. In 1949 the figure decreased, but it increased again in 1958, when it was 927 per thousand.

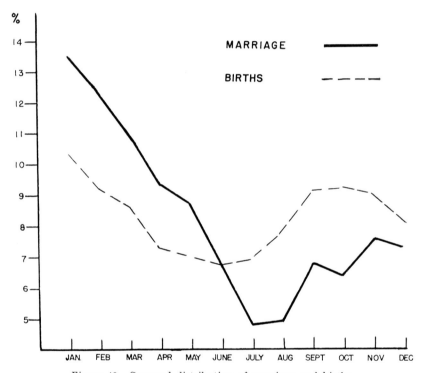

Figure 49.—Seasonal distribution of marriage and births

Why is Taiwan's fertility rate so high? There are three answers to this question.

(1) Chinese tradition places a high value on having many children. As an old Chinese saying has it, "Among offenses against filial piety, to be without children is the most serious." The culture of China has been strongly influenced by a morality that stresses the importance of progeny.

(2) Moved by this pressure to produce numerous children, people marry young. In Taiwan most men are married before they become 25 years old, and most women even younger. Family life is so strongly emphasized that the reason for living is to have children.

(3) Means of adjusting the size of families are not available. At present in Taiwan it is extremely difficult to effect any limitation of births.

224

The types of contraceptive practices common in other countries are unpopular and considered immoral on the island. Other disadvantages also handicap their use. Advice and care are required, and these are too expensive for the average couple; therefore, some couples produce more children than they desire.

Thus the large-family tradition, early marriages, and little or no use of contraceptives, keep the fertility rate of the island high.

It is a common phenomenon in European countries that after the birth rate rises to a certain level, it starts to decline. For example, in France in 1814, the birth rate reached the highest point in its history, 33.9 per thousand population, and it immediately began to decline. In the 1860's a similar sequence took place in Sweden, in Australia, in Switzerland, and in the Netherlands. In the 1870's it took place in Britain, and in the 1880's in Hungary and in Italy. Among Asiatic lands, Japan was the first whose birth rate began to decline; its decline occurred in the 1920's.[4] In Taiwan the birth rate rose after 1906 and attained its peak in 1926–1939. After that it started to decline.

Many explanations of the decline of birth rates are proposed, but one point is almost unanimously accepted, that such a decline begins with the development of industrialization and urbanization. This explanation may be correct for European countries and also for Japan. Can it explain the decline of Taiwan's birth rate after 1939?

In 1920, the total population of Taiwan's cities with 100,000 or more persons amounted to 5 per cent of the total population of the island. It increased to 12.3 per cent in 1940. Urbanization was still generally low, but its rapid development between 1920 and 1940 was noteworthy. The composition of the population changed greatly after Taiwan's restoration to China in 1945, but no evidence can be found to show with certainty the cause of the declining birth rate in Taiwan. Two explanations are possible for the cause of the declining birth rate in Taiwan.

One is the influence of two wars, the Sino-Japanese War in 1937 and World War II between 1941 and 1945. During the war years, with the scarcity of daily necessities and the conscription of youth, the marriage rate declined, as did the birth rate.

The second possible explanation of the decline has to do with the change in age composition among the Taiwanese. Of the married women in Taiwan, those in the age group between 20 and 24 years have the highest fertility rate, and the change is much influenced by any change in the number of persons in this age group. Between 1935 and 1940 the proportion of married women from 15 to 19 years of age increased by 25 per cent, and the proportion of those between 25 and 29 years old increased by 15 per cent, but the age group from 20 to 24 years old increased by only 2 per cent.

The proportional decline found in this highly fertile age group would naturally be reflected in the decline in Taiwan's birth rate after 1940. The cause of that group's proportional decline lies in the fact that the women aged 20–24 years were born between 1915 and 1919. In that period malaria and influenza were very prevalent, and they caused a decrease in the number of births and an increase in infant mortality. These losses later caused the decline of the birth rate after 1940.[5]

DEATH RATE

The death rate in Taiwan has been declining rapidly for the past half century. From 1906 to 1910, the average annual death rate (rounded off) was 32 per thousand population; from 1916 to 1920, it was 31; from 1926 to 1930, 22; from 1936 to 1940, 20; and from 1951 to 1955, 10 (*Table 45*). This remarkable decline in the death rate reflects the improvement of medical care, strengthening of public-health measures, and the general improvement of social conditions.

The death rate in Taiwan is lower than that in other Asiatic lands, and about the same as the rates in European countries. The rate of 10 deaths per 1000 persons for the years 1950–1955 is even lower than that in the United States during the same period.

As for the seasonal distribution of death in Taiwan, more persons die in summer than in any other season, and the least die in spring. For example, in 1943, 28 per cent of the total deaths took place in June, July, and August; deaths in spring amounted to only 25 per cent of that year's deaths.

Different areas have different predominating causes of death which are closely related to the area's social and economic conditions. From the point of view of curability by present-day medicine, diseases that lead to death can be divided into two groups:

    Group A—Diseases curable by present day medicine:
        Epidemic diseases, especially malaria. Pneumonia, diarrhea and
        enteritis, tetanus, tuberculosis.
    Group B—Diseases not curable or not sufficiently curable by present-
        day medicine:
        Heart diseases, cancer, cerebral hemorrhage, and nephritis.

It is the generally accepted view that the diseases in *Group B* are the leading causes of death in industrialized countries with advanced technology and a comfortable material life and that those in *Group A* are the leading causes of death in underdeveloped societies.

Sociologist S. H. Chen of National Taiwan University has made a study comparing the leading causes of death in Taiwan and in the United States. From *Table 46*, which is based on Chen's study, it is evident that the leading causes of death in these two places are quite different. In Taiwan the four leading causes of death, pneumonia, diarrhea and enteritis, infectious and parasitic diseases, and bronchitis, are all curable by present-day medicine. They are acute diseases, and they occur mostly among infants and children. In the United States the four leading causes of death are diseases of the heart, cancer, cerebral hemorrhage, and nephritis, all of them diseases not sufficiently curable by present-day medicine. They are chronic and constitutional diseases and occur mostly among the aged. This indicates that the American lives longer than the Taiwanese, so they die of degenerative diseases.

From *Table 46* it can be seen that the proportion of deaths from four leading diseases of *Group B* to the total deaths in 1940 was 41 per cent among the Taiwanese, but was only 6 per cent among Americans. In other words, the death rate from diseases that are curable by present-day medicine was nearly seven times as high in Taiwan as in the United States.

On the other hand, the death rate from *Group B* diseases—including those diseases that are not sufficiently curable by modern medicine—was five times as high in the United States as in Taiwan. This shows there is an intimate correlation between leading causes of death and the degree of social improvement.

Thus the question arises, "Will Taiwan's leading causes of death switch from *Group A* to *Group B* as the island's economic development advances?"

Table 46. Leading Causes of Death Among Taiwanese and Americans, 1940*
(number of deaths per 10,000 population)

	Taiwanese	Americans
Crude death rate (*C*)	201.43	107.64
Disease group (*A*)	82.49	6.67
Pneumonia	46.41	5.48
Diarrhea, enteritis, etc.	15.91	0.76
Infections and parasitic diseases	10.83	0.13
Bronchitis	9.34	0.30
Ratio *A/C*	41%	6%
Disease group (*B*)	22.09	58.52
Diseases of the heart	4.67	29.25
Cancer	3.27	12.03
Cerebral hemorrhage	5.52	9.09
Nephritis	8.63	8.15
Ratio *B/C*	11%	54%

* Chen Shao-Hsing, "Population change in Taiwan," *Bull. Arch. Anthrop. Taiwan Univ.* 6, 37 (1955).

If the changes in the mortality from the various causes of death in Taiwan and in the United States are examined, the answer must be "yes," for the trend in both places is in the same direction. The difference between them in this respect is the enormously faster shift from *Group A* to *Group B* in the United States. With the advancement of medical techniques and the rise in the level of material life in the United States, epidemics have practically been eliminated and pandemic diseases greatly reduced. From 1900 to 1948 changes in the mortality from different causes of death in the United States show that 80 per cent fewer deaths were caused by pneumonia in 1948 than in 1940; 96 per cent fewer by diarrhea and enteritis; and 85 per cent fewer by tuberculosis.

On the contrary, again in the United States, certain degenerative diseases caused a smaller proportion of deaths in 1948 than in 1940; other causes of death showed a sharp rise. Deaths from nephritis decreased by 40 per cent between 1900 and 1948; and deaths from cancer by 16 per cent; but deaths from cerebral hemorrhage origin increased by 111 per cent; and deaths from heart diseases increased by 134 per cent.

Taiwan first suffered principally from the epidemic diseases, especially malaria, then from the pandemic diseases such as pneumonia, diarrhea and enteritis, and tuberculosis. During the later years of Japanese rule, the degenerative diseases, nephritis, heart disease, cancer, and cerebral hemorrhage, became prominent. Up to 1906 malaria was the leading cause of death; but in 1912–1914, it was exceeded by diarrhea and enteritis. In the period from 1917 to 1942, pneumonia was the chief cause of death. In this period malaria and diarrhea and enteritis alternately occupied second and third places. In 1922 deaths from malaria suddenly dropped, as a result of preventive measures. Only once again, in 1942, during World War II, owing to a shortage of drugs, did malaria regain its position as the leading cause of death.

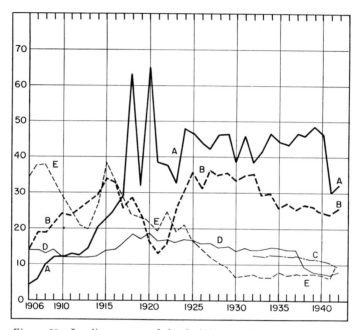

Figure 50.—Leading causes of death (1906–1942) per 10,000 persons

A. Pneumonia
B. Diarrhea, enteritis, etc.
C. Other infectious and parasitic diseases
D. Tuberculosis of the respiratory system
E. Malaria

From 1942 on, nephritis, a degenerative disease, ranked high as a cause of death in Taiwan. This is clearly an example that the degenerative diseases are gradually gaining importance among the leading causes of death in Taiwan. It can be seen that there has been a gradual increase in deaths from diseases of the degenerative kind and a gradual decrease in deaths from epidemic and pandemic diseases.

REFERENCES

[1] Chen Shao-hsing, "Population growth and social change in Taiwan," *Bull. Arch. Anthrop., Taiwan Univ.* **5,** 80 (1955).
[2] —, *Ibid.,* 84.
[3] George W. Barclay, *A Report on Taiwan's Population* (Princeton University Press, Princeton, N. J., 1954), pp. 48–50.
[4] Chen Shao-hsing, "Population change in Taiwan," *Bull. Arch Anthrop., Taiwan Univ.* **6,** 37 (1955).
[5] Chen Chen-hsiang, "The fertility and mortality of Taiwan's population," *Quart., Bank of Taiwan* **VII,** No. 4, 49–50 (1955). [In Chinese].

EIGHTEEN

Settlement and Transportation

CITIES AND TOWNS

THE URBAN UNITS in Taiwan can be classified in two groups: cities, each of which has a population of at least 50,000 persons; and towns, each of which has a population of at least 2500 persons. As a rule, a town functions as a market center for the surrounding rural area, and it has a long main street. By these criteria, Taiwan has twelve cities and ninety towns. These cities and towns have a total population of about 2.2 million people—20 per cent of the population of Taiwan. All the cities except Taitung were established by the Chinese. They are surrounded by protective walls with four gates such as those common in China. The walls are built of stone, brick, or mud blocks. The outline of a city is always a quadrangle or circle. In early days, as soon as the walls had been constructed, people were attracted by the safety of living within them, and the compact urban settlements developed rapidly.

Two characteristics are noticeable in the distribution of cities and towns in Taiwan. First, 90 per cent of the cities and towns are located on the plains and, since the broadest plain is in the western part of the island, most of the cities and towns are located there. In the eastern mountain regions, the cities and towns are found only in the two flat areas, namely, the Ilan plain and the Taitung rift valley. The second characteristic is that the cities and towns are located in an elongated pattern extending the length of the island, from north to south. They are divided into three rows: coastal ports, inland cities, and foothill towns (*Figure 51*).

Among the coastal ports, Keelung on the northern coast and Kaohsiung on the southern are the two leading ports; other ports include Tamshui,

Chiukong, Houlung, Wuche, Tungshih, and Anping on the western coast, and Taitung, Lukong, Hualien, and Suao on the eastern coast.

The inland cities, located between the coast and the mountains, are cities that were originally trading centers for agricultural products; they have since become economic, political, and cultural centers. They include Taipei, Hsinchu, Miaoli, Taichung, Changhua, Yuanlin, Hsinying, Tainan, and Fengshan.

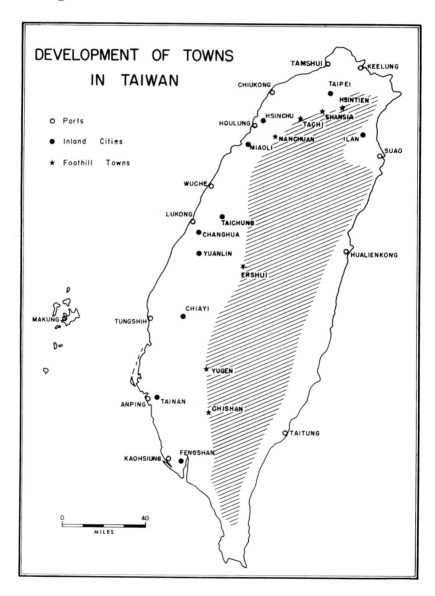

Figure 51

On the eastern edge of the western plain a number of towns have developed in the foothills of the Central Mountains. They are usually located at the mouths of rivers flowing from the mountains, such as Hsintien on Hsintien Creek, Shansia on the Tamshui River, Ershui on Choshui Creek, Yugen on Tsengwen Creek, and Chishan on the lower Tamshui River.

The coastal ports, the central inland cities, and the foothill towns lie in a north–south line. At the same time, from the coast to the inland plain and to the foothills, because of the link of transportation by rivers, the towns form trading groups in lines crossing the north–south line. For example, Tamshui, Taipei, and Hsintien are in one combination. Other combinations include Houlung, Hsinchu, and Nanchuang; Lukong, Yuanlin, and Ershui; Tungshih, Chiayi, and Yugen; and Anping, Tainan, and Chishan.

The causes of this belt distribution of towns are related to the history of the island. Most of the cities and towns were developed during the period of early Chinese immigration. The Chinese settled in the ports on the western coast, where the rivers empty into the sea. These rivers generally flow in parallel courses from the Central Mountain region to the west coast. Gradually the Chinese immigrants moved inland along the rivers, pushing the aborigines up into the mountains. Although conflicts arose between the Chinese and the aborigines, the two groups often carried on trade with each other, and in order to effect a convenient exchange of goods at a spot distant from the ports, the Chinese built inland cities. When the plain was settled, the aborigines were pushed farther up the mountains. The area between the mountains and the plains became an important trading center for the Chinese and the aborigines; and here developed the foothill towns to carry on trade.

The ports declined rapidly in importance, and the foothill towns expanded very slowly; only the cities of the western plains grew and prospered.

The decline of the ports was due to two factors: After the great wave of immigration was past, the difficulty of crossing Taiwan Strait to and from the Chinese mainland led to a drop in business for the ports. Another factor in the decline was the silting of the mouths of the rivers, which eventually made the ports useless. Only the cities with good natural harbors, such as Keelung and Kaohsiung, continued to be important ports; they remain so today.

The foothill towns did not grow and prosper because the nature of the landform restricted their expansion, because their trading goods were rather limited, and because they suffered sporadic attacks by the aborigines.

The cities on the western plain have the greatest natural advantages and developed to the greatest degree; today they are the most important urban areas on the island. Their growth was stimulated greatly when the Japanese came to Taiwan and connected them by a railroad.

Taiwan was first settled and developed in the southern part of the island, with the city of Tainan as the center of colonization. Taipei, the main city in the north, developed at a much later date. The establishment of cities and towns did not extend from south to north as might be expected, but rather from west to east. The westward flow of the rivers made traveling in a northerly direction difficult; a more convenient method was to follow the course of a river to the source, establishing towns along the way. Also, the settlements of the aborigines, strung out over the plains, discouraged northward expansion. The cities and towns, therefore, developed eastward from the ports along the coast to the plain, and finally to the foothills.

THE MAJOR CITIES

Taipei and its old port, Tamshui

Taipei, the capital of Taiwan, is the political, economic, and cultural center of the island. With a population of approximately one million persons, it is one of the main cities in southeast Asia. Located in the middle of the Taipei basin, it is surrounded by hilly land with an elevation of from 500 to 2000 feet. Most parts of the city have an elevation of less than 30 feet, but the highest point rises to 2000 feet. The floor of the basin slopes gently from southeast to northwest. The Tamshui, Keelung, and Hsintien Rivers break the surrounding hilly land and provide outlets to the sea.

At the beginning of the 18th century, when the Chinese migrated to Taipei, the land was all swamp and forest and was inhabited by aborigines. The Chinese started to cultivate the land and trade with the aborigines. One of the important trading items received from the aborigines was sweet potatoes. This early trading area was the original site of the city. About 1720 a small market called *Meng-Chia* was formed along this old street. The city developed from that and two other sections, *Tai-tao-chen* and the inner city. These three commercial centers of Taipei were not connected (*Figure 52*), but were separated by paddy fields, swamps, and graveyards.

MENG-CHIA (THE OLDEST MARKET).—The name *Meng-Chia* is the Chinese phonetic version of the aborigines' word *Moungar* which means "canoe." In the early days of the settlement, the aborigines who lived along the upper courses of the Tamshui River and Hsintien Creek often came to town in canoes with their goods to trade with the Chinese.[1] At that time, Meng-Chia was simply an area for trading with the aborigines.

Later, in 1735, more Chinese migrated to the Taipei basin and cultivated the land in the eastern part of the basin. Being located at a point where the Tamshui River joined Hsintien Creek, Meng-Chia gradually developed into the trading center of this new agricultural area. With the increase of Chinese migration and colonization, trade at Meng-Chia expanded rapidly. When the port of Tamshui, at the mouth of the Tamshui River, was opened by the government in 1788 for trade with the Chinese mainland, junks sailed up the Tamshui River. This gave Meng-Chia an important stimulus, and it rose rapidly in importance. This is evidenced by the shifting of the Chinese naval base to Meng-Chia in 1808 and also by its becoming the seat of Taipei county in 1809. As the Chinese settlers poured into this river-bank market, they forced the native aborigines back to the mountainous area, and by about 1820 there were few aborigines left in the Taipei basin.

The Tamshui River was then relatively deep, and ships found no difficulty in coming and going. Big junks from the mainland could reach Meng-Chia. It was a political center, a naval base, and the most important trading center in the northern part of Taiwan. The period 1820–1850 was the golden day of Meng-Chia. With the increase in inhabitants, the market extended eastward; business was booming. At that time many Chinese temples were built in Meng-Chia and the trading center was reported to include 5000 households. Its importance was next only to that of Tainan in the south and Lukong in the central part of the island.

The golden day of Meng-Chia soon passed. The rapid silting of the Tamshui River made it difficult for large ships to reach the town, and the failure to build a bridge across the Tamshui River to extend the market to Hsinchuang also contributed to the decline of the market town of Meng-Chia. The factor that caused its decline most directly was a conflict between two groups of Chinese settlers, which lasted from 1851 to 1861.

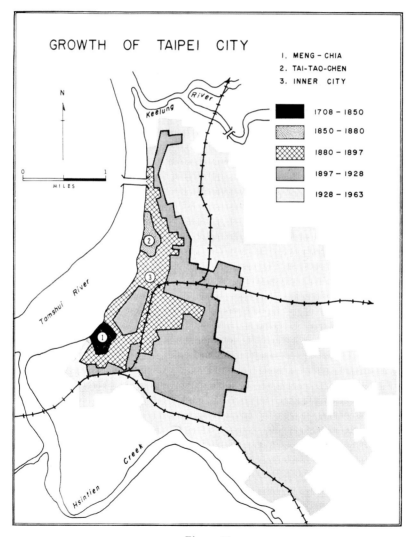

Figure 52

The result of this conflict was that the defeated people moved a short distance north and built a settlement known as Tai-tao-chen. The trading center shifted from Meng-Chai to Tai-tao-chen, which later was to become the commercial core of Taipei.

TAI-TAO-CHEN.—The word *chen* means "open space." It is usually a high flat area located in the midst of paddy fields; it is used for drying rice. *Tai-tao* means "big rice."

In 1853 the defeated group of people who had successfully settled in this area and set up commercial buildings entered into competition with Meng-Chia.

During the years 1860–1870, tea plantations were established at Tai-tao-chen. In 1860, when the port of Tamshui was opened, the Dutch, the Germans, and the Americans set up their consulates there. Thus Tai-tao-chen rose to challenge the dominance of Meng-Chia and became the trading center. Later, in 1887, the governor-general of Taiwan constructed many buildings in the city. Tai-tao-chen had become not only a tea-trading center, with three or four thousand girls working every day in more than sixty tea-processing factories, but also the center for trade in camphor, Taiwan's other chief export; and the chief residence center for foreigners as well.

During the Japanese occupation, the tea-processing industry, with tea representing a large proportion of the island's total exports, expanded still more; by 1915 the factories numbered 100. Even today Tai-tao-chen is the main tea-shipping center and one of the principal commercial cores of Taipei. When navigation became difficult with the silting of the Tamshui River, Taipei then expanded eastward from the river; thus, most commercial activities removed themselves from Tai-tao-chen to the eastern side of the inner city.

THE INNER CITY.—The inner city is the area within Taipei's old city wall, which lies east of Meng-Chia and south of Tai-tao-chen. Even though the inner city developed twenty-five years later than Tai-tao-chen and seventy years later than Meng-Chia, or perhaps because of that fact, today the most important and impressive buildings and the broadest streets are concentrated in the inner city.

LATER HISTORY OF TAIPEI.—In 1875 the Chinese government established Taiwan as a prefecture and chose today's inner city as the seat of the administrator's office. Taipei became one of the important political centers, comparable to Tainan in southern Taiwan.

In 1885 Taiwan became a Chinese province and a governor-general was appointed. He constructed his official residence and other government offices in the inner city of Taipei and established a revenue bureau, a general telegraphy center, a power plant, and machinery factories. At that time, the first railway in Taiwan was laid, connecting Keelung in the north and Hsinchu in the south, and passing through a number of cities, including Taipei. In 1891 Taipei was officially designated as the capital of Taiwan and became the political center of the whole island, with Keelung as the city's outlet port.

In 1895, when the island was ceded to Japan, the Japanese kept Taipei as the capital. At that time the population of the three parts of the city totaled 47,000 persons. Among the three, Tai-tao-chen had the largest proportion of the inhabitants, 50 per cent; Meng-Chia was next with 42 per cent; and the inner city had only 8 per cent. Within ten years the Japanese made much progress in construction in the city; traffic facilities were improved, a city sewage system and flood control dikes along the Tamshui River were built, and the city walls were torn down and built into a three-lane boulevard. Only the wall's gates were left, as historical monuments. The typhoons of August, 1911, which destroyed many of the natives' houses in Taipei, offered the Japanese a good opportunity to rebuild the city thoroughly. Especially in the inner city, where most governmental offices and financial buildings were concentrated, the Japanese used steel and concrete in the western style, in contrast to the brick and clay of the Chinese style, which was used in Meng-Chia and Tai-tao-chen.

At present Taipei is the capital of Taiwan, the seat of the Chinese Nationalist government and one of the important cities in southeast Asia. The airport of Taipei has become an international terminus, where the passengers number 15,000 per year.

The population of Taipei is concentrated in two areas, each having a population density of more than 260,000 persons per square mile. One, the northeast part of the city, roughly coincides with the old Tai-tao-chen area. The other, the southeast part, is approximately the old Meng-Chia, which is now called Wanhua.

About 74 per cent of the working inhabitants of Taipei are engaged in industry, commerce, government service, or professional occupations. This is a usual phenomenon in cities. However, in 1930 about 30 per cent of the inhabitants were in industry, and another 30 per cent were in commerce; only 17 per cent were in government service or a professional occupation.

TAMSHUI.—Tamshui, located at the mouth of the Tamshui River, was the oldest seaport outlet for northern Taiwan. As such it was the door to Taipei and carried on heavy trade with the mainland cities, Foochow, Amoy, and Shanghai, opposite it on Taiwan Strait. Later the appearance of a sandbar in the river bed and the silting of the harbor, which made anchoring difficult, brought on the decline of the port. The decline was hastened by the completion of the Keelung harbor and also of the island's main railroad; and Keelung replaced Tamshui as the island's chief harbor.

Tamshui has facilities for ocean bathing and is a tourist center. The streets present a terraced form, and schools and residential areas are located on the upper terraces. Along the river, the street is lined with shops.

Keelung and Kaohsiung—twin doors to the island

Keelung, located in the northeast, and Kaohsiung, in the southwest, are the two main entrances to the island. They are the terminals of the north–south railroad, and they afford elaborate facilities for importing and exporting. Both Keelung and Kaohsiung were opened as ports in 1860 under the Tientsin Treaty between China and Britain, which also opened Tamshui and Anping, the two formerly important ports.

KEELUNG.—This city, only 16 miles away from Taipei, the present capital of the island, is Taipei's seaport. Kaohsiung, only 25 miles away from Tainan, is the seaport for that city, which was the most important political center of Taiwan in the early period and is now its cultural and historical center.

In the early days, Tamshui and Anping were Taiwan's main harbors and served as outlets for the cities of Taipei and Tainan, dominating northern and southern Taiwan respectively. Owing to the silting of their rivers and the expanding of sand bars, both harbors declined and were replaced by Keelung and Kaohsiung.

There are differences between Keelung and Kaohsiung, as follows:

(1) Keelung developed much earlier in history than Kaohsiung, but Kaohsiung is presently the fastest growing city in Taiwan. It is also the second largest city on the island, with a population of 490,000 persons; Keelung is the fifth largest, with a population of 240,000.

(2) Keelung is located on a deep gulf with a rocky shore; Kaohsiung is on a shallow lagoon, surrounded by sandbars.

(3) The development of Keelung was closely related to the local production of coal; Kaohsiung was originally developed from a fishing village.

(4) Keelung is one of the rainiest ports in the world, which makes the loading of goods difficult; Kaohsiung has a mild winter and few rainy days. Its abundant sunshine and mild temperature make it convenient for the loading of sugar, salt, cement, and other agricultural and industrial raw materials.

(5) Keelung's main export is rice; Kaohsiung's is sugar. This is natural, as rice cultivation is concentrated in the north and sugar cultivation in the south.

Keelung has increased its population by 83 per cent in the last 16 years. Chinese mainlanders occupy 26 per cent of the city. The city is located around the harbor and on irregular narrow strips of land at the base of steep mountains. The city limits extend 2.5 miles from northeast to southwest and 1.9 miles from southeast to northwest. The business district is concentrated at the inner end of the harbor; the public buildings are dispersed through the same general area. The industrial areas are small and scattered.

The harbor of Keelung can be divided into three parts, namely, the inner harbor, the outer harbor, and the fishing harbor. The bottom of the inner harbor consists of clay, and that of the outer harbor of sandstone, neither of which offers any difficulties for docking. The flat land of the city is found only near the bay, and the streets press close to the bay head. The western part of the city, called "great Keelung," is the old city; the eastern part, called "little Keelung," was built by filling in part of the bay; it was the commercial area for the Japanese during their rule. Public offices, banks, and commercial offices stand high above the bay. The expansion of the commercial area of the city has gradually pushed the residential areas and schools to the high elevation in the back mountains.

There are several causes for the development of Keelung Harbor. First, it is a natural harbor, surrounded by rock banks. No big river empties into the harbor; thus, there is no problem of silting. Second, being the northern terminal of the main railroad of the island, it is connected with Taipei on the southwest. Also, it is connected by highways with Ilan and Suao on the east. Third, for exporting goods, the port is not too far from Japanese and Chinese ports. In this it has an advantage over Kaohsiung. As for importing, Keelung is nearer than Kaohsiung to the main urban centers of the island, such as Taipei, Hsinchu, and Taoyuan. Fourth, near Keelung

Harbor are coal and gold mines and sources of marine products, which have helped the harbor's development. Water supply is no problem.

Keelung has disadvantages also. First, the harbor is surrounded by mountains, and there is little flat land for future expansion. Second, the rainy season of Keelung is long, and there is too much rainfall for the efficient discharge of goods in the harbor. This is especially true in view of the fact that the main exports from the harbor are rice, sugar, tea, and cement, all of which are easily ruined by rain. Third, in the winter, the northeast monsoon is very strong; it makes navigation outside the harbor very difficult. Fourth, the harbor is a little too far from the agricultural processing regions of the island.

Few Chinese settled in the northern part of the island until 1723 when they began to live in the place that was the original site of Keelung. (Previously the Spaniards and the Dutch had occupied it.) During the period 1736–1795, the Chinese settlers spread out to other parts of the city. In 1800 they built a road to Ilan, and the number of Chinese settlers increased; in 1840 there were 700 Chinese households in the city.[2]

In its early stage, Keelung had a close relationship with the coal-mining industry. In 1851 foreign steamboats began to do business at Tamshui and Keelung. In 1860, under the terms of the Tientsin Treaty, Keelung was designated an open port. In 1875 the prefecture government's administrative office at Taipei set up a branch office at Keelung.

KAOHSIUNG.—This city is an important naval base and industrial center in southern Taiwan. Kaohsiung Harbor is a long lagoon running east and west between two sand bars. It is 7.5 miles long and 4900 feet wide—6.5 square miles in area—although the mouth is only 500 feet wide. The bottom consists mostly of sand, which is good holding ground for ships' anchors. It is easy to deepen and presents no silting problem. The quality of the water is excellent, good enough for drinking purposes. The harbor facilities, including a storehouse and a railroad station, as well as dock space enough to accommodate six 8000-ton ships at one time, were built by the Japanese, who made Kaohsiung an important port.

During World War II, Kaohsiung developed into an important naval base, ranking with such important ports in Japan proper as Osaka, Kobe, and Nagasaki. The Japanese even planned to reconstruct the harbor within twenty-five years to allow the port to accommodate 150 ships of 10,000 tons—a total carrying capacity of 1,500,000 tons—at the same time. It was only because of their deteriorating war situation that the plan was dropped.

Kaohsiung has a hinterland, including extensive plains in the southwest part of the island. Its commercial influence even extends to Taitung, in the eastern part of Taiwan, and to Taichung, in the central part. No longer is it important, as it was before 1949, for such imports as fertilizer from Japan, soy beans from Manchuria, and jute bags from India; rather, it is an exporting center for the rich agricultural products of the hinterland, including sugar, rice, pineapples, bananas, peanuts, and sweet potatoes.

The surrounding salty soils have turned many lagoons into fish ponds. Kaohsiung was developed from a fishing village and today it still is a fishing port; about 10,000 of its inhabitants are engaged in the fishing industry. The boats sail as far as the sea near Indonesia. During the Japanese occupation, 40 per cent of the fish exported was sent to Japan. Now most of it is locally consumed, although canned spearfish is an important export item. In the city there is a fishing fair, an icemaking plant, and oil storage tanks.

Kaohsiung is not only an important port but also an important industrial center. Oil refining and the production of salt, petroleum, limestone, alkali, cement, and aluminum are well developed. Other industries include fertilizer manufacturing, tile making, and shipbuilding. The port is near Fukien and Kwangtung provinces on the Chinese mainland, 395 miles from Hong Kong and 215 miles from Amoy, the two commercial ports on the Chinese coast. It is a terminal for scheduled shipping lines to Hong Kong, Manila, Yokohama, and points along the Taiwan coast. Backed by high mountains and facing the ocean, Kaohsiung has beautiful scenery.

Tainan and its port, Anping

Tainan is the oldest city on the island, and it is the third largest. The Chinese settled there as early as 1590, and today the population is composed of more than 350,000 persons. The city is a center for marketing and processing of sugar cane, rice, peanuts, and salt. The fish industry is important in Tainan, especially fish culture.

At the beginning of the 17th century, when the Dutch settled the southwestern part of the island, their headquarters was Tainan. Later in the same century, under Chinese rule, it became the capital of the island and remained so for two centuries, with the name Taiwan-fu. Early in the 18th century the Chinese constructed a half-moon shaped earth wall around the city. Gates were placed at the east, north, and south sides; on the west, the city is bounded by the ocean. During those days the city enjoyed great prosperity as the political, commercial, and educational center of the island. In the 19th century, when Taiwan became a province of China, the capital was moved from Tainan to Taipei; then the importance of Tainan became chiefly commercial.

During the Japanese occupation, the old Chinese walls and nearly all the gates were pulled down to permit building of a railway and highways.

Tainan is rectangular in form. On the western side there is a small harbor and extensive brackish fish ponds; on the other sides are paddy fields. The city is located on terraces. Settlement started at the west side of the present city limits, the place nearest to the city of Anping, which is Tainan's port. In the early days, the western side was a swamp beside the seashore. Since then the swamp has been displaced by fish ponds.

In the early days the core of the city remained on the western side, but during the Japanese period, when the railroad tracks were built, passing through the east side of the city, the railroad station became the city's main entrance and the streets radiated from there. Thus the railroad station, in the eastern part of the city, replaced the western part near the port as the city's center. Tainan is bounded by military establishments; only its southern part has developed into a residential area.

Tainan is also a center for a number of industries, including the rice-processing, textile, machinery, ice-making, soybean sauce, wine, and fruit industries. The city specializes in making silver and gold ornaments and tinfoil. The city abounds in historical relics, which are well preserved, and for that reason it is an important tourist center.

TAINAN'S PORT.—Anping, which is Tainan's port, is the oldest settlement in southern Taiwan. Thousands of mainland Chinese have migrated to Taiwan via this port. It lies 3 miles west of Tainan and it is connected with the city by a canal and a trolley line. The city was formerly a thriving port; but, with the completion of the main railroad on the island, the progress of harbor construction at Kaohsiung, and the silting of the bay, its importance declined. Today the port is but an open roadstead, with vessels anchoring almost 2 miles off the beach. Passengers and goods are conveyed between land and sea by lighters and bamboo catamarans.

Taichung

Taichung lies between Taipei and Tainan. It is the principal city in central Taiwan and the fourth largest on the island. It is relatively new and is growing rapidly; its population of today, 310,000 persons, has nearly trebled since 1937. Chinese mainlanders make up 18 per cent of the residents. With the transfer of the seat of provincial government from Taipei to Taichung in 1959, the latter has become an important political center. As the seat of the provincial government, with the palace museum located in the city, as well as several institutions of higher education, Taichung is noted in Taiwan as an educational and cultural center and a fine residential city. Located in a fertile paddy-field basin between the low west coast tablelands and the extensive high mountains on the east, the city is on the "mountain line" of the north–south railroad.

In the 18th century, when Taiwan became a province of China, the governor of the island suggested Taichung as the administrative capital of the island, but Taipei was chosen instead.

Immediately after the cession of the island to Japan, a plan was made for the construction of a modern city. Thus the city, in contrast to other cities in Taiwan, is in modern Japanese style. The streets are well arranged and regular in pattern, resembling Kyoto in Japan—the city has even been called Taiwan's "Little Kyoto." However, because it was built later than the other cities, Taichung has little historical flavor. During World War II, Taichung suffered the least damage among all Taiwan's cities.

Situated in the middle of the island, where rice, sugar, and bananas are produced in large quantities, Taichung is the central distribution market for these products. It also has many small manufacturing plants.

When the main railroad, passing through Taichung, was completed, development of the city's commerce was stimulated, and Taichung superseded the old business center of the island, Changhua. But with the opening of the railroad along the west coast, Changhua again became important, and Taichung is no longer important in transportation.

Hsinchu

Hsinchu, about 50 miles southwest of Taipei, is located on the north–south railroad and highway. It is 7 miles inland from Taiwan Strait. The city is associated with bamboo and its original name meant "bamboo fort." In the 18th century the city wall was constructed, and in the 19th century the city name was changed to *Hsinchu*, meaning "new bamboo." The city is as famous for strong winds as is Ilan for heavy rainfall.

When the early Chinese immigrants came to the island, they formed a small colony on the site of what is now Hsinchu, driving away the aborigines. Since then, this locality has become a thriving business center as well as the seat of Chinese learning in northern Taiwan. The surrounding area is well known for the production of tea, rice, oranges, and fibrous plants, as well as for petroleum. During World War II, the Japanese built their largest airfield nearby.

The city is surrounded on three sides by mountains, and the west side is open to the sea. Along the seashore trees are planted as protection from the strong winds; the protection is especially needed in the winter.

The city is generally regular in design, though far from compact; and its oldest street is in Chinese style.

Chiayi

Chiayi is one of the largest cities in southern Taiwan, with a population of more than 200,000 persons. It is backed on the east by Ali Shan and faced on the west by extensive fertile alluvial plains. There are paddy fields on the west side of the city and low-lying hills to the east. Chiayi is on the main north–south highway, and a branch railroad to Ali Shan starts at this city. The city has good connections with the sugar-producing centers, by private railways. The headquarters of the great Chianan irrigation system is located at Chiayi.

Because of the city's easy access to transportation, many merchants have gathered there, and a hotel business is now well developed. The city is a timber-processing center and also a center for farmers' supplies and for marketing of rice and of other products such as mangoes and betel nuts. The city's manufactured products include plywood and paper, wine and alcohol, ice, cement, small machinery, and tires.

The Tropic of Cancer passes near Chiayi; a tower marking this important parallel of latitude stands a few miles south of the city.

Changhua

Changhua is about 12 miles southwest of Taichung. It is an old town, formerly well known for textile manufacturing. Located at the juncture of two railroad lines, the mountain line and the coast line, the city is important in the marketing of rice, oranges, and pineapples. Sugar manufacturing is well developed.

The original city was established in the 17th century, when the Chinese settled there. In 1734, the city walls were built of bamboo, and Changhwa became a city of strategic importance in central Taiwan.

Lukong

Lukong, situated 7.5 miles west of Changhua, is one of the oldest seaports on the island. In early days it was the main door for immigrants to central Taiwan. At its peak the population amounted to 100,000 persons. Because of the movement of trade to the central part of Taiwan, the silting of the harbor, and the completion of the main railroad from north to south, the port of Lukong declined. It has few commercial activities, but it is a famous salt field and hat manufacturing town. A railroad and a highway connect Lukong with Changhua.

Hualien

Taitung and Hualien are sister cities, both being gateways to the eastern part of Taiwan. Their relative inaccessibility from the west coast is an economic handicap.

Hualien, on the northeast coast, is the largest city on the eastern or Pacific side of the island. Its position there makes it an important port. However, the seas are usually high, especially during the winter months, when the strong northeast monsoon prevails; at such times, landing a cargo and passengers through the surf is too dangerous to undertake. The city is served by a one-way cliff road leading north to Suao, by a narrow-gauge railroad south to Taitung, and by intra-island plane flights. Highway and railroad transportation is quite often interrupted by severe typhoons and landslides.

Hualien has its problems: a low and sinking terrain that makes it vulnerable to damage from typhoons, and the prevalence of earthquakes—the city suffered much damage from one in 1951. It may be necessary to move the city to higher ground immediately to the north, where, in the Japanese era, streets were laid out for the development of an industrial harbor. Some settlement has already occurred in that area, and recently new government buildings were constructed there. During World War II, the Japanese planned to make Hualien a great port. The surrounding area produces sugar cane, rice, jute, and camphor, and Hualien has become a trading center for these products. With the completion of the cross-island highway, the city has grown in importance.

Hualien's first streets were laid out in the 19th century, but about fifty years ago, Hualien was still a small, insignificant village bordering on the aboriginal frontier. With the establishment of a local government in the locality in 1910, however, agricultural, forestry, and mineral enterprises were begun. Immigration of Japanese farmers to this region in 1909 and construction of the railway added to the city's importance. As a result of those developments, the little town has grown steadily, so that it has now assumed the aspect of a modern city with a fine future before it.

Taitung

Taitung has no connection with the west coast, and the city has no harbor facilities. The lack of a good harbor has retarded industrial progress and development of the local natural resources. Also, the city is subject to frequent typhoons. The city of Taitung is built on the coastal plain which has been built up by the deposits of three rivers at the southern end of Taitung rift valley. Formerly Taitung was near the aborigine territory and less than eight per cent of the total county was under cultivation. Rice, sugar cane, and peanuts are the three leading crops. Livestock and poultry are produced in some quantity.

Ilan

Ilan is one of the biggest cities in eastern Taiwan; it is located in the middle of the extensive Ilan delta, which is the rice production center of the east, and the city is the largest rice market in eastern Taiwan. With the connection of the railroad north to Keelung and south to Suao, the importance of the city has been increased.

Suao

Suao is on the Pacific Coast, about 40 miles from the northern end of the island. It is at the northern entrance to a one-way mountain road to Hualien. It was the first natural harbor to be developed on the east coast, and it is the southern terminal of the Ilan-Suao railway. Two miles east of Suao there is a fishing port, which during the fishing season accommodates 100 boats. In summer, the people are employed in collecting coral, and in winter, in catching spearfish.

URBANIZATION

In recent years urbanization (*Table 47*) has taken place rapidly; the rate of population increase in urban areas is more than twice as high as in rural areas. In almost every available space in the cities, small dwellings have been erected; and growing lines of temporary sales booths are appearing on downtown streets. There has been a considerable increase in the number of itinerant peddlers and other marginally self-employed people. Pedicabs swarm in every busy street. The rapid urbanization of Taiwan can also be noticed in the increase in the percentage of households having piped water, electric irons, radios, newspapers, and motor vehicles. To supply the food demands of city residents, more fowl and hogs are being raised.[3]

Table 47. Percentage Distribution of Taiwan's Total Population, by Size of Communities, Specified Years, 1920–1952.*

	20,000 persons or less				More than 20,000 persons					
Year	Total	Less than 5,000	5,001– 10,000	10,001– 20,000	Total	20,001– 30,000	30,001– 40,000	40,001– 100,000	100,001 or more	Others**
1920	75	2	19	54	24	11	5	3	4	1
1930	59	1	10	48	40	22	2	8	5	3
1940	36	1	6	30	63	34	7	8	12	2
1952	23	—	—	—	77	25	17	12	21	2

* ARTHUR F. RAPER, *et al.*, *Urban and Industrial Taiwan—Crowded and Resourceful* (National Taiwan University, Taipei, 1954), p. 255, with modifications.
** "Others" include aborigines' settlements and other living places, such as boats.

Taipei, Kaohsiung, Tainan, and Taichung, already the four largest cities of the island, more than doubled in population between 1937 and 1953; Keelung, Hsinchu, and Hualien almost doubled their population. The smaller cities have had smaller increases, ranging from 35 to 60 per cent. Only one city, Juifang, a mining area in northern Taiwan, has had a population decrease.

The increase in urban residents is due chiefly to three factors. First, the movement to Taiwan of the Nationalist government in 1949 brought nearly 1.5 million mainlanders, most of whom moved into the cities. The second factor in population growth has been an annual increase of more than three per cent of births over deaths in cities. The third factor has been the movement into the urban areas of many young rural Taiwanese seeking better economic opportunities.

During the period 1920–1960, the proportion of the population of Taiwan living in the cities quadrupled. The population increase is greatest in the larger cities; the smaller cities have lost much of their population to the larger ones.

As is seen in *Table 47*, in 1920 the cities with 20,000 or fewer people made up 75 per cent of the island's total population, as compared with 59 per cent in 1930, 36 per cent in 1940, and 23 per cent in 1952.

The greatest decrease occurred in cities with less than 5000 population, the next greatest in the 5000–10,000 population group, and the third greatest in cities with 10,000–20,000 population.

The increases in cities with more than 20,000 people accounted for the marked increase in the cities' proportion of the island's total population. The proportion of Taiwan's total population living in cities of 20,000–30,000 persons doubled between 1920 and 1952; in cities of 30,000–40,000, the proportion more than tripled; in cities of 40,000–100,000, it quadrupled; and in cities of more than 100,000 it increased more than five times.

SOCIAL CHARACTERISTICS OF URBANIZATION

Some distinctive social characteristics may be noted in the urbanization of Taiwan.[4] First, the people who have moved from the rural areas to the cities have done so fairly recently. As the 1953 survey conducted by the Chinese-American Joint Commission on Rural Reconstruction shows, a third of the people in the nearly 1400 sample urban households in the cities and towns had been city dwellers less than five years, and 27 per cent, from five to ten years. In short, three-fifths had lived in the city for only ten years or less. In contrast, only ten per cent of the more than 500 sample farm-owning households in the survey had lived on the farms less than ten years.

Second, the survey showed that the urban residents were rather young. In families who had moved to the cities from the rural areas, two-thirds of the heads of households and three-fourths of their wives ranged in age from 16 to 35 years. Thirty-six per cent of the urban population is made up of this highly productive 25–35 age group; only 24 per cent of the rural population was of this age group.

Third, as for the reasons given for moving to the city, 76 per cent reported that they wanted to find a job, 8 per cent came as refugees from the mainland, 8 per cent followed parents, and 8 per cent came for other reasons. Nearly three-fifths of the women came to the cities with their husbands, one-fourth came to get married, one-tenth followed parents, four per cent came to find jobs, and three per cent for other reasons.

Fourth, because of urbanization, households in the cities are becoming smaller and more independent. The traditional family group often includes members of three or four generations, but now many more urban households than rural ones are made up of two generations only, parents and children. Family life in urban Taiwan is in a state of transition from the traditional large rural household to the smaller and more independent urban one. The average size of the urban household is 5.4 persons, compared with the general rural average of 6.9. A factor in lowering the number of children in urban families is the delay in the marriages of young urban residents because of financial difficulties; the divorce rate in urban areas has been increasing for the same reason.

Observations of urban households have shown that, on the average, employers have the largest families, eight members; the self-employed are second, with 6.2; and civil servants and laborers have the smallest families, averaging 4.6 and 4.7 members respectively.

Fifth, as a result of their greater independence, members of urban households have more opportunities to determine how they will make a living, and how they will use their money and their leisure, to plan the number of years their children will stay in school, and to make other decisions.

The traditional large family, which is the center of Chinese life, has less influence in the urban area. In the rural areas agriculture has solved the basic problems of food, shelter, and survival for the Chinese, and most facets of life have centered on the maintenance of family solidarity. In the struggle for existence they have felt that only the family could be relied upon; and, in turn, the individual, on the grounds that the greatest virtues were family loyalty and filial piety, owed primary allegiance to the family. Many cultural characteristics of the Chinese, such as politeness, friendliness, consideration for others, and willingness to compromise, have been necessary for survival in crowded living conditions.

Last, the increased number of people in the cities has outrun employment opportunities, with the result that households are less secure and that there is a marked increase in the marginally self-employed. Such workers are numerous in urban areas, where their small shops can be seen, one little stall after another on one or both sides of the street, block after block. They display all sorts of items for sale: foods of many kinds, ready-made clothes, fruits and vegetables, pots and pans, cut flowers, and potted plants. On one side may be a shoe mender, and on the other, an umbrella-repair man. Many of these marginal businesses are conducted on a cash basis with a very small capital investment. The goods are carted home at night and are not displayed on rainy days. Besides these marginal businesses that have fixed locations, there are also street peddlers who carry their small wares in baskets swinging from the end of a pole over the shoulder. Other movable businessmen are the pedicab pullers, always ready on a second's notice to serve a paying customer. This is the most convenient means of transportation in cities.

In the city of Taipei, these marginally self-employed constitute more than one-fifth of the total population, and the proportion is much the same in other large cities. In most of the smaller cities and towns, the proportion is slightly smaller.

HOUSING SHORTAGE.—Bomb damage to dwellings during World War II created a housing shortage that has been aggravated by the rapid population increase in urban areas since the island was restored to China. As a result, temporary housing is very much in evidence in all of the larger cities and towns. Most of the new temporary houses have been built of whatever inexpensive materials could be found. They are located along the banks of canals, on the parkways of wide but little-used avenues, on the strip of land between a street and the city wall, around a schoolyard, or in a vacant right-of-way along railroad tracks running through a city.

TRANSPORTATION

In recent years, the economic development of Taiwan has resulted in an increase in farming, forestry, manufacturing, and mining, as well as in expansion of foreign trade. All these increased economic activities have demanded coordinated improvements in transportation. In turn, improvement of transportation accelerates the progress of farming and industry.

The island's transportation facilities can be divided into four categories: railroads, highways, shipping, and aviation.

RAILWAYS

In transportation the western half of Taiwan has always been of greater importance than the eastern. The first railroads were built in the west; and the main railroad line, the principal artery of the island, is located there. Totaling more than 250 miles in length, with 79 stations, the government enterprise starts at the port of Keelung in the north and extends the entire length of the island along the western coastal plain to Kaohsiung in the south, the other great port of the island, bringing the northern and southern extremities of Taiwan into direct communication. Most of the island's principal cities, where the greatest portion of staple products, such as rice, sugar, and tea, are accumulated for transportation, are located along this line (*Figure 53*). The line carries passengers as well as freight.

From this main line stretch six branch lines, also goverment-owned, which have a total length of about 200 miles.

(1) The Tamshui branch line (from Taipei to Tamshui) was originally built to transport materials for improving the main railroad. It was built in 1899–1900, and is about 14 miles in length.

(2) The Ilan branch line (from Keelung to Suao), about 62 miles long, traverses the coal fields of Taipei county and runs to the Suao delta. It is important in the development of the northeastern part of Taiwan.

(3) The Pinchi branch line (from Santiolin to Tsintonkun) was originally the main line, with a length of 8 miles. This line is built on a mountainside and is called the mountain line. With the development of economic activities, the line's traffic increased and made it necessary for another line to be opened. The newer line runs along the west coast, from Chunan to Changhua, via Mialoi, Taichung, and Wangtien. It was first called the coast line. Later, it became the main line and the mountain line became a branch. The coast line was then named the Taichung line; more than 55 miles in length, it has fourteen stations. One of the stations is located at an elevation of 1300 feet, the highest railroad station on the island.[5]

(4) The Jiji branch line (from Ershui to Watsurchen), with a length of 18 miles, was originally built for carrying engineering equipment to the Sun-Moon Lake electric station; but since 1922, the line has provided public transportation.

(5) The Pintung line (from Kaohsiung to Linpien). When this branch,

40 miles long, was being built, it was necessary to construct a bridge for it, more than 4900 feet long, a famous feat of engineering.

There would be a railroad line around the whole island if the line between Suao and Hualien and that between Taitung and Linpien had not been demolished during Wold War II. Transportation between these points is now being taken care of by truck service.

(6) Besides the western main and branch lines, there is an eastern railroad, the Taitung Main Line, running in the long, narrow Taitung valley,

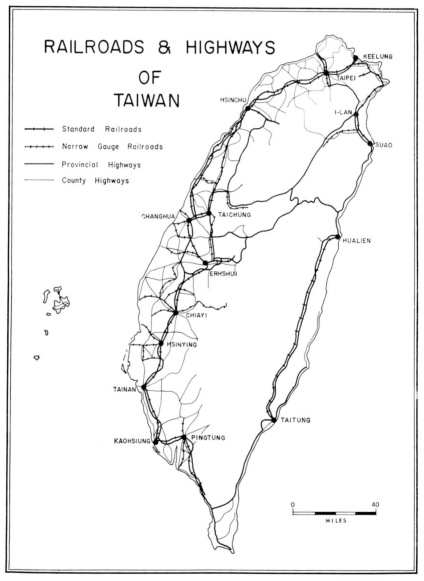

Figure 53

connecting two main ports in eastern Taiwan—Hualien and Taitung. The eastern main line is about 110 miles long and has 39 stations.

In addition to the public railroads, there are also quite a few private lines on the island, which ship raw material. They are owned by the Taiwan Sugar Corporation, the Taiwan Forestry Administration, and others. These private railroads, mostly of the narrower gauge, comprise a network of almost 1900 miles, of which a stretch of nearly 500 miles is open for public traffic. They are not competitive with the public railroads, but rather serve as feeder lines. In 1956 about 20 million passengers and 3.5 million tons of freight were handled by these private lines.[6]

The length of the public railroads combined is more than 450 miles; that of the private lines is almost 1900 miles, giving a total of about 2350 miles. For the whole area of the island, this is a ratio of approximately 10 miles of railroad per 50 square miles of area.

Because of the rugged terrain of the island, many tunnels had to be built through hills, and bridges over the rivers, during the construction of the railroads.

Starting from Changhua, which is located in the central part of the island, the general movement of goods by railroad in Taiwan is either northward to Keelung or southward to Kaohsiung, depending upon the season and upon import and export conditions. But the primary movement of goods is as follows: Coal, produced mainly in northern Taiwan, is shipped to the central and southern parts of the island. Fertilizer, besides being produced locally, is brought in at Keelung and Kaohsiung and is then shipped to other locations, such as Hsinchu and Chiayi. Sugar is produced mainly in central and southern Taiwan, and most of it is shipped to Kaohsiung for export. Rice is produced in central Taiwan and is shipped north to Keelung for export. Lumber is produced in central Taiwan and is shipped north and south. Cement is produced both in northern and in southern Taiwan; it is also an import item, shipped in at Keelung and Kaohsiung and transported to other cities, such as Taichung and Tainan. Salt is produced in the southwest and is shipped to Kaohsiung for export. Sandstone is quarried in the mountainous areas and near the headwaters of rivers; it is shipped to other localities.

HIGHWAYS

The highways in Taiwan are well developed. The most important highways are located, of course, on the western plain of the island, and they run north and south, parallel with the mainline railroad. The highways on the eastern coastline and the southern circular line are also important. With the railroad on the eastern coasts, the island transportation system is thus completed. Most of the highways were built during the early part of the Japanese rule as a military project. Though they were irregular and poorly graded, being based on the footpaths of earlier days, they formed the foundation of the present highway network.

The total mileage of the highways in Taiwan is nearly 10,000 miles, approximately 7 miles of road for every 10 square miles of the whole island. This ratio is greater than the ratio that most countries in southeast

Asia can boast. The highway mileage in western Taiwan is 11 miles per 10 square miles; in eastern Taiwan, it is only 4.

Of the 910 miles of provincial roads, the 670 miles of round-the-island trunk lines constitute the major part. The maximum grade of most of these provincial roads is 10 per cent, and the minimum radius of curvature is 32 feet; the roadway width varies from 13 to 46 feet. Since the main line from north to south crosses many parallel rivers, it has more than 1000 bridges, with a combined length of nearly 21 miles. Silo Bridge, which is the longest, not only in Taiwan, but also in the entire Far East, consists of 31 spans, totaling more than a mile. The bridge is located at the midpoint of the north-south truck highway.

The plan for future development of the island's highways includes improvement of the Suao–Hualien highway and restoration of the Hualien–Taitung highway, improvement of access roads to scenic spots, and the maintenance of the cross-island highway.

The Suao–Hualien highway on the east coast is an important link of the round-the-island trunk line, with a total length of nearly 75 miles. The road is carved out of the precipitous cliff of the coastal mountains facing the Pacific Ocean. The roadway is narrow throughout its length, passable by only one car at a time. Besides, many curves make the road even more difficult to travel. Perennial typhoons, floods, and earthquakes have caused landslides and washouts, often closing the road to traffic.

SHIPPING LINES

Being an island, Taiwan naturally depends upon ships for trade and other communication with neighboring areas such as Korea, Japan, the Ryukyus, Hong Kong, the Philippines, and Malaysia. Far-off areas also, like Australia, New Zealand, the east and the west coasts of North America, South America, the Middle East, and Europe, have trade connections with Taiwan.

For trade with nearby areas, there are at present three main shipping lines: the Taiwan–Japan, Taiwan–Korea, and Taiwan–Hong Kong, of which the first carries the greatest amount of cargo. Besides, there are many tramp services between Taiwan and the Ryukyus, the Philippines, Malaysia, and Thailand. At present the main destinations of the ocean-going vessels are ports on the east and west coasts of the United States. At times those vessels also ply the coasts of South America, Europe, and the Middle East, as well as of islands in the South Pacific.

Harbor facilities

Lacking indentation of its coastline, Taiwan has but few good ports. The eastern coast is nearly a continuous wall of high cliffs, and precipices rise almost perpendicularly out of the sea, whereas on the western coast there are shoals running miles out into the sea with many shallow sandbars. Despite these disadvantages, Taiwan, like any island, must maintain overseas trade. The extension of Taiwan's seaports has become an urgent necessity as a result of her industrial development and the growth of her foreign trade.

Of the island's seventeen harbors, Keelung, Kaohsiung and Hualien are the three biggest.

KEELUNG HARBOR.—This is the main entrance to northern Taiwan, and the northern terminus of the main railway in the western coastal region. A number of railways and a network of highways place Keelung within easy reach of all the important centers of the island.

The harbor basin is very shallow and, owing to the strong monsoon, its seas run so high that for fully half of the year all vessels of 1000 tons or more have to drop anchor about a mile offshore.

Keelung Harbor is surrounded by mountains on three sides and the entrance is on the north side. The size of the whole harbor is 4,354,430 square yards, of which 1,357,000 constitute an inner harbor, 2,603,930 an outer harbor, and 393,490 a fishing harbor. In 1945, when the harbor was returned to the Chinese by the Japanese, it was entirely paralyzed; more than 150 vessels had been sunk within its confines. After extensive rehabilitation, Keelung Harbor has emerged as one of the best international commercial ports in the Far East.

In the first ten months of 1957, Keelung's tonnage—export and import—amounted to 1,793,640 tons. In comparison with 887,665 tons in 1946, this represents an increase of 100 per cent. Major items of export are rice, pineapples, tea, camphor, bananas, bamboo poles, and hardwood; imports include wheat, cotton, fertilizer, iron ore, soy beans, phosphate rock, and machinery, as well as general cargo.

Keelung Harbor is one of the few deep-water harbors in southeast Asia. Although its cargo-handling capacities have increased steadily, thus far only the inner harbor has been used. With a narrow waterway and mountainous surroundings, the harbor is unable to handle cargo effectively on account of inadequate wharf and berth facilities.

Completion of the outer harbor breakwater will make it possible for the outer harbor to increase its cargo handling capacity and to meet the growing demands of military transportation.

A grain elevator more than 1300 feet high is being constructed, which will help in handling the wheat, which alone reaches an annual total of around 220,000 tons.

A tunnel has been completed, which is accessible to both highway and railway. In the shape of a horseshoe, the tunnel is a link between the city and the outer harbor. It is 1300 feet long, 26 feet wide, and nearly 23 feet high. After the completion of the outer harbor extension projects, an adequate means of transportation must be provided for incoming and outgoing cargo, which is likely to reach an annual total of 550,000 tons. The tunnel shortens the communication lines between the city and the outer harbor by nearly 2 miles. Other connection lines, 2 miles of railway and 1 mile of highway, are being constructed between the outer harbor and the city; since those lines bypass the inner harbor, the transportation burden on the latter will not be further increased.

A 1650-foot special cargo wharf is being planned. Such a wharf will have several advantages: First, grain can be discharged in all weather, and losses can be cut to a minimum. Second, vessels can get under way quickly as a result of those time-saving facilities. The handling charges on grain will be lower. Gunny sacks for packing will no longer be necessary. Third, the new wharf will form a loop with the highway and the railway, so that in case any part of the loop is damaged, the wharf will not be paralyzed.

Fourth, the wharf will relieve the congested land traffic near the inner harbor, and will increase, by 30,000 square yards, the space used for handling cargo.

KAOHSIUNG HARBOR.—This harbor is as important in the south as Keelung is in the north. It is more suitable than Keelung for export, since it is in an area within easy reach of agricultural production as well as manufacturing. Nearby are rice- and sugar-producing centers, also industrial centers processing aluminum, alkali, oil, sulfuric acid, and so forth. Major commodities exported from this harbor are sugar, salt, molasses, bananas, and cement; those imported are crude oil, fertilizer, ore, timber, and soy beans. The total tonnage of export and import in the first ten months in 1957 was more than 2 million tons, compared with some 110,000 tons handled in 1946.

The harbor is situated on Kaohsiung Bay in a lagoon 4900 feet wide and 7.5 miles long. A long sand bar forms half the side of the bay, separating it from the open sea, which is on the southwest. A waterway only 344 feet wide forms its entrance, connecting the basins with the open sea. The lagoon is extremely shallow, and the entrance is strewn with rocks, so that even junks and small steamers find it difficult to approach. The need for improving the port is urgent. Steps preliminary to construction include reclaiming the foreshore and dredging the harbor basin. The port city is the southern terminus of the island's main railroad line. Thus, it not only is the most important traffic center of the southern section of Taiwan, but promises to be a great industrial metropolis in the near future.

Owing to the recent rapid development of industry and agriculture in Taiwan, the volume of ocean shipping at Kaohsiung Harbor has taken an upward turn, increasing by 16 per cent each year since 1947 and reaching a total of 2,890,000 tons in 1957. As a result, the existing harbor facilities are overloaded and have long since become inadequate. At present there are 840 factories in active operation in the Kaohsiung metropolitan area. The multiplication of industrial plants has been rapid and is reflected in the annual increase of electric power consumption in Kaohsiung, an increase which has averaged 18 per cent a year in the last few years. Today Kaohsiung consumes one-third of all the power produced on the island.

Kaohsiung Harbor is the largest fishing base in Taiwan. In the last five years, the total fish catch and the tonnage of fishing craft in Kaohsiung have doubled. As a result the existing facilities for fishing are very much overtaxed; and, more than this, insufficient land area is available for construction of additional shore facilities such as ice and cold-storage plants.

Traffic congestion presents another problem for the operation of this port. In recent years, more ships have been visiting the port than it could accommodate. On many occasions vessels have had to await their turn to discharge their cargoes and to load. At present, the amount of railway and highway transportation is also limited by the inadequacy of existing switch operations and of available lines accessible to the port. New outlets for inland transportation must be found, and this can be done only after the harbor area is further expanded. As was indicated previously, five-sixths of the water area still awaits development. The extension of this port will not only increase the port's capacity to meet the growing shipping demand, but also will contribute to the growth of industry, fishing, and trade and to city development.

At present such extension is being planned. The completion of this project will increase the harbor area sixfold, increasing the port's ability to handle the expanding import and export business. The project will lengthen the existing fairway from 10,170 feet to 33,785, will reclaim 9,000,000 square yards of land, and will construct 119,400 feet of shallow-water wharf and 655 feet of deep-water wharf. The reclaimed land will provide suitable sites for four times as many plants as are now located in the industrial area. The creation of new (reclaimed) land has manifold advantages for the city of Kaohsiung. It is a requisite for expansion of the fishing base, for improvement of railway and road transportation accessible to the harbor areas, and for development of the city.

HUALIEN HARBOR.—This is the only large port in eastern Taiwan. In that part of the island, frequent landslides, occurring during the typhoon and wet seasons, make the roads and the railways of very little practical use, thus emphasizing the need for sea transportation. In 1939, Hualien Harbor was opened as an international port. The harbor entrance is narrow, and prevailing strong winds make it difficult to navigate. To expand the port, it is planned to build a deep-water wharf of 1050 feet and a shallow-water wharf of 655 feet, with a protecting levee of 985 feet; this will enable the port to handle 440,000 tons. Though Hualien Harbor has few goods to transport, it is important in the development of forestry and water power. In the fall of 1963, Hualien was opened to international shipping.

CIVIL AVIATION

The Taiwan Flight Information Region (FIR) was established in 1953. Its geographical boundaries as approved are: longitude 117° 30′ E., latitude 20° N.; longitude 123° E.; latitude 29° N.

Before 1950 all airports and navigational aid facilities in Taiwan were managed and operated by the Chinese Air Force (CAF). The runway on Taipei Airfield, originally built by the Japanese and later extended by CAF is 4590 feet long and is paved with 6-inch-thick concrete. It can sustain aircraft no heavier than the DC-4 type.

In 1956 the total number of flights was 6000; of passengers, 81,000. These figures represent an increase of more than 100 per cent in flights and more than 400 per cent in passengers over the 1950 figures—3000 flights and 19,000 passengers.

There are eight airlines now using the Taipei International Airport, five of them foreign companies and three Taiwanese-Chinese.

REFERENCES

[1] CHENG-SIANG CHEN, "The growth of Taipei," *China Today* **7**, 23 (1958).
[2] —, *The Gazeteer of Keelung* (Historical Research Commission of Taiwan Province, Taipei, 1954), p. 16. [In Chinese].
[3] ARTHUR F. RAPER et al., *Urban and Industrial Taiwan—Crowded and Resourceful* (National Taiwan University, Taipei, 1954), p. 1.
[4] *Ibid.*, pp. 255–280.
[5] *The Gazeteer of Taiwan*, Economic Volume (The Historical Research Commission of Taiwan Province, Taipei, 1958), p. 107. [In Chinese].
[6] *Transportation in Taiwan*, Taiwan Research Monograph No. 63 (The Bank of Taiwan, Taipei, 1958). [In Chinese].

NINETEEN

Agriculture

CHARACTERISTICS

THE SUBTROPICAL CLIMATE of Taiwan has been beneficial to the development of agriculture, which is the foundation of the island's economy. The high temperature, abundant rainfall, and long growing season combine to make the island an excellent place for cultivating crops (*Figure 54*).

However, not all the physical features of the island favor agricultural development. The surface configuration and the poor soil are formidable handicaps. Arable land is chiefly limited to the western plains. In the east rise high mountains, and only the narrow elongated Taitung valley and the Ilan plain are agriculturally significant. Thus, it is not surprising to find that on the island of Taiwan only 24 per cent of the land surface is under cultivation. This figure compares favorably with Korea's 20 per cent, Japan's 16 per cent, and southeast China's estimated 14 per cent, but unfavorably with France's 46 per cent and the high percentages found in other western European countries.

In addition to the surface configuration, the condition of the soils of the island also restricts the land area available for cultivation. Centuries of irrigation and heavy year-round cropping have leached much soil of plant nutrients. In the north the soils are primarily old leached alluvials or diluvials; some are residuals of acid volcanic rocks. In the southwest most of the soils belong to red and yellow laterities, which require careful management. In the east and in the Central Mountains the soil is usually thin, immature, and infertile. On the western plain the soils are, in most cases, more fertile, but they are mixed with sand, gravel, and boulder debris left by the short, swift-flowing rivers that rise in the Central Mountains.

Because of the heavy population pressure on the island the cultivated area in Taiwan increased rapidly. In 1910 the total area of cultivated land was 1,665,000 acres. By 1920 it had increased to 1,850,000 acres. In 1930

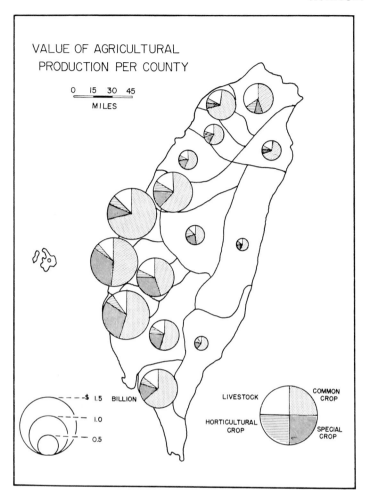

VALUE OF AGRICULTURAL
PRODUCTION PER COUNTY

0   15   30   45
MILES

$ 1.5   BILLION

1.0

0.5

LIVESTOCK

HORTICULTURAL
CROP

COMMON
CROP

SPECIAL
CROP

Figure 54

it amounted to slightly more than 2,000,000 acres, and in 1940 it reached 2,124,000 acres. In 1950 it increased to 2,149,000 acres and was increased to 2,166,000 acres in 1959.[1]

However, compared with the population increase, the expansion of cultivated land is slight. With 2,166,000 acres of cultivated land, there are 621,000 farm families and an agricultural population of 3,900,000. The farms average only 3.5 acres in size, and an individual farmer cultivates only 0.58 acre of land (*Figures 55 and 56*).[2]

In Taiwan over 85 per cent of the farms are less than 7.5 acres in size. About 46 per cent of the farms are smaller than 2.5 acres, and more than a quarter of those are less than an acre in area. Only one per cent of the farms are larger than 25 acres.[3] The constantly increasing size of the agricultural population of Taiwan, combined with the limited amount of cultivated land and farm division through the inheritance system, further reduce the average farm size. To an American this is not farming, but gardening.

253

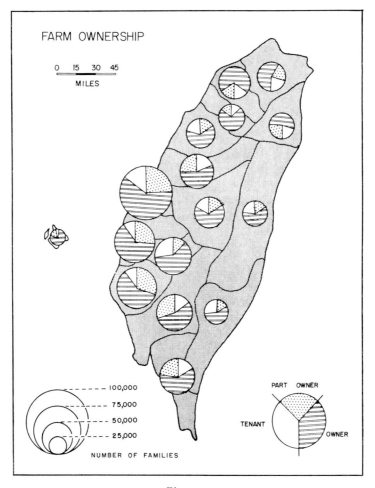

Figure 55

In spite of these small holdings, Taiwan's farmers are not only able to support themselves with the basic foodstuffs, but they are also able to export a surplus of rice, sugar, tea, fruit, and other products.

The high crop yields of the farms in Taiwan are the result of the diligent work of the farmers as well as of the intelligent application of various agricultural practices, such as (*a*) irrigation, (*b*) fertilization, (*c*) the rotation system, and (*d*) the introduction of new crops.

IRRIGATION

Water is the lifeblood of Taiwan's agriculture, because rice, which is the principal product of the island, is a water-loving crop. Level land, high temperatures, and abundant rainfall are the three basic physical requirements for rice cultivation. The alluvial plains of the western coast, where the temperature is high, the growing season long, and the annual rainfall adequate, are suitable for rice cultivation. However, the problem there is that the rainfall is not evenly distributed. Too much rainfall is concentrated in a few months, leaving a long dry season. The only solution to this problem is the storing of water during the dry season. Through irrigation a definite water supply is obtained and a harvest assured (*Figs. 57* and *58*).

Long before the Japanese period, the Chinese had designed an irrigation system. The first part of their system consists of a pond constructed with mud and rock in a low area; this stores the water for use in the dry season. The other part consists of a network of river tributaries, creeks, canals, and ditches to conduct the water from a pond to the farm. Before the development of cement, which made dams available, this system provided the irrigation for the island. This method was efficient because the rivers

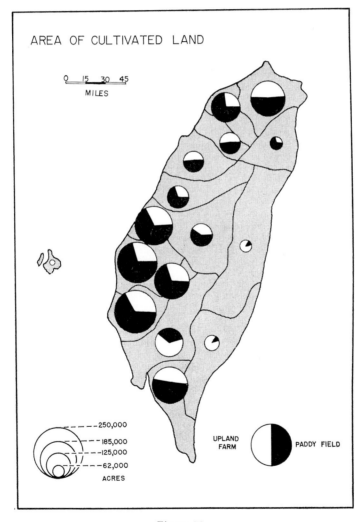

AREA OF CULTIVATED LAND

0 15 30 45
MILES

250,000
185,000
125,000
62,000
ACRES

UPLAND FARM   PADDY FIELD

Figure 56

255

in Taiwan have wide beds and many tributaries, and the lands to be irrigated are scattered and isolated. However, the materials used in those systems are easily destroyed by storm and flood.

Under the Japanese rule the irrigation systems were greatly expanded and improved. There are many irrigation systems in different localities in Taiwan, but two of them are most important. One is the Chianan irrigation system, and the other is the Taoyuan irrigation system.

Almost thirty years have passed since the Chianan irrigation system was completed. At present the system is gradually deteriorating, owing mainly to water erosion and silting. The water in the reservoirs is leaking and the water level has been lowered. The irrigation canals have not been kept in

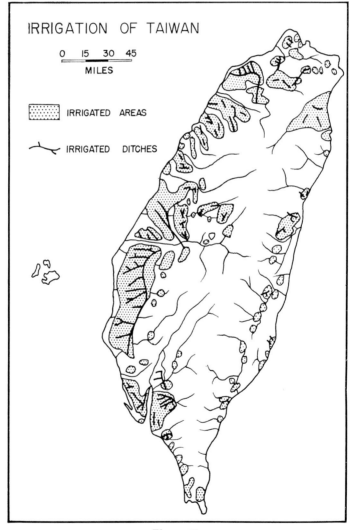

Figure 57

good shape, and much mechanical equipment at the water gates has broken down. Many suggestions have been offered for remedying the situation. It has been suggested that another reservoir be built, that the Coral Reservoir be expanded, and that the height of the dam at the present reservoir be increased. However, it will be difficult to follow these suggestions because of the shortage of capital. A more practical way would be to dredge the deposited sand from the present dam, to cultivate forests, and to give attention to the soil erosion at the upper part of the Tsengwen River, which was the original water supplier of the irrigation system.

Figure 58.—Initial construction of a new irrigation project (AID/JCRR photo)

The Taoyuan irrigation system is primarily a Chinese irrigation method, improved by the Japanese. Taoyuan tableland is located in the northwestern part of Taiwan. It has a gently sloping surface, rising from the eastern foothills and gradually lowering to the west coastal area. It is 232 square miles in area and includes a large portion of a paddy farm. In order to have the farmland well watered, the Chinese built about 800 ponds on the gentle, sloping land to store water for irrigation. These ponds vary in size, ranging from 2.5 to 75 acres, and are dammed on one side with earth and rocks. On the dammed side of a pond the water is deeper than on the other. The total area of the ponds amounts to about 19,300 acres.

Starting in 1916, the Japanese built an aqueduct at Shihmen to conduct water from Takekan Creek to irrigate the Taoyuan tableland. The engineering work on this project was completed in 1924. Since then a total of

56,800 acres of land has been irrigated and has been turned into paddy farm land. This irrigation system utilizes the many pre-existing ponds, which relieve the burden of the main canals. It also re-uses the irrigation water; owing to the slope of the region, after irrigating the farms the irrigation water flows back to the natural rivers. If river dikes were built, the used water could be conducted back to the irrigation canals or the pond to be used again. This irrigation system brought about an increase in rice production from 37,000 tons to 81,000 tons.

FERTILIZATION

For producing efficiently the major crops of rice and sugar cane, irrigation and fertilization are the two most important practices of Taiwan's agricultural economy. Since a piece of land produces more than one crop each year and the demand for increased productivity is rising, the use of large quantities of fertilizers on the island is necessary. As in other densely populated parts of southeast Asia, a variety of indigenous fertilizers is widely used. The use of compost, green manures, human excrement (night soil), straw, ashes, and other materials is an integral part of the farming system of Taiwan. Every year the island uses indigenous fertilizers amounting to more than 14 million tons. Unlike farmers in most Oriental societies, Taiwan's farmers also make extensive use of commercial fertilizers. This is a result of the Japanese rule, which aimed to develop the island as a rice and sugar supplier to the Japanese Empire, and is a continuation of a program established since the Chinese restoration, to increase the yield production per unit area. In the use of abundant amounts of fertilizer Taiwan outranks all neighboring rice-producing areas excepting Japan.

Because of the heavy rainfall, the continued flushing with irrigation water, and the alluvial origin of most of the agricultural soils, humus content is low in almost all parts of the cultivated areas. Since optimum moisture characteristics, soil structure, and the capacity of plants to derive mineral nutrients from the soil depend upon that organic constituent, efficient utilization of farm manures is essential to sustained crop production.

In the Far East, Taiwan's utilization of commercial fertilizers is notable. In southeastern Asia few countries use commercial fertilizer even though its importance in increasing crop yield is now widely appreciated.

Although it is difficult to make an exact estimate of the amount of fertilizer that should be applied to a given soil and crop for economically optimum returns, there is clearly a correlation between fertilizer application and crop yield. In Japan, where application of fertilizer per unit area is much higher than in Taiwan, rice yields are substantially greater; approximately 2850 pounds of rice per acre in Japan as compared with 1780 pounds per acre (single crop) in Taiwan. Although many other factors are involved, an important part of the contrast in yield must be attributed to differing intensities of fertilizer use. There is little question that attainment of peak yields is heavily dependent upon sustained use of large quantities of chemical fertilizers, supplemented by organic farm manure.

Nitrogenous fertilizers comprise 70 per cent of the gross weight of the chemical fertilizers in Taiwan; phosphoric fertilizers, 25 per cent; and potassic fertilizers, about 5 per cent.

Since Taiwan has no domestic reserves of either potash or phosphate, imports of these two essential items will have to be continued.

CROPPING SYSTEM

The island of Taiwan has developed a special system of cropping to compensate for its small crop-producing area. This system, which has increased the production of crops per unit area, includes multiple cropping, crop rotation, and interculture.

MULTIPLE CROPPING.—Because of the favorable climatic conditions, most cultivated lands in Taiwan have two harvests a year. This means that the crop area is much greater than the cultivated area. For example, in 1960, the cultivated land amounted to more than 2,151,000 acres, but the crop land amounted to 4,142,000 acres. Thus, the multiple-crop yield was 193 per cent of the single-crop. Among the counties, Taichung has the highest multiple-crop yield—219 per cent of the single-crop; Penghu has the lowest—147 per cent.

Among different kinds of cultivated land the double-cropped paddy rice fields have the highest multiple-crop yield. Those paddy fields occupy about 38 per cent of the total cultivated area. Besides the two rice harvests per year, other crops are planted between seasons or between the paddy rows. Therefore, there may be five harvests in two years, or three harvests in one year.

CROP ROTATION.—This is another characteristic of Taiwan's agriculture. The cycle of rotation for paddy fields ranges from one to four years; one-year and two-year cycles are the most common. The rotation cycle for dry-farming fields is mostly limited to one or two years. In the central part of the Chianan irrigated area, sugar cane, paddy rice, and mixed crops rotate every three years.

The typical cultivation pattern of the island includes a first and second rice crop. This is followed by an unirrigated winter crop; usually sweet potatoes, grains, vegetables, and green-manure plants. In addition, a leguminous summer catch crop for green fertilizer may be grown.

INTERCULTURE.—The interculture of four crops—the first rice crop, the second rice crop, the summer catch crop, and the winter catch crop—varies through the year within a given region. The first paddy crop is planted and harvested much earlier in the south than in the north. The second paddy crop is also planted and harvested earlier in the south, even though the difference in time is slight. Thus, the summer intermediate crop season begins earlier in the south and lasts longer.

The summer catch crop season, because of its shortness and the heavy rainfall, is suitable only for green manure or for two or three kinds of vegetables. On the other hand, the longer duration and better weather of the winter intermediate crop season make possible the cultivation of many kinds of crops. The duration of the winter intermediate crop season increases progressively as we move northward. The middle part of the island, in spite of the rather dry winter, is the best area for winter intermediate crops. Taichung County, in the middle area, has the highest multiple-crop index.

Introduction of new crop species

Under Japanese rule much effort was dedicated to the improvement of crop qualities and the introduction of new crop species. Among the most successful species introduced was Ponlai rice, which has approximately a 20 per cent higher yield than that of the native variety. Among other products or varieties successfully introduced were tea from Assam, groundnuts and sugar cane from Java, jute from India, and pineapples from Borneo. The present provincial agricultural experiment station of Taiwan also has developed many new crop varieties of good quality. For example, recent plant breeding has contributed to the list by producing fast-maturing sugar cane and wheat.

LAND UTILIZATION

More than one-half of Taiwan's total land area is covered by mountain forests, and of the remaining land only 66 per cent is cultivated. Paddy fields cover about 62 per cent of this land (*Figure 59*); the balance is used for upland dry farming. The forest, paddy, and dry-farming areas vary in different counties. Taipei County has the largest forest area, Hsinchu, the largest percentage of paddy-land, and Penghu, the largest dry-farming area.

Other land in Taiwan is used for graveyards and for irrigation ponds, both of which occupy a large area. Pastures account for only a small percentage of the land; pasturage is not well developed. The area occupied by temples is about the same as that used for pastures.

In each county the land use depends considerably on local conditions. For instance, 56 per cent of the island's irrigation canals and ponds are located in the Tainan County area. This irrigation system is closely related to the Chianan irrigation system. About 70 per cent of the irrigation ponds are concentrated in Hsinchu County. This is due to the fact that Hsinchu and Taoyuan counties are located on a tableland and that the landform favors the construction of ponds. Ninety-six per cent of the fish culture ponds are found in Tainan and Kaohsiung counties, owing to their location on the southwestern coastal shallow area, with lagoons and shallow bays, which are easily dammed to form ponds. About 89 per cent of the salt fields are found in Tainan County, for it has a shallow-water seacoast and dry, sunny winters, both of which favor the salt industry. Penghu County has the largest graveyard area; graves there represent 10 per cent of all the graves on the island. This large percentage is related to the fact that Penghu is the area of the oldest settlement and the earliest development.

Land utilization is affected by landforms and soils. Taiwan has four types of landforms: mountains, hills and tablelands, plains, and dunes and reefs.

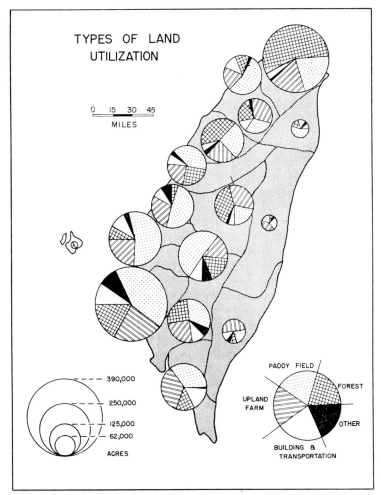

Figure 59

LANDFORMS

The mountains occupy about 8900 square miles, which is nearly 64 per cent of the total area of Taiwan. From the steep slopes of the high Central Mountains, landslides, rockfalls, and mudflows are constantly spilling into the deep, narrow, stream-filled valleys. These occurrences are increased by earthquakes and typhoons, which are common in this subtropical climate. Somewhat more than one-half of this vast mountainous area is now in an economically unproductive state, but hardly any conservation program has received wholehearted support in the past. However, proper utilization of the mountain land in the future should also improve the use of Taiwan's lowlands.

Even though the mountain land is not suitable for crop cultivation, its abundant rainfall and wide range of altitude provide excellent conditions

261

for the growth of useful trees. The trees are needed, for without forest cover the mountain soil would be vulnerable to the destructive erosive forces of the rain that is so heavily concentrated in these highland regions.

The mountains of Taiwan are the source of only small quantities of minerals, such as gold, copper, manganese, sulfur, pyrite, and asbestos. But with dependable and abundant rainfall, together with steep slopes, the mountain area is an ideal place for generating hydroelectric power and providing usable water for irrigation as well as for household and industrial uses.

Every change in the condition of the mountains, such as timber cutting and sporadic clearing, may affect the land use in many lower parts of the watershed area. Through elimination of the forest and vegetation cover, much rocky debris, gravel, silt, and sand are flushed downhill by torrential rains and runoff water. These are then deposited on the lowlands. Every year these deposits damage hundreds of acres of farming lands, villages, highways, irrigation canals, and so forth, and costly repairs have to be made.

Plains, located mostly on the western coast, occupy 3100 square miles, which is about 23 per cent of the total land area of Taiwan. Compared with other landforms, the plains have many advantages, especially in agriculture. Constituted largely of fine-grained sediments that have been washed down from adjacent mountains and hills, the soils have higher fertility than most others in Taiwan. The most important element in agricultural production in the plains is water supply, and both surface and underground water are normally present in plains areas.

The plains of Taiwan are readily accessible to urban concentration, to transportation routes, and to potential markets, and they support the largest number of people per unit area in Taiwan—approximately 3600 persons per square mile. In the mountain areas there are only 65 persons per square mile.

Between the mountains and the plains are located foothills and gravel tablelands, which occupy 1700 square miles, or 12 per cent of the total land. They are composed of unconsolidated materials, mostly gravels and boulders. The land use of these hills and tablelands depends on several factors. The lateritic soils on top of the gravel beds, which have a high dispersion ratio of clayey soil, are highly vulnerable to water erosion. Because of prolonged exposure and desiccation of land surface resulting from denudation and from long cultivation (since early settlement days), these soils are notably low in organic content, a condition that results in low fertility. The area is not directly connected with high mountains, and irrigation cannot be easily developed. Agricultural production suffers because of the unpredictable rainfall and the unreliable irrigation system. Surface reservoirs, occasionally supplemented by canals, can serve only as temporary fish-culture ponds. Closer to the plains and more accessible than the mountains, the hills and tablelands are ever increasing in importance as areas suitable for agricultural expansion, despite a high proportion of slopes, deeply incised stream valleys, and active soil erosion.

Along Taiwan's western coast there are many tidal sand flats and actively migrating sand dunes, which occupy about one per cent of the total land. They are formed from the periodically receding tidal or stream waters that expose the otherwise submerged sand along the beach, in the stream beds, and on the river banks. The strong north-northwesterly monsoon winds, blowing from September to April, and the south-southeasterly winds, blowing from May to August, carry the quickly dried-up sand particles often as far as three miles. The erosive force of wind in the dune areas has many implications for agricultural production. The wind damages not only the soil, but also, directly, the crops.

SOILS

The soils used mainly for agriculture are of two kinds: paddy and alluvial soils, and red and yellow soils.

Paddy and alluvial soils are found in the southwest plains. Farming in Taiwan was first developed many years ago in the coastal plain area because it had, and still has, the most productive soils. Gradually farming was extended toward the Central Mountains. Artificial irrigation has been established for most of the fertile plain areas. In the areas characterized by unusual stoniness, light soil texture, excessive internal drainage, and inadequate irrigation, the land is commonly used for production of dry-farming crops. The soils in those areas, as a rule, preserve the distinctive features of their alluvial origin.

Red and yellow soils are mostly intermingled in foothills and table-lands. The red soils, characteristically acid to strongly acid, are examples of soil subjected to prolonged leaching, excessive surface runoff, and water erosion. The high dispersion ratio of their colloids, infrequent accessibility to irrigation, low organic-matter content, and high rate of potash and phosphate fixation form the clay complex for general crop production. The yellow soil areas are generally better suited for forest than for agricultural use, yet cultivation has found its way into many yellow-soil areas.

MAN-MADE CONDITIONS

Land use in Taiwan is affected not only by physical forces, but also by man-made conditions. Because the amount of arable land is limited and the population growth rapid, quick returns are needed, and the land is mistreated. Examples of mistreatment include attempts to use land far beyond its capabilities and inadequate or improper maintenance practices. Such mistreatment is common, especially in areas adjacent to the foothills. Methods of farming that illustrate the misuse of land may be described in relation to three types of crops as follows[4]:

CITRONELLA.—In 1945, when the island was restored to China, only 141 acres were in citronella grass. By 1951 the area for this crop had increased to 44,500 acres. Most of it was cleared from the forest land in the foothills in Miaoli, Taichung, Nantou, Hsinchu, and Taoyuan counties. When the price of citronella oil dropped, the farmers discontinued to cultivate the crop, but the hilly areas previously cleared of their forest cover could not be restored quickly to timber production. On some hillsides, abandoned citronella plantations were converted to different food crops such as peanuts, sweet potatoes, corn, and cassava. All of these crops require cultivation after planting as well as soil excavation during harvesting. Citronella growers did not have either the funds or the incentive to

263

establish soil-conservation measures such as terracing, contour planting, strip cropping, and protective waterways. Concentrated runoff water through the deserted citronella fields rapidly carried away the surface soil from the hillside, and in a few years extensive areas were depleted.

TEA.—Similarly, new tea plantations also accelerated soil erosion. Over 80 per cent of the tea plantations are located on steep hillsides on 20–40 degree slopes. Tea farmers do not like to see water standing on their plantations, and painstakingly they will dig up-and-downhill drainage ditches, which often develop into gullies as a result of concentrated runoff water.

Whenever tea is cultivated on a hillside, cultivation extends from the very top down to the foot of the hill, which is all planted with this one crop. This not only exposes most of the vulnerable soil but also prolongs the continuous slope and accelerates the erosive action of runoff water.

Soil-erosion damages on these lands are irreparable in many cases. Because of the soil-impoverishing methods used, the losses suffered on the whole become much greater than the meager income temporarily realized by the individual.

BANANAS AND CASSAVAS.—The misuse of soil is at its worst in the recently expanded cultivation of bananas and cassavas on the steep hilly lands originally under brush or forest in many parts of central Taiwan. Not only has much of the soil been eroded away from most of such cultivated slopes, owing to tillage and harvest operations, but also the excessive runoff waters have exposed and moved boulders of all sizes and have frequently caused damage in the lower areas to highways, railroads, irrigation channels, and productive paddy fields.

THE CHANGE IN LAND USE

The use of land in Taiwan has changed, mainly owing to the rapid increase of the population. The changes are observed through aerial photographs taken from 1947 to 1951 and in comparison with the 1957 report of a ground field survey. The aerial photographs showed one type of land use; the later field survey showed another.

There were changes from brushland to dry-farming land and from grassland to banana, tea, cassava, or castor bean plantations. There were also changes from tropical and subtropical hardwood forests to bamboo groves, because bamboo has wider usage and higher economic value than hardwood forests.

Sand flats or shallow sea beaches became fish ponds, salt fields, or farmland for sweet potatoes and peanuts and even for some paddy rice.

Paddy fields were converted to urban and industrial uses, such as schools, military establishments, and roads.

Recent trends to urbanization have converted hundreds of acres of good paddy lands in the plains or near big cities to various urban uses.

Generally, when the acreages are compared with those for the years before the war, it is found that the acreage for food crops increased while the acreage of cash crops decreased.

There were two rapid changes in land use on the island. One was the sharp decrease in forest areas from 64 per cent of the total area in 1948 to 55 per cent in 1955. The other was the rapid rise in cultivated upland fields, which increased by five per cent from 1948 to 1955. In 1948 the cultivated area amounted to 2,119,000 acres; in 1958 it amounted to 2,717,000 acres. Most of the increase in cultivated land is used for dry-farming in the foothill regions.[5]

The trends show considerable increase in cultivated areas, particularly in those used for upland crops. There was also a definite increase in grassland areas, and a significant decrease in forest areas. The increase in paddy and other areas was insignificant as to area but very important to the island's economy.

RECOMMENDATIONS FOR LAND USE

Rather than focus so much attention on the plain areas, the general public should become more interested in the conservation and development of the foothills, mountain areas, and tablelands, which, combined, constitute almost 70 per cent of the island's total land area.

Each year erosion, floods, and runoff deposits, caused partly by misuse of the land, results in extensive and costly damage to the soil and public and private property. This indicates the necessity of more intensive protective and conservation measures.

To accommodate the increase in population and maintain the crop output has created a two-fold problem in food production. On the one hand, there is diminished use of paddy lands for agricultural purposes because of the increase in their conversion to urban and industrial uses. On the other hand, the hilly uplands used to replace the fertile paddy fields are only about one-seventh as productive.

Portions of the many acres of grasslands could be developed for livestock production, if steps can be found to overcome their multiple disadvantages, including lack of water, inaccessibility, steep slopes, and, in particular, the fire hazard they constitute.

With technical training and financial aid, the government must convince the farmers of the benefits derived from individual soil and water conservation. Large-scale conservation cannot be achieved by compulsory measures, but by the incentive of thousands of individual farmers assured of its advantages.

AGRICULTURAL PRODUCTS

More than seventy kinds of crops are grown in Taiwan; rice, sugar cane, and sweet potatoes represent nearly three-fourths of the total production (*Figure 60*).

The increase in production of some crops can be seen in *Table 48*. Per acre yields have been increased for every crop. The per acre yield of rice, for example, has gone from 1856 pounds in 1953 to 2340 pounds in 1962, an increase of 26 per cent. During the same period, pineapple yield increased from 5534 to 8353 pounds, or by 50 per cent. Tea has gained 100 per cent, from 122 to 240 pounds. The total production of sugar declined because of lower international demand, but the per acre yield has increased 9 per cent.

Table 48. The Increase in Production of Selected Crops Between 1953
and 1962 (in tons)*

crop	1953	1962
Rice	1,805,712	2,324,161
Sugar (decreased)	9,233,782	6,756,648
Pineapple	75,318	101,537
Bananas	105,711	148,786
Tea	13,093	21,728
Citrus fruits	32,292	73,855
Vegetables	685,577	925,549

* Based on Republic of China Today (Overseas Chinese Affairs Commission, Taipei, 1963), p. 61.

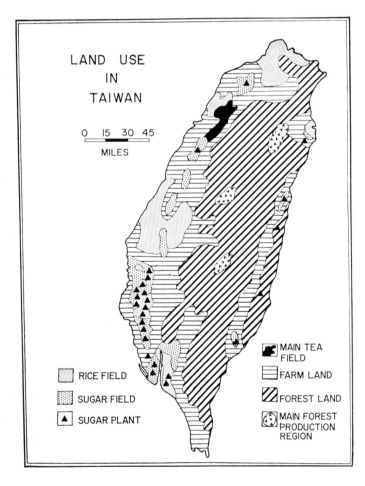

Figure 60

Rice

Rice is the leading crop and it accounts for more than half of Taiwan's total agricultural production. Of all Taiwan's crops, rice has the highest yield per unit area. The yield is much higher in Taiwan than, for example, in Burma, but it is lower than in Japan (*Figures 61 and 62*).

Rice not only is a staple article of the people's diet, but its cultivation is also Taiwan's most effective means of preventing soil erosion, checking flooding, and conserving soil fertility.[6]

World War II reduced Taiwan's rice production considerably. The Japanese government in Taiwan, supplying rice to its army, controlled rice production, storage, milling, transportation, and selling. Because of compulsory selling of rice at an official price, the farmers could hardly make a living and became reluctant to increase production. A labor shortage, due to the army draft, and a shortage of fertilizers from Japanese manufacturers worsened conditions.

In the fall of 1945, when Taiwan was restored to the Chinese National government, food control was abolished and agricultural production was rehabilitated. After that, the production of paddy rice and the area of its cultivation increased steadily.

Also, the area devoted to native rice was now greater than that devoted to Ponlai rice. Two conditions account for this. First, although Ponlai rice has a higher yield per unit area than native rice, it needs much more chemical fertilizer. Such fertilizer had been supplied by Japan, but the

Figure 61.—Through improved farming practices, Taiwan's rice production has attained record highs (AID/JCRR photo)

267

supply was cut off when the island was restored to China. Second, the political pressure exerted by the Japanese in expanding the cultivation of Ponlai rice, because it was more palatable to Japanese consumers, was removed. Those two conditions led Taiwan farmers to return to the cultivation of native rice. However, since 1950 the provincial government of Taiwan and the U.S. Economic Cooperation Administration's China Mission have purchased chemical fertilizer for the island, and the area of cultivation of Ponlai rice has increased again.

Under the Japanese rule more than 90 per cent of Taiwan's annual rice production was exported to Japan. However, since 1945 and the restoration of Chinese rule, seven-eighths of its rice is consumed on the island, leaving little for export.

Figure 62.—Terraced rice paddy fields appear to overlap like roof tiles in northern Taiwan (AID/JCRR photo)

Past increase in rice production was chiefly the result of restored and improved irrigation and an improved fertilizer and seed program. Any further improvement in production will depend to a great extent upon cultivation methods. Experimental deep-plowing methods have already improved the structure of the soil and facilitated growth of the rootlets. This increases the amount of nutrients available for the crop.[7] Other methods of improving rice production include seed disinfection, better arrangement of seedbeds, transplanting in closer rows, and pest control.

Sugar cane

Second only to rice, sugar cane is the most important agricultural product of the subtropical island. Before World War II, the world's sugar production averaged 22 million tons annually. In that time, Taiwan's average was 1.1 million tons, nearly five per cent of the world's sugar production; Taiwan was fourth in sugar production, outranked by India, Cuba, and Java.[8] In the export of sugar, Taiwan was surpassed only by Cuba and Java, for India consumed all the sugar she produced. Before the war, the average annual world export of sugar amounted to 11.5 million tons. During the same period, Taiwan's sugar export averaged 1.1 million tons, or eleven per cent of the world export.

Before World War II, Taiwan's sugar industry reached its peak; but during the war it declined rapidly owing to the following conditions. First, since rice was in greater demand than sugar, cane fields were converted into rice fields. Second, the Japanese did not need Taiwan's sugar for they occupied Java and the Philippines, two places where sugar was plentiful. Third, wartime caused reduced shipping facilities and sugar factories were converted for other uses.[9]

Sugar cane is planted from June to November and harvested about 18–20 months later. Sugar cane cultivation has a long history, but in Taiwan it remained undeveloped until the modern plantation sugar industry was introduced by the Japanese in 1938. Before the outbreak of World War II, sugar refining accounted for more than half of the total manufacturing industry of Taiwan. There were 51 sugar mills on the island, and, at that time, the island normally supplied nearly 90 per cent of the sugar requirements of Japan.

Sugar cane has been the leading cash crop in Taiwan for more than half a century, but the climatic conditions there are by no means ideal for its cultivation. In the northern part of the island, the absence of a dry season hampers the harvest and lowers the sugar content of the cane. In the south, during the dry season, irrigation becomes necessary, for sugar cane cultivation requires at least 24 inches of rainfall annually.

Sugar cane can be grown almost anywhere in the agricultural area of the island, and 45–50 per cent of the arable land is devoted to it. Its greatest acreage is on the western plain, especially south of the Choshui River, where cultivation is benefited by the Chianan irrigation system, and where 80 per cent of the sugar cane of the western plain is grown. However, the area shifts with the price of sugar cane. With high prices, the cane area pushes northward; in a low price year, it retreats south of the Choshui River.

For many years there has been competition between sugar and rice for available irrigated land. The farmer profits more from the growing of rice, owing to its shorter growing period, which permits two crops in a year, whereas the sugar cane requires an 18-month growing period. Also, rice may be stored, but sugar cannot. If the Japanese government had not encouraged the sugar cane industry in Taiwan, that industry would not have attained its present status.

There can be no doubt that continued export of sugar is vital to the maintenance of the island's economy. Sugar earns more in foreign exchange than any other agricultural product.

In view of the ecological handicaps and the competition with rice cultivation, increasing the sugar cane yield per unit area would be one of the most important steps toward improving the sugar cane industry, for Taiwan's cane yield per unit area is low in comparison to the yield in other places, such as the Philippines and the United States.[10] Efforts have been made in this direction since the war, and as a result, the average cane harvest per acre has doubled. Sugar yield per acre increased correspondingly. This increase took place in spite of the fact that the acreage devoted to cane fluctuated widely. That acreage may be reduced in the future because the rice acreage is increasing as a result of increased population. On the other hand, cane production could maintain and even surpass its present amount, if the yield per unit area is increased. Steps toward the increase should include improvement of cane varieties, with an increase of the sugar content of the cane; extension of irrigation facilities; improved use of fertilizers; tractor cultivation; deeper plowing; and efforts to decrease wind damage and to prevent destruction by insects.

Sweet potatoes

The sweet potato ranks third among Taiwan's crops in acreage and in total value of production. It is an indispensable article of diet in Taiwan and is next in importance to rice and sugar. As a cash crop it ranks behind tea, pineapples, and bananas. The warm, nearly frost-free climate of the island is very well suited for its growth. This plant is cultivated nearly everywhere on the island and during all seasons. A little over 40 per cent of the amount produced is consumed in Taiwan, much of it for other than direct food purposes; some is used as fodder, and some for making alcohol.[11] The maximum concentration of sweet potato cultivation takes place in the Chianan irrigated area, where sweet potatoes are used as a rotation crop.

Wheat

Wheat is a minor food crop in Taiwan. Its production is low and fluctuates greatly. Its highest production—29,800 tons—was registered in 1956; its lowest—407 tons—in 1929.[12] Wheat cannot compete with sugar, rice, or sweet potatoes, nor with jute or peanuts. The per unit area earnings from wheat are also lower than those of the other crops. The farmer plants it mainly because it is a cash crop. During the Japanese colonial period, the government tried to advance wheat production in Taiwan, but failed. During that period, flour was imported almost without interruption. When Taiwan was restored to China after World War II, and a large number of Chinese came to the island from the mainland, wheat production was encouraged. As a result, wheat production increased to more than three times the highest record set during the Japanese period in 1941.

Even so, the yield of wheat in Taiwan is exceedingly low when compared to that in some European countries. It is only about one-third of the yield in Belgium, Denmark, or the Netherlands, and about one-half of the yield in many other European countries. It is, however, higher than the yield in any other Asiatic country except Japan.

The climatic conditions in Taiwan do not favor wheat cultivation. In southern Taiwan, the humid atmosphere and high temperature and the scant and uneven distribution of rainfall have limited wheat planting.

In the north, the excessive precipitation and the insufficient winter sunshine have almost excluded it. The central part of the western plain is the only region where wheat can be produced without much natural risk.

In Taiwan wheat is planted in October and November, right after the harvesting of the second rice crop. Harvesting of wheat generally takes place some time in late February or early March, before the transplanting of the first rice crop. Wheat mostly grows between the first and second rice crops, and its growing period in Taiwan is relatively short compared to that in other countries. Thus the island requires a variety of wheat that not only matures early, but also grows quickly and gives a good harvest within a short period of time.

The relatively low price of imported wheat has unfavorably influenced local wheat production. Many farmers feel that in addition to the natural risks in wheat production they have to take the chance of a sudden drop of wheat prices, resulting from the influx of cheap imported wheat. Flour mills in Taiwan prefer imported wheat to domestically produced wheat for the following reasons:

First, imported wheat is supplied in large quantities with standard grades and specifications, but local wheat is not standardized and contains a high percentage of moisture and foreign material.

Second, imported wheat, particularly hard red winter wheat, contains a high percentage of gluten. This is necessary for manufacturing high-class flour and monosodium glutamate, a food additive.

Third, the extraction rate of imported wheat is higher than that of local wheat.

A shortage of suitable seeds, an insufficient supply of chemical fertilizer, and inadequate facilities for storing wheat are problems experienced by many farmers in the production of wheat in Taiwan.

Tea

Since 95 per cent of Taiwan's tea crop is exported, tea occupies an important position in its international trade. It is the island's fourth most valuable export, ranking after sugar, rice, and bananas. About 27,000 families, or five per cent of the agricultural families, depend on the tea industry for a living.[13] Before World War II, 95 per cent of the crop went to Japan; now only 80 per cent is exported and most of that goes to the United States and southeast Asia. Tea planting in Taiwan is limited to the hill slopes of the north and the northwest. In this area rainfall of moderate intensity nourishes the tea shrub all year round. Attempts to cultivate tea shrubs in the southern and eastern parts of the island have proved unsuccessful owing either to the scarcity of rainfall or to its erratic nature.

Unlike rice and sugar cane, the tea plant is not a serious competitor for land. It is suited to steeply sloping sites and to relatively infertile acid soil that is little adapted to other commercial crops except citrus fruits.

In 1865, an Englishman distributed tea seeds brought from mainland China to Taiwanese farmers and encouraged tea cultivation by lending them cash. In 1869, he sailed with two ships containing oolong tea, trademarked "Formosa Tea," for sale in North America. From then on, tea from Formosa gradually became known outside the island.[14]

271

The tea bushes in Taiwan are plucked from early April to the middle of November. Three types of tea are generally processed on the island: oolong tea, paochung tea, and black tea. The production of oolong tea, which is semi-fermented and which was once exported in large quantities to the United States, has declined greatly in recent years. Paochung tea, also semi-fermented, is scented and is mostly exported to southeast Asia. More than half of the tea now produced in Taiwan is black tea, which the world market prefers, especially in Europe and America.

Taiwan's tea is mainly for export, and production is always influenced by the international market. From oolong tea to black tea, the manufacture of tea on the island experienced many changes. In 1906, 73 per cent of the tea produced in Taiwan consisted of oolong tea; 25 per cent was paochung and one per cent, black tea. From 1934 to 1939 the production of black tea increased to one-third and exceeded that of oolong. In 1940 black tea amounted to 56 per cent; paochung, 32 per cent; and oolong diminished to 12 per cent of the amount produced.[15]

Tea cultivation requires much labor; labor costs account for about 65 per cent of the production expense. In locations near paddy ricefields, the male laborers in the vicinity are usually occupied in those fields; therefore, tea workers are usually women.

Fruits

The climate of Taiwan is suitable for the production of a large variety of tropical and subtropical fruits—82 kinds, 14 of which have large acreage.[16] The land used for the cultivation of fruit is estimated at 1,480,000 acres, with the largest acreage allotted to cultivation of the banana, which is the king of Taiwan's fruit. Next to bananas in acreage among fruits are pineapples and oranges.

Bananas which were exported totaled 45–75 per cent of its production; pineapples, 72–93 per cent; and oranges, 23–35 per cent. The profit realized from oranges and bananas is larger than that from tea, sugar cane, and rice because the fruits are mostly exported.

BANANAS.—Bananas are high in nutritional value, easy to store, and not difficult to cultivate. Together with low cost of cultivation, these factors combine to encourage banana production. Bananas are grown in many parts of the island, but 90 per cent of the crop is raised in the central and southern parts. In the central part, bananas are cultivated on hilly land without fertilizer. In the south, they are planted on the plain, with many trees per unit area. Therefore, even though the central part has a larger cultivation area, the production in the south is almost as large. Planting and harvesting of bananas requires one year in the southern part of Taiwan, 15 months in the central part, and 18 months in the north. The grade of the slope for the ideal banana farm is not more than 30 degrees.

The cultivating time for bananas in the central part of Taiwan varies with the temperature. As a rule, they are planted from January to April. Then, during the summer typhoon period, the trees are still small and do not suffer much harm from the wind.

On the plain, banana trees are planted 100 feet apart, with about 3500–4400 trees per acre. In the mountains, 2500 trees are planted per acre.

Taiwan's success in banana growing can be explained as follows. First, the physical conditions of the central and southern parts of the island are suited for banana cultivation. Second, there is a large market for bananas in Japan, Korea, and Hong Kong. Third, transportation of bananas for export is easy. Fourth, cultivation is not handicapped by fruit disease. Fifth, there is close cooperation among banana growers.[17]

PINEAPPLES.—Pineapples were introduced into Taiwan from south China in 1650. In 1911 the island had only two canning factories; by 1925 this number had been increased to 26. Although pineapples were cultivated in Taiwan before the Japanese occupation, their cultivation did not become a large-scale enterprise until 1920. That cultivation reached its peak in 1939, when the island's production—160,000 tons—was exceeded only by Hawaii's and Malaya's. That year Taiwan was the third largest producer of pineapples in the world. At that time, the entire crop was exported to Japan. As a result of the loss of the Japanese market at the end of the Japanese occupation in 1945, many farmers shifted from pineapples to cassavas.

In selecting land for pineapple growing, drainage is the first concern. Usually hilly land is used. As the pineapples are usually canned, the plantation should be near a canning factory. At present, half of the pineapple-cultivating area lies in Taichung county.

The pineapple industry had a successful past in Taiwan during the days before World War II, but experienced serious setbacks during the war. The strains of pineapple became badly mixed, owing to the appearance of numerous off-types. There was negligence in type selection. After the war, a long-range plan was established for rehabilitating pineapple production in Taiwan. This dealt with seedling selection and purification of strains. Cultivation methods were improved, as well as pest-control methods.[18]

In 1939, more than 24,000 acres were devoted to pineapple growing. In 1958, the pineapple planting area amounted to 23,500 acres, about half of it in the central part of the island. Southern Taiwan planted more than 9000 acres in pineapples—40 per cent of the total; and the east coast had about 2300 acres—ten per cent of the total. In 1957, a modern cannery was established in the city of Taitung and, as a result, in the near future eastern Taiwan should become an important pineapple-producing area.[19] In the north, the temperature during the growing season is too low for profitable planting of pineapple. The hills of the north are now planted in citrus fruits and tea.

In the past, pineapple growing in southern Taiwan has been limited by the prevalence of pineapple wilt, caused by mealy-bug infestation. With the extension of chemical control of that pest, the acreage of the crop in the south is expected to expand rapidly.

At present, though its acreage and production have not yet reached the prewar record, the pineapple is among the principal fruit crops of Taiwan, ranking second to the banana. It is also one of the most popular table fruits, either fresh or canned, on the domestic market.[20]

CITRUS FRUITS.—About 30,000 families are engaged in working some 20,000 acres of citrus plantations—oranges and tangerines. The total acreage is lower than that of the banana and of the pineapple. Owing to limited production, export of citrus fruits has been very small in recent years.[21] The citrus trees are mainly concentrated in the northern part of Taiwan; 72 per cent of the total citrus acreage is located there. In central and southern Taiwan, where the climate is warmer and drier, pineapples and bananas dominate. Only eastern Taiwan is a promising area for improved citrus varieties.

The citrus fruits grown in Taiwan have definite drawbacks. Though they have excellent flavor, their loose skin makes them unsuitable for storage or long-distance shipping.

The citrus harvest season is from October to March. The varieties grown are mixed. To avoid competition with other crops, citrus trees are planted on hilly slopes with a grade of from 15 to 20 degrees. Citrus areas are similar to tea plantations, but are not so concentrated.

Very little chemical fertilizer is applied to citrus trees, but the farmers do apply compost and barn manures. In recent years, some citrus farmers have learned to use calcium cyanamide, a locally-produced chemical fertilizer.

After the restoration of Taiwan to China in 1945, it was found that the citrus groves were generally infested with injurious insects and diseases. This was a result of wartime negligence and a lack of pesticides at that time. This negligence inflicted heavy losses on the farmer. The warm, humid climate of Taiwan leads to the development of insects and diseases injurious to plant growth. As a result of the close spacing of trees, ventilation of the trees is poor, and this, coupled with the high humidity in the groves, aggravates the situation.

The foreign markets for citrus crops can be improved by planting many high-quality nursery trees and by giving special attention to planting distance, fertilization, pest control, and orchard sanitation.

Other crops

Groundnuts.—The groundnut is the most important legume grown in Taiwan. As a rotation crop, its distribution is similar to that of sweet potatoes. Roughly one-fourth of the output is pressed for oil; the remainder is consumed in its natural state. Other leguminous crops grown in Taiwan include peas, beans, and soy beans.

Jute.—Jute is Taiwan's most important fiber crop. It is used for weaving sugar bags and rice bags for use in export. The island has always been dependent upon imports to meet its requirements, although 10,500 tons of jute were produced in 1960. More than 90 per cent of the crop is grown on the coastal plain in the west.

Cotton.—Under Japanese rule, efforts were made to encourage cotton planting; however, insects and devastating typhoons constituted great obstacles to its production. In some years, there were complete crop failures. During the period between 1937 and 1945, the cotton acreage on the island averaged 10,500 acres a year; the average yield was 980 pounds per acre.

Peanuts.—Peanuts are grown on sandy soil throughout the island. The heaviest concentration is in the drier parts of the western plain. About 25 per cent of the crop is pressed for oil.

Vegetables.—Vegetables form an important part of the Taiwanese diet. There are 107 kinds, but the principal types grown are radishes, cabbages, garlic, taros, onions, melons, celery, cucumbers, leeks, eggplants, string beans, peas, and pumpkins.[22]

Tobacco.—The growing of tobacco in Taiwan was promoted by the Japanese during their occupation. This policy, aiming at self-sufficiency with regard to that product, has been continued by the Chinese, especially since 1948. Tobacco growing is controlled by a government monopoly. Annual consumption on the island is about 4400 tons.

Grains.—In Taiwan, grains other than rice and wheat—barley, millet, and sesame—are grown in small quantities. In the south, these grains are often a third crop; that is, a winter crop grown after the two successive rice crops are harvested.

AGRICULTURAL REGIONS

Several attempts have been made to delimit the agricultural regions in Taiwan. Some specialists use a statistical approach to set the boundaries of the regions; others use a system based on the distribution of the major crops, choosing the dominant crop of the area to determine a distinct agricultural region. Still others use one map, superimposing symbols showing the limits of each of the major crops, and consider those as determining the regions.

Ten agricultural regions are recognized by Jen-hu Chang.[23] He calculates on a county basis the ratio of cultivated to total land and that of cropland to cultivated land and uses an isopleth that indicates equal acreage as the criterion to delimit the agricultural regions. Such a boundary, figured according to acreage instead of the value of products, not only is less subject to fluctuation from year to year but also conveys an areal concept, which is the central theme of geography. In determining the exact location of critical isopleths, he consults the dot maps of important crops. In a region like Taiwan, where statistics are adequate and the culture more or less uniform, a numerical comparison employing the isopleth to delimit agricultural regions may be stimulating and useful.

H. T. Chang presents another approach to dividing Taiwan into agricultural regions.[24] He bases the classification on the distribution of the major crops and selects the dominant crop representative of the agricultural regions. He delineates four major agricultural regions and thirteen subdivisions. In determining the agricultural regions, he also pays attention to the special agricultural problems confronting each region, such as the need for improvement of crop varieties, of cultivation methods, and of pest control.

The agricultural regions delimited by Willert Rhynsburger do not have definite boundaries to emphasize the dominant crops in each area.[25] Instead, he has put the limits of the island's fourteen major crops on one map. Rhynsburger's map, which shows the overlapping of several crops in one area, is logical and presents a true picture of the land use. Also, by avoiding set boundaries of the agricultural regions, he gives an impression that is less subjective than are the former two classifications. However, the map is hard to comprehend; it is less clear in its classification than are those of the Changs.

These three ways of dividing Taiwan into agricultural regions exemplify different methods and different viewpoints, but many of the agricultural regions the three authors present are identical. The new map presented here, which divides Taiwan into ten agricultural regions, uses a combination of the above three classifications (*Figure 63*).

In classifying Taiwan land into agricultural regions, it is worthwhile both to examine the distribution of the major crops and to consider important physical boundaries. There are two such boundaries on the island that interestingly coincide with the agricultural boundaries. The first one is the 1600-foot contour line that roughly separates the Central Mountain land from the hilly land. In agriculture this contour line also serves as a boundary between the forest lands and the mixed crop-forest lands. The other important physical boundary is the 300-foot contour line. This line roughly separates the hilly land from the plains, the plains including the basins, alluvial fans, and rift valleys. It is also roughly an agricultural dividing line, separating the mixed crop-forest land from the farmland.

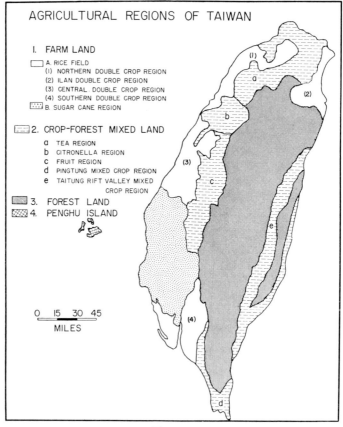

AGRICULTURAL REGIONS OF TAIWAN

1. FARM LAND

A. RICE FIELD
(1) NORTHERN DOUBLE CROP REGION
(2) ILAN DOUBLE CROP REGION
(3) CENTRAL DOUBLE CROP REGION
(4) SOUTHERN DOUBLE CROP REGION
B. SUGAR CANE REGION

2. CROP-FOREST MIXED LAND

a TEA REGION
b CITRONELLA REGION
c FRUIT REGION
d PINGTUNG MIXED CROP REGION
e TAITUNG RIFT VALLEY MIXED
    CROP REGION

3. FOREST LAND
4. PENGHU ISLAND

0   15   30   45
    MILES

Figure 63

276

With these two contour lines, three kinds of landforms, which coincide with the three major agricultural regions, can be outlined. They are: low, flat farmland; hilly, mixed crop-forest land; and mountainous forest land. If the Penghu Islands are considered as a unit, four major agricultural regions are found in Taiwan.

Not only do the 300- and 1600-foot contour lines separate the three types of landforms that coincide with the three major agricultural regions, they also coincide roughly with the 80- and 120-inch isohyets, which indicate equal rainfall. The 300-foot contour line coincides with the 80-inch isohyet, and the 1600-foot contour line with the 120-inch isohyet.

In the flat, low farmland, with an elevation of less than 300 feet, an annual rainfall of less than 80 inches, and alluvial soils, the major crops are rice, sugar cane, sweet potatoes, peanuts, and wheat.

The hilly mixed crop-forest land has an annual rainfall of between 80 and 120 inches, an elevation of 300–1600 feet and reddish-brown and yellowish-brown lateritic soils. Its main crops are tea and citronella in the north, and bananas and pineapples in the central and southern regions.

In the mountainous forest region, the annual rainfall exceeds 120 inches, the elevation is more than 1600 feet, and the soils are of the podzolic type.

FARMLAND

Rice is the major crop in Taiwan, accounting for more than half the total value of the island's agricultural products and also for half of the cultivated area. When the population of the island increased, the paddy fields were extended at the same rate. However, population increase is without limitation, while the area of the paddy fields is limited by the sloping of land. With the passing of time, the paddy fields' rate of increase has slowed down, and their expansion has been retarded as they approach the foothills. Most paddy fields are located in areas less than 300 feet in elevation. Much of the flat land is occupied by the paddy fields.

Taiwan's extensive western alluvial plains have become its most important farmland. The Choshui River divides the western plains into two parts; the northern part grows rice and the southern part sugar cane.

Northern double-crop rice region

The northern region includes a lake basin and plains. The basin is a flat surface surrounded by hills. The basin's limits are rather clearcut; the plains have less definite boundaries.

The region's heavy loam clay, soaked with rain, is particularly suited to rice cultivation, and two crops a year are harvested; greater stress is put on the first crop of rice than on the second. More rice is grown here than in any other region of the island, and more than 60 per cent of the cultivated land in this region is devoted to it.

The northern area is also important for producing oranges and vegetables. Also, a fair amount of flax, ramie, and peanuts is raised in the area. Several of the leading cash crops grown widely in other parts of Taiwan are rather insignificant in this region. Among those crops are sugar cane, bananas, pineapples, tobacco, and cotton, all of which are better suited to southern Taiwan. For all such crops the determining factor is the climate.

Since the northeasterly winter monsoon serves as a rain carrier, the rainfall during the winter season is much more abundant in the north than elsewhere in Taiwan. The rain facilitates the growth of rice during the first half of the year. However, it is unfavorable for the maturing of sugar cane, which is generally planted in the early months and harvested during the spring of the following year. For tobacco and cotton the rainfall in this region is overabundant and the rainy season too long. The growth of bananas and pineapples is handicapped in this region by the shortness of the summer season.

To improve the agriculture of this region, the winter leguminous green manure crop should be planted during the period from November to February after the second crop of rice is harvested, because the region's cool, rainy winter permits sufficient growth of the leguminous crop. The irrigation system in this region should be improved to meet the frequently recurring drought. Also, an efficient means of drying the paddy field before transplanting should be developed, because after the second rice harvest much paddy soil is lost during the winter rainfall owing to sprouting of the grains.

The northeastern double-crop rice rotation region

The northeastern basin is the delta of the Ilan-Choshui River. The network of the river's tributaries provides natural irrigation ditches for the thirsty rice crop. The region resembles the northern one in three ways. First, a high percentage of cultivated land is in rice, which in both amounts to more than 60 per cent. Second, the boundaries of both agricultural regions are well defined; the area contrasts sharply with the surrounding forested hilly land. Third, the agricultural problems here are similar to those of the northern region. Here also the growth of the leguminous green manure crop should be extended to the cool and rainy winter after the second crop of rice has been harvested and the fields are ready for the planting of the first crop. To prevent the loss of the paddy soil there should also be a more efficient means of drying the fields after the second rice crop is harvested.

The middle double-crop rice region

The boundaries of the middle double-crop rice region are defined not by landforms, but by the use of the land. On the northeastern border of this region are plantations of tea and citronella; on the eastern, of bananas and pineapples; and on the southern, of sugar cane. Unlike the surrounding area, it lacks an important cash crop. Its crops differ also from those of other double-crop rice regions in some respects. Sweet potatoes and sugar cane are more important in this region than in other regions, and peanuts less so. In this region, the first rice crop is more profitable than the second. The percentage of cultivated land in rice here is lower than that in the northern and northeastern regions, but the yield per unit area is higher. In fact it is among the highest on the island, owing mainly to the irrigation facilities. This region does not receive an extreme amount of rainfall, but its extensive irrigation ditches help greatly in the cultivation of rice. In the central part of the region less irrigation is available, the percentage of cultivated land in rice is accordingly lower, and other crops are planted among the rice plants. In recent years, winter crops such as wheat, sweet potatoes, vegetables, tobacco, jute, and flax have rapidly expanded their acreage and will soon compete with rice for use of the land.

Southern double-crop rice region

This region has the warmest winter on the island and as a result three crops a year can be grown there. Rice is the leading food crop, but here its importance in acreage is less than it is in the other double-crop rice regions. As for the minor crops, this region contributes the largest share of soy beans, peanuts, and sesame. Sweet potatoes, bananas, and pineapples are produced in substantial quantities. Jute and ramie are also of some importance, but cotton is rare, and flax is out of the picture completely. On the whole, only a few types of crops are significant in the region.

In this region the earlier harvesting of the second rice crop enables the farmers to grow a winter crop of soy beans. To help reduce damage to the fields caused by the summer showers, facilities for quick drying of paddy fields after the first rice crop is harvested should be provided.

Sugar cane region

The sugar cane region is located on the western plain, a rather dry area where rainfall is slight and very variable. The dry season extends over seven months, from October until spring, and is the longest on the island. However, sugar cane needs less rainfall than rice. This area has become Taiwan's most important sugar cane planting region; about one-half of the island's sugar cane acreage is concentrated here. Because of the water shortage, only one crop of rice a year can be harvested in this region; rice and fruits are restricted to places that have been especially adapted by irrigation. In this region sugar cane occupies more than 20 per cent of the cultivated land, but a great variety of crops, in addition to rice and fruit, is grown here—jute, soy beans, wheat, sweet potatoes, pineapples, bananas, and vegetables.

The prolonged dry period was formerly a great obstacle to the development of this region, but the difficulty was solved through construction of an irrigation system, which brought about a phenomenal increase in the sugar cane yield. Today this area is Taiwan's most productive agricultural region. The landscape here is a checkerboard of sugar cane plantations and paddy fields, crossed by a network of irrigation ditches and narrow-gauge rails and dotted with sugar refineries. In the future, with the planned development of underground water, this region will become a place of sharp competition among sugar cane, rice, sweet potatoes, peanuts, jute, and so forth.

While the relatively low rice production is presently necessary for maintaining the production level of sugar, the potential for expansion of rice acreage in this area is greater than in any other area of Taiwan. The production of peanuts as a source of protein food and that of jute as packing material for rice and sugar should increase greatly. Despite the competition for acreage among these crops, technical improvements bringing about an increase in the yield of rice per unit area and a reduction in loss of paddy soil after the harvest are most necessary for any agricultural betterment in this region. Also, improvement is needed in the utilization of the saline soils and "planosol"-like soil in this area. Since the necessity for increasing the acreage and production of rice and peanuts is so great in this region in order to meet the increasing food demands of the island, recommendations for improving the region include the following: That the planting of sugar cane be gradually transferred to the soil that is best for it; that the planting of jute be transferred to another region or that substitute fiber crops be sought; that the sweet potato acreage be reduced; that irrigation be further improved; that winter crops be encouraged.

THE MIXED-CROP FOREST LAND

For increasing the variety and volume of agricultural products, the mixed-crop forest hilly land holds the only hope.

Since rice is the most important staple food in Taiwan, it occupies every suitable piece of plain. In contrast, the hilly land is used for tea, bananas, pineapples, and citronella. With the increase in population, the rice fields are expanding further inland. The cash crops cannot compete with the precious rice, and thus the acreage devoted to tea and to bananas has retreated to the eastern foothills.

One of the important steps in the future agricultural plans of Taiwan is the diversifying of exportable goods so as to include such products as tea, citronella, pineapples, and bananas. With the exception of the pineapple crop, very few crops grown on the hilly land are now chemically fertilized. The potential for increasing the crop yield of these areas is greater than that of the plains and can be realized if more fertilizer is applied. Economically important crops such as ramie, coffee, nuts, and pasture crops should be developed on these sloping lands whenever possible. Also, much attention should be paid to soil conservation, since soils in this hilly mixed crop-forest land are easily eroded.

Tea region

The area for the cultivation of tea has the most clear-cut boundaries in Taiwan. The tea shrubs are grown in the northern gently-rolling hilly lands, where the well-drained, reddish, acid soils are particularly suited to tea cultivation. The eastern and western limits of the tea plantations are flanked by the expanded rice fields, and their southern boundary is the Central Mountain forest lands. The area for planting oranges in Taiwan coincides with that for tea, but the plantations of oranges are not so concentrated as are those of tea shrubs. There are more varieties of oranges grown on the island than of tea, and each requires a different type of physical environment. This factor contributes to the trees being scattered.

Citronella region

The distribution of the citronella grass is quite distinct. Its area of concentration is the middle of the island with its yellowish-brown lateritic hills. Eighty per cent of all the citronella on the island—almost 50,000 acres—is grown there. Before World War II, the area was occupied by forests and tea plantations. After the war, tea was difficult to export. In the meantime, the overseas demand for citronella had so increased that the whole area was given over to its cultivation. However, citronella's acreage is influenced by fluctuations in the world market.

Banana and pineapple region

The central part of the hilly region is the banana and pineapple area. Under the present pressure of population increase, the islanders cannot afford to plant either pineapples or bananas on the plains, where those fruits would have to compete with rice; instead, they grow them on the interior hilly land. Both bananas and pineapples are tropical fruits, unable to stand the cold, and are therefore grown in the southern part of the island.

This region has the highest percentage of dry farmland on the island. Bananas and pineapples are the major crops of the region, but more than 80 per cent of the island's tobacco and cassava are planted here. Rice is also found, but the yield per unit area is rather low. In recent years the effort to produce more rice for the increasing population, an effort that is indicated by the construction of more irrigation ditches and by the advance of terraced fields further up the slopes, has caused the western boundary of this region to retreat gradually.

Pingtung mixed crop region

Located at the southern tip of the island, the Pingtung region has low elevation and high temperatures—the lowest temperature is more than 68°F. Rice is the leading food crop, but it is not so important in acreage here as in other double-crop regions. Other crops produced in substantial quantities in the region include bananas, sisal, sweet potatoes, soy beans, jute, and millet. The main crop is sisal; more than 80 per cent of the island's yield of sisal is planted in this lowland.

Taitung Rift Valley mixed-crop region

The Taitung valley's isolated location, rather than any distinctive agricultural feature, leads to its being an agricultural unit. Because of its considerable extension from north to south, its climatic conditions show greater variation than do such conditions in other parts of Taiwan, and the crops raised here are representative of nearly the whole island. Of the mixed crops, rice, sugar cane, fruits, sweet potatoes, tobacco, peanuts, and millet are grown here, but not tea. The cultivation of rice is concentrated in the flood plains of the rivers, sweet potatoes are cultivated on the hilly land, and fruit trees further up the slopes. Almost all the crops produced here are consumed locally; little is exported.

A noticeable feature is that the percentage of proprietary farmers is highest in this region; this is because a large number of "civilized aborigines," who customarily own their land, live here. The chief handicap of this region is the scarcity of level land. Hence the total area of cultivatable land is only a fraction of what is found in other regions.

FOREST LAND

The forest land lies in the inaccessible high mountains, where less than 10 per cent of the land is devoted to crops. It is inhabited chiefly by aborigines. Rugged terrain, severe climate, and serious soil erosion discourage agricultural development, and the region is practically devoid of agriculture. As a matter of fact, the boundaries of this area are considered the limits of agriculture.

Trees, of course, are the most important products. Cedar, pine, fir, spruce, and so forth, are grown, and also camphor, the most valuable tree on the island.

The cultivated area accounts for less than 2 per cent of the total area of the forest land and the population is small. Sweet potatoes, grown by the aborigines, are the most important crop.

Especially in recent years the wooded mountain areas, because of their beautiful scenery, have become the tourist center of the island.

PENGHU ISLANDS

The islands of Penghu, which are politically part of Taiwan, as an agricultural region are strikingly different from the other regions. The cultivated area is extremely restricted. Rice, the most important food crop on the main island, fails to take hold and sugar cane is not grown here either. Sweet potatoes and peanuts are the only staple crops. Even vegetables are rare and the amount of fruit is negligible. Scanty rainfall, poor soils, and strong winds are primarily responsible for the island's backwardness in agricultural development. Located in Taiwan Strait and lying in the rain shadow of the high mountains of Taiwan, Penghu has an annual rainfall of about half the average of the main island and its rain is deficient for most crops. Moreover, the strong wind, which helps evaporation, makes the area arid and the soil too sandy for irrigation (*Figure 64*).

Figure 64.—A farmer on Kinmen Island waters his vegetables. New wells have been dug to serve for irrigation of the fields and for drinking purposes (AID/JCRR photo)

THE PROBLEM OF MECHANIZATION

In order to meet the needs of the increasing population and to maintain the economic stability of the island, Taiwan has continued to make an effort to increase agricultural production. Possibilities for the extension of cultivated land are limited, for the area already cultivated is near its upper limit. The alternative then is to increase the yield per unit area. Besides expanding irrigation facilities, applying more fertilizer, controlling drainage and flood water, eliminating plant disease, and controlling insect pests, which are the primary means for increasing yield per unit area, an important and effective method is the mechanization of agriculture. However, mechanization has been slow to be adopted on the island.[26]

Optimists consider that agricultural mechanization is a world-wide trend in agricultural improvement and that Taiwan should follow that trend. They say that although farm machinery cannot yet be manufactured on the island, the idea of mechanization should not be given up forever. They point to the fact that the island has not been able to manufacture automobiles, locomotives, or airplanes but has been using them for years. Nowadays agricultural machinery is widely considered necessary in farming, as are automobiles, locomotives, and airplanes in communication. An adequate supply of farm machinery will no doubt stimulate and help farm mechanization. It is not technically difficult to produce simple farm machinery if markets for it exist. Bicycles, for example, have been successfully manufactured on the island in recent years.

Pessimists, however, maintain that owing to overpopulation, full employment has not been attained, so that it is not wise now to substitute machinery for manpower. Again, they note that most farms in Taiwan are small and scattered, and this makes the use of machinery on them difficult. Furthermore, farm machinery, fuel, and so forth, all have to be imported and it is clearly not economical to spend foreign exchange money at this time of national financial stringency.

Both the pro and the con of this problem have reasonable grounds, and it seems worthwhile to explore the question in more detail.

There is abundant manpower on the island, but there is a lack of draft cattle, and the surplus manpower cannot replace the needed animal power. Because of the insufficient supply of animal power, the land for the second rice crop is usually very poorly prepared; this of course affects the yield.

In Taiwan, each head of cattle has to work 5.5 acres of cropland. The excessive workload imposed on the cattle has resulted in crude land preparation, delay in planting, and delay in harvesting. Therefore the highest potential production of cropland is not attained. The overworking of the draft animals also reduces the number of the animals' serviceable years. Also, there is little chance to raise more cattle.

In some other countries farm machinery has taken over most of the work from draft animals. In the United States since 1902, when the first tractor was put into use, there has been a steady change to farm mechanization, and more than 69 million acres of land that were formerly used to produce feed for draft animals are now used to produce food and clothing materials. In Japan at the end of 1953, 113,000 households were using farm machinery to replace cattle in order to increase the area of land for producing food and clothing.

The strongest point noted by persons who are against mechanization is the fact that the farms in Taiwan are small and scattered. But fortunately, with today's technology, it is possible to manufacture small farm machinery to cultivate the small farm. The widespread "gentleman farming" in England and the victory gardens in the United States during the second World War, inspired development of garden tractors of various sizes. The small power tiller requires only three–five horsepower and is relatively simple in structure. It is smaller than a buffalo and costs only two–three times the price of that animal. It can be used in all fields where draft cattle work and it plows deeper and faster than does the animal. Moreover, the machine can be stored safely and needs no more care than the animal (*Figure 65*).

Figure 65.—Small power tillers do some work better, cheaper, and faster than cattle. Here farmers are instructed in the use and operation of one of the machines (AID/JCRR photo)

However, buying a power tiller in a rural area is not as easy as one might think. It has to be adapted to the farm conditions. If complete success is to be attained in the use of imported farm machinery, the machinery must be improved. The Taiwan Sugar Corporation, which has been using farm machinery for many years, found that imported farm machinery does not fulfill the special needs of the corporation's sugar cane farms and is now devising plans to change the machinery to improve production. Small power tillers present similar problems, and only after the machines have been adapted to different conditions and the psychological reactions of the farmers have become more favorable can there be a beginning of machine use.

Also, if the small power tillers are to come into use, the supply of fuel should be studied. In Taiwan it is easier to get gasoline than either diesel oil or kerosene. It has been estimated that to put to use in Taiwan 50,000 power tillers—the equivalent of 100,000 head of cattle—10 million gallons of gasoline will be needed annually. This amounts to about 24 per cent of the present annual output of the China Petroleum Corporation. However, the 50,000 power tillers will not be put to use at once; it may take eight or ten years to reach that goal. With the gradual increase in the number of power tillers, a system of supplying gasoline should not be too difficult to develop. Besides, there is always the possibility of finding a substitute for gasoline, and it is also possible to use alcohol in gasoline engines. Therefore, use of the gasoline-powered tillers should be encouraged and also the search for a gasoline substitute.

The key to the problem of agricultural mechanization is the use of these small power tillers. When those are used, other power machines for cultivation, pest control, processing of the crop, and so forth, will undoubtedly be adopted.

Finally, where can Taiwan get the foreign exchange to be spent on purchase of power tillers? It has been estimated that it can be raised with the resulting increased rice output within a year (two crops of rice). Not only would the agricultural output be increased, but the manufacture of agricultural machinery would be helped in Taiwan. It would be a very profitable investment on the part of the government.

All the above points suggest the possibility of success for the agricultural mechanization program. As a matter of fact, the Chinese-American Joint Commission on Rural Reconstruction has already given power tillers to twelve agricultural research stations in Taiwan for experiments in their use. With the concentrated efforts of all concerned, it should not be long before Taiwan's agricultural system will enter the age of mechanization.

THE "LAND TO THE TILLER" PROGRAM

The "land to the tiller" program, a system of land reform that was carried out chiefly under an act passed in 1953, has been a great achievement of the Nationalist Government of Taiwan.

As in other parts of the world, Taiwan farmers have a deep urge to own the land they till; but that urge could not be fulfilled until the government established the land-reform system described below.

Taiwan has a small amount of cultivatable land, and before the reform took place, little land was available for sale. Also, the prices were so high that tenant farmers could hardly afford to buy, especially in places where irrigation facilities were good and the rice fields fertile. Most farmers were tenants and paid high rents. Farming was on a small scale, and earnings were low.

The concept of "land to the tiller" is nothing new in Chinese history. In the 10th century, in the 11th, and again in the 19th century, such programs had been tried but had failed. In 1924, Dr. Sun-Yat-Sen, founder of the Republic of China, advocated such a program; and as the first step, planned a 25 per cent reduction in farm rents, but the reduction could not be enforced.

In the recent land-reform program, the first step—taken in 1949—was a government-ordered reduction in annual rent from the usual 50 per cent of the year's major crop to 37.5 per cent. The second step was the sale of public land to tenant farmers at a specified price, including 4 per cent interest, to be paid in twenty installments. No installment was to be greater than the rent the tenant had been paying. The third step was compulsory sale to the government of privately owned, tenanted farmland, and resale, at the same price, to the tenant farmers under the same conditions as the public land.

The Chinese-American Joint Commission on Rural Reconstruction has given the Chinese Nationalist government technical assistance in planning and also financial aid in administering the program.

The principal provisions of the "land to the tiller" act are as follows:

(1) Each landlord shall be permitted to retain not more than seven acres of paddy land or 14 acres of dry land that he is now leasing to tenants. All excess acreage over this maximum retention limit shall be purchased by the government and resold to tenant farmers. Allowable retentions are proportionally smaller for the better grades of land.

(2) The purchase price for the land is to be set at two and one-half times the value of the average yearly main crop; 30 per cent of the price shall be paid in government enterprise stocks and 70 per cent in land bonds redeemable in kind. The latter shall bear interest at the rate of 4 per cent per annum and shall be redeemable in 20 equal semi-annual installments, including interest.

(3) The tenanted land that is purchased by the government shall be resold to the present tillers. The resale price shall be the same as the purchase price and shall bear interest at the rate of 4 per cent per annum.[27]

To a poor tenant farmer the saving through ownership represents a considerable improvement in his standard of living. Most tenant farmers have had, since 1948, sufficient rice to feed their families, and many are even able to sell surplus rice to buy other necessities. They are working harder to increase rice production because of the greater share accruing to them. This incentive was one of the important factors in the big increase in rice production in the years 1950–1952.[28] Since the program went into effect, the farmers have been able to develop irrigation and to buy more fertilizer, pesticides, farm implements, and draft animals.

Before the program went into effect, 39 per cent of the island's farmland was tilled by tenants; under the program, only 15 per cent with the remaining 85 per cent tilled by owners.

It would be premature to say that Taiwan's land problem has been solved once and for all. The land problem is only one aspect of the economic problem, and it is always influenced by changes in the national economic policy. If, owing to heavy taxes or lack of ready cash to buy seeds, implements, and so forth, the tiller feels that owning his land is not benefiting him, the government's effort for land reform will have been in vain.

REFERENCES

[1] *Taiwan's Economic Statistics* (Committee on American Aid, Taipei, 1960) p. 17.
[2] T. H. SHEN, "Food production and administration in Taiwan," *Sci. Mon.* **LXXIV**, No. 5, 253 (1952).
[3] C. S. CHEN, *Land Utilization in Taiwan* (National Taiwan University, Taipei, 1950) p. 95 [In Chinese].
[4] E. C. HSIA, *Land Use Conditions in Taiwan* (Chinese-American Joint Commission on Rural Reconstruction, Forestry Series No. 5, Taipei, 1957) p. 11.
[5] ——, *Ibid.*, pp. 42–43.

[6] Jen-hu Chang, *Agricultural Geography of Taiwan* (China Cultural Service, Taipei, 1953) p. 54.

[7] Jing-rang Yu, "Rice culture in Taiwan," in *Rice in Taiwan* (Bank of Taiwan, Taipei, 1949) p. 7. [In Chinese].

[8] S. K. Lu, "Taiwan's sugar and its research," in *Sugar in Taiwan* (Bank of Taiwan, Taipei, 1949) p. 22. [In Chinese].

[9] T. C. Sun, "Taiwan's sugar," in *Sugar in Taiwan* (Bank of Taiwan, Taipei, 1949) p. 33. [In Chinese].

[10] Arthur A. Simpson, "Postwar economy of Taiwan, a crucial area of East Asia," *Foreign Commerce Weekly* **XI**, 4 (1949).

[11] C. S. Chen, "Taiwan's sweet potatoes," *Quart., Bank of Taiwan* **III**, No. 3, 140 (1950). [In Chinese].

[12] Young-chi Tsui, *A Study of Wheat in Taiwan* (Chinese-American Joint Commission on Rural Reconstruction, Taipei, 1957) p. 1.

[13] P. N. Li and H. Y. King, "The manufacturing of tea in Taiwan," *Quart., Bank of Taiwan*, Taipei, 1949) p. 5. [In Chinese].

[14] N. C. Chang, "Taiwan's tea," in *Tea in Taiwan* (Bank of Taiwan, Taipei, 1949) p. 5. [In Chinese].

[15] C. S. Chen, *Land Utilization of Taiwan* (National Taiwan University, Taipei, 1950) p. 217. [In Chinese].

[16] K. C. Shen, "Taiwan's fruit," in *The Fruit in Taiwan* (Bank of Taiwan, Taipei, 1955) p. 2. [In Chinese].

[17] C. S. Chen, "Taiwan's banana," in *The Fruit in Taiwan* (Bank of Taiwan, Taipei, 1955) p. 36–37. [In Chinese].

[18] S. M. Chen, "Taiwan's pineapple," in *The Fruit in Taiwan* (Bank of Taiwan, Taipei, 1955) p. 78. [In Chinese].

[19] Chi-lin Luh, *Recent Improvement on Pineapple and Citrus Fruit Production in Taiwan* (Chinese-American Joint Commission on Rural Reconstruction, Taipei, 1958) p. 3.

[20] ——, *Ibid.*, p. 6.

[21] ——, *Ibid.*, p. 15.

[22] P. N. Li, "Taiwan's vegetables," in *Vegetables in Taiwan* (Bank of Taiwan, Taipei, 1955) p. 6. [In Chinese].

[23] Jen-hu Chang, *Agricultural Geography of Taiwan* (China Cultural Service, Taipei, 1953) p. 70.

[24] H. T. Chang, *Natural Environment and Crop Distribution in Taiwan* (Chinese-American Joint Commission on Rural Reconstruction, Taipei, 1956) p. 39.

[25] Willert Rhynsburger, *Area and Resources Survey, Taiwan* (International Cooperation Administration, U. S. Mutual Security Mission to China, Taipei, 1956) p. 60.

[26] Fengchow C. Ma, *On the Agricultural Mechanization in Taiwan* (Chinese-American Joint Commission on Rural Reconstruction, Taipei, 1958) pp. 1–4.

[27] Hui-sun Tang, *Land Reform in Free China* (Chinese-American Joint Commission on Rural Reconstruction, Taipei, 1954) pp. 14–22.

[28] T. H. Shen, "Land to the tiller in Free China," *Ann, Acad. Sinica*, No. 2 (part 1), 3, (1955).

TWENTY

Livestock
Fisheries
and Forestry

LIVESTOCK RAISING

As IN OTHER Far Eastern regions, livestock plays a role in the rural economy of Taiwan. Almost every farm family raises hogs and poultry and some cattle also are raised. In contrast to northwestern China where animals are raised for milk, hides, and wool, in Taiwan they are used for cultivation, hauling, and meat. Again, in northwestern China there are large pasturelands; in Taiwan, owing to the pressure of increasing population, as much as possible of Taiwan's land must be used for crops. The pastureland occupies only one-tenth of one per cent of Taiwan's total area. These pastures are located on dry river beds, foothills, and mountain grasslands.

The subtropical climate is also a handicap to livestock raising; the high temperature and humidity encourage livestock diseases and make it difficult to preserve fodder.

The number of livestock on the island in relation to population is far below that of western countries. There are only 4 head of cattle per 100 persons in Taiwan, as compared with about 60 head per 100 persons in the United States; 30 hogs, as compared with 45 in the United States; and 60 chickens as compared to 300 per 100 persons in the United States. There are fewer animals per capita in Taiwan than in mainland China.

Livestock raising, however, has a close relation to agriculture and is profitable for Taiwan's farmer. In 1962, for instance, the value of livestock production represented about one-third of the total value for agricultural production.

About 7,000,000 tons of hog and cattle excrement a year are used to maintain soil fertility. It not only supplies organic content, but also increases the water storage capacity of the soil and thus prevents serious soil erosion.

As for feed for cattle and hogs, soy beans are easy to grow, and are an economical feed. Cattle fodder is also obtained from the leaves available after the harvesting of agricultural products.

For poultry an economical feed is found in the fish and oysters that abound in the island's many ponds and irrigation canals.

The number of hogs, cattle, chickens and ducks on the island is increasing and the raising of livestock provides the most promising avenue of development in Taiwan's agricultural area. However, much improvement is needed, which will require the prevention of diseases, better selection of breeds, improvement of feeding, and carefully supervised raising techniques. In the United States, one hen can produce 365 eggs per year, and one duck, 360; one dairy cow can produce 17,500 gallons of milk a year. But in Taiwan one hen can produce only 70 or 80 eggs a year and one dairy cow can produce only 3000 gallons of milk per year.[1]

Livestock raising has always been secondary to crop production in Taiwan and all livestock breeds were much neglected and characteristically poor in quality. The hogs on Taiwan, being closely confined, are subject to the rapid spread of disease, plague, influenza, and enteritis. There is little occurrence of cattle diseases and, among the large poultry population in 1960 for example, deaths due to disease amounted to only three-tenths of one per cent. Sheep and goats are so scarce that little is known of the occurrence of diseases among them. However, the failure of sheep raising has often been attributed to the inroads of parasitic diseases.

Hogs

Pork is the basic meat in Chinese society, and hog raising is of much importance to the farm economy of Taiwan. Hog production amounts to 10 per cent of the total agricultural production; it is surpassed only by rice and sugar. Hogs represent 74 per cent of the island's livestock production. It is estimated that the sale of hogs brings in one-sixth of the island's farm income. Slaughter taxes, chiefly from hog butcheries, are reported to account for 30 per cent of each county's revenue. Although in the beginning meat and bristles were the only hog products commercially usable, pigskin is now being used in the manufacturing of footwear. This reduces the island's dependence on imported hides.

In 1898 there were only 430,000 hogs in Taiwan and it was necessary to import more than 100,000 to meet the demand. In 1910 hog production reached 1,200,000 and was sufficient for the island's needs, but it was not until more than two decades later that there was enough for export. In 1934 Taiwan was able to export hogs. In that year the island exported nearly 3600 to Hong Kong. In 1889 the average number of hogs per family on the island was only one. In 1913 it was three hogs per family. In 1933 it was 4.5 hogs per family, more than four times the figure for 1889.[2] In 1962, Taiwan had 3 million hogs.

Taiwan is one of the leading hog-producing areas in the world—not in the total number of hogs produced, but in the ratio of hog production to population and to land area. In 1939 Taiwan had 280 hogs per 1,000 persons and was fifth in the world in that respect. The first four places were held by Denmark with 869, Brazil with 501, Canada with 500, and the United States with 418. In the same year the number of hogs per square mile of land in Taiwan was 119; this was second only to Denmark's figure of 197. Again, with respect to the number of hogs per square mile of cultivated land, Taiwan was second in the world in that year with 497 per square mile.

Unlike farmers in the United States, who feed their hogs on corn, and unlike European farmers, who feed them on potatoes, Taiwanese farmers feed their hogs mainly on sweet potatoes and for protein, soy bean cakes.

During the years 1929–1938 Taiwan improved greatly in hog raising. Breeding programs improved the quality of the hogs for market. Feeding was better; more soy beans for hog feeding were imported. Owing to further improvements in hog raising, the number of hogs produced on the island increased more than eight times between 1945 and 1962.

In the future a hog improvement program should direct more attention to disease control. Although the program has benefited by the import of soy beans, dependence upon this import should be decreased because peanuts, potatoes, molasses and other feeds can be produced locally.

Cattle

There are two kinds of cattle in Taiwan: water buffalo and yellow cattle. The buffaloes raised for farm work constitute four-fifths of all the cattle on the island.[3] They are ubiquitous in the rural area. The buffaloes are used on paddy fields; the yellow cattle on dry-farm land.

In 1962 the total number of cattle in Taiwan numbered 420,000. The island average is 32 head of cattle per square mile. There are about 40 head of cattle per 1000 persons on the whole island.[3]

Poultry

Poultry outnumber all other livestock in Taiwan. Export of feathers and of ducks is higher than the United States' total, and Taiwan's poultry sales rank high in world exports. But poultry, despite large numbers, remains distinctly a farming sideline on the island.

Denmark, the chief poultry producer in the world, averages 5.8 birds per person; Canada is second (5.2); the United States third (3.4); and Belgium is fourth (1.5). Taiwan is the fifth on the list with 1.3 per person. Taiwan's poultry production is twice that of Japan and four times that of Korea. In 1962 the production of all poultry combined totalled 14 million head of which chickens amount to 56 per cent, geese 12 per cent, and turkeys 2 per cent (Figure 66).[4]

Chickens are the most numerous of the poultry, amounting to five million. Unlike ducks, which are raised cooperatively, chickens are raised on the plains; fishermen also raise them along the coast, and even city dwellers raise them. The ponds and irrigation canals and ditches are used for raising geese and ducks. Hybrid chickens are the most profitable because they are able to resist pests and diseases.

Combating livestock diseases on an island is easy. The spread of disease can be controlled by careful scrutiny of imported animals. During the Japanese period the authorities made every effort to eliminate this problem. They set up an investigation system for imported animals, established an institute of animal diseases, and undertook the training of veterinarians.

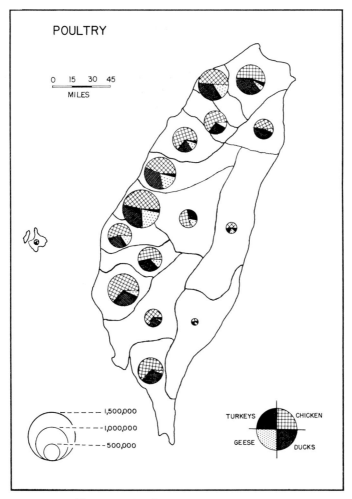

Figure 66.—Poultry production in Taiwan

FISHERIES

With shallow sea on the western coast, Taiwan has a good foundation for fisheries. Huge quantities of plankton are constantly being renewed by streams draining into the seas and they attract a wealth of fish that spawn and feed in the shallow water each season. Shore facilities for landing, storage, refrigeration, marketing, and transportation of fish are generally adequate.

However, the fisheries of Taiwan are not highly developed. The fish catch amounted to only 62 pounds per capita in 1962, as compared with Japan's 108. In that year yield of the fisheries constituted less than 3 per cent of the total value of Taiwan's production, including agriculture, forestry, mining, manufacturing, and fishing. The fish industry employs about 240,000 persons. Assuming three dependents each, a total of 720,000

291

persons are wholly or partly dependent on the fisheries for a livelihood. This is 7 per cent of the island's population. Added to these are a somewhat smaller number of persons engaged in or dependent upon fish handling, processing, transportation, and marketing. Most of the offshore islets are comparatively barren, and their inhabitants rely upon sea products for a living to a greater extent than do those on Taiwan proper. It is reported that four-fifths of the employed population of the island of Penghu are fishermen, either full time or part time.

Twenty varieties of fish and shellfish usually account for more than 80 per cent of the total fishery production, figured either in volume or in value[5]. In order by volume the varieties are: milk fish, sardines, bonito, sharks, lizard fish, black and white croakers, mackerel, mouthbreeders, oysters, tuna, sea bream, spearfish, cuttlefish, hairtail, shrimp, horse mackerel, flying fish, mullet, carp, and ray.

Physical conditions

Compared with the highly indented and irregular coast of Fukien, Kyushu Island of Japan, and Western Korea, the shoreline of Taiwan is relatively unbroken and affords few anchorages or harbors. Located between the East China Sea and the South China Sea and separated from the mainland of China by the Taiwan Strait, the island is surrounded by a continental shelf with a depth of about 660 feet.

Scattered along the Taiwan coastline there are 42 major fishing ports, but only three of them are prominent—Keelung and Suao in the northeast, and Kaohsiung in the southwest. These three centers supply one-half of the total fish catch. Other important fishing ports include Makung, Hualien, Hsinkong, Anping, Tungkong, and Tamshui.

An ideal fishing port should provide ice plants, cold storage, shipyards, machine shops, processing factories, transportation, and other related industrial installations. Keelung and Kaohsiung best meet these requirements.

The western coast, along the Taiwan Strait, has gentle slopes averaging 160–330 feet in depth. It provides an ideal marine environment for bottom-dwelling fish. The fish catch along the western coast represents about 80 per cent of Taiwan's total fish production.

On the eastern coast—the Pacific side—the ocean floor drops immediately to a depth of 9800–13,500 feet, eliminating the possibility of catching bottom-dwelling fish. However, here are found large deep sea species such as tuna, spearfish, bonito, mackerel, sharks, and sardines.

Taiwan is benefited by ocean currents. The Kuro Siwo or Black Stream (Japan Current), a warm current flowing northward along the east Asian coast, approaches Taiwan from the southeast. Near the southern tip of Taiwan it flows along both east and west shores of the island. The China coastal cold current flows southward along the mainland shore and meets the warm current in Taiwan Strait. Thus the strait is the area where food for fish is plentiful; and it becomes the fishing grounds located north and northwest of the Penghu Islands.

This type of physical environment generally favors the development of fisheries. But in Taiwan that development is handicapped by the climate. From October to April the northeast monsoon is so strong, reaching 26 feet per second, that fishing is then a dangerous business, and this naturally lessens the catch. In the summer months, from July to September, the island suffers from typhoons. From 1945 to 1949 no less than 67 fishing steamboats were destroyed, as well as 286 rafts. This caused the drowning of 322 men.[6]

Types of fisheries

On the basis of fishing methods, the fisheries of Taiwan are classified in four main categories: deep-sea, inshore, coastal, and fish culture (*Figure 67*). The 1962 catch was 359,700 tons, 2.5 times that of 1953. This catch was broken down into 40 per cent coastal, 35 per cent deep-sea, 10 per cent inshore, and 15 per cent cultured fish.

DEEP-SEA FISHING.—This consists of otter-trawling with a powered craft in the 50–110 ton class, and tuna longlining with a powered craft in the

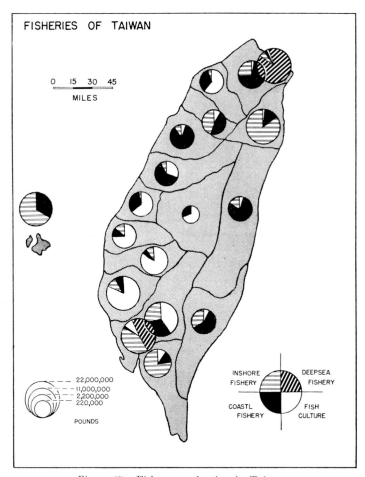

Figure 67.—Fishery production in Taiwan

293

100 ton or heavier class. The trawlers are operated generally in the southern waters of the East China Sea and in Taiwan Strait. The tuna longliners carry their activities as far away as the southwest Pacific and the Indian Ocean.

Before World War II, deep-sea fishing was the poorest of the four types of fisheries in Taiwan. Most of the yield from the deep sea off Taiwan was deposited directly at Japanese ports. The modest deep-sea fleet which did exist before 1940 was destroyed during the war and that type of fishing ceased entirely. Tuna fishing is now undergoing active improvement and expansion.

For development of deep-sea fisheries emphasis should be placed on exploration of new fishing grounds and resources, advancement of technology, and construction of modern fishing boats. Also urgent is the need for sound programming and industrialization of deep-sea fisheries in coordination with shipbuilding and other related industries. If advancements are to be made, the shipbuilding industry must work along with the fishing industry.

INSHORE FISHING.—Most of the boats used on the island for inshore fishing are small powered craft averaging 10 tons each. The majority of the inshore fleet are less than 20 gross tons in weight. Their operation is generally confined to the waters 10–80 miles off the shores of Taiwan, a one-day trip from port. After World War II, because of the high cost of replacing or rehabilitating boats, engines, and gear, inshore fishing revived less rapidly than did coastal fishing. But the inshore catch increased from 19,600 tons in 1947 to 35,970 tons in 1962—the largest amount ever taken in Taiwan. The main products of inshore fishing from Taiwan Strait are bream, mackerel, croaker, and mullet. Off the southwest coast, spearfish, sailfish, shark, and tuna are found. These are caught in the nearby waters of the South China Sea and the Philippine Sea.

Unlike coastal rafts and sampans, which can be based almost anywhere, most inshore fishing vessels operate from the larger ports. About half of the boats weighing less than 50 gross tons are registered in Kaohsiung, Tainan, Keelung, and Suao and adjacent smaller ports. Kaohsiung is the principal port and it has more than 400 vessels in the 5–50 ton category. Makung, on Penghu Island, is also a major base for inshore fishing.

COASTAL FISHING.—Coastal fishing includes all fishing conducted without the use of powered vessels; that is, fishing from sampans or rafts, or from the shore with nets, traps, or lines, and hand gathering of marine shellfish, seaweed, and so forth. People who reside in coastal regions can engage in this type of fishing with little investment and equipment, and this is the most common type of marine fishing.

Because of the modest capital requirements for simple individual operating units, coastal fishing made rapid recovery after World War II. Sardines, mackerel, mullet and shellfish make up the bulk of the coastal catch. Many species are taken in lesser quantities. Oysters, shrimp, clams, and crabs constitute 90 per cent of the shellfish yield and make up from one-fourth to one-third of the total coastal catch. Since the number of potential fishermen is virtually unrestricted and the physical area of operation rigidly limited, coastal fishery resources are in danger of overexploitation.

FISH CULTURE.—Fish culture or pond fishing is widely practiced in Taiwan. The early immigrants from the mainland were experts in it.

There are two types of pond fisheries. One type is carried on in specially-constructed brackish water ponds near the shore. These are found chiefly along the southwest coast from Changhua to Pingtung. The other type is carried on throughout western Taiwan in fresh-water farm ponds, ditches, lakes, and reservoirs, and in rice paddies with the growing crops. Brackish water culture is the more important type. It yields almost three-fourths of the total pondfish production.

Fishing culture is especially prevalent in the south, where milkfish are raised in 35,000 acres of brackish water ponds. Along the western coast, in the central and southern parts of the island, oysters are cultivated in about 15,000 acres of shallow water. In the northern and southern parts carp and mouthbreeders are raised in about 12,000 acres of fresh-water ponds and in 18,500 acres of reservoir water; mouthbreeders are also raised in 18,500 acres of paddy field.

The southwest coast of the island is easy to convert into brackish-water fish ponds, for the coastline is dotted with tranquil bays and lagoons. Also, the land on that coast is too salty for any other use.

The major species of fish raised in brackish water are milkfish, mullet, carp, and prawns. Milkfish are by far the most important and they comprise two-thirds of the yield of brackish-water ponds. Its culture is thought to have been introduced from Indonesia during the period of the Dutch occupation in Taiwan, because brackish-water fish culture is known to have been common in Java as early as 1400.

The brackish-water ponds are concentrated in the southwest near Tainan and Kaohsiung, where high winter temperatures combine with level shore land to provide favorable physical conditions for fish culture, and where brackish-water fish-raising is a long-established industry. The shores of Chiayi, Yunlin, and Changhua counties in the west are also used for such ponds. The northwest coast is not, as it is more exposed to north winds and experiences lower winter temperatures.

The raising of fresh-water fish has been of comparatively minor importance, chiefly because of the rather low return per unit of labor required. The most important areas are in Taoyuan and Hsinchu. Here vast numbers of farm reservoirs are suitable for raising fresh water fish. Taoyuan tableland has a gentle surface sloping toward the sea on which it is easy to build a pond for irrigation and fresh-water fish culture. In Tainan and Kaohsiung, temperatures are more suitable for tropical species. Until recently carp has been the principal freshwater fish.

Future of Taiwan's fishing

In 1962, Taiwan had 700 motorized fishing vessels, 240 of them of more than 20 tons in weight and suitable for long cruises.

A total of 240,000 persons are engaged in various fishing activities. About eight per cent of them were employed in the deep-sea and inshore fishing. About 68 per cent of them were employed in the coastal fisheries. About 22 per cent were employed in fish culture. Deep-sea fishing firms totaled 55, and inshore 1800.

The postwar increase in production of fish occurred not in the deep-sea and inshore fisheries, but in the coastal fisheries and fish culture. But neither of the latter two categories is capable of large-scale expansion owing to the limited availability of land and fishing grounds. Therefore in the future the deep-sea and inshore fisheries will most certainly become the important sources of substantial increase in production.

The future development of the deep-sea fisheries depends on many factors. There is a need for improved personnel to make a systematic investigation of possible fishing grounds now unexploited in the central part of the South China Sea and thus to further the development of deep-sea fisheries. Harbor facilities for ship maintenance should be improved. An international fishing convention should be arranged with the governments of Japan, the Philippines, and Indonesia in order to set up mutually-agreed-upon fishing areas. This would prevent the constant conflicts over territorial rights. The market for fish should be ascertained before the fish are caught—too large a catch without an available foreign market lowers the price.

The coastal fisheries and pond fisheries have improved in sales, but production is limited by the size of the fishing grounds. In the future, attention should be paid to obtaining more fishing grounds, especially on the new beach reclaimed land.

In order to develop the inshore fisheries, it will be necessary to improve fishing methods and increase the mobility of fishing boats and add better equipment.

The sale of all fishery production except that of the coastal fisheries and fish culture is transacted in wholesale fish markets. Taiwan has at present 43 such fish markets located in places where the fish are landed and 35 in places near the consuming public. The sale of fish is done entirely by auctioneers, employed by the market. The market charges a commission on each transaction—a maximum of 2.5 per cent—in order to provide for necessary expenses, maintenance, and improvement of its installations. The fish are transported to retail markets.

The total fishery production in Taiwan usually reaches its height in May and drops to its lowest in January. Among the four kinds of fisheries, deep-sea fisheries are affected least by the climate and seasons.

For the deep-sea and inshore fisheries the period from March to May is the most productive; but for the coastal fisheries and fish culture it is the period from June to October.

FORESTRY

Importance of forestry in Taiwan's economy

With high mountains, high temperature, and abundant rainfall, Taiwan has rich flora. However, different groups of settlers who came to the island at various times cultivated the western plain where the natural vegetation disappeared and was replaced by rice paddy fields, sugar cane, sweet potatoes, tea, peanuts and beans. Today, forest is Taiwan's only natural resource which has a large reserve, covering over 55 per cent of the entire land area. Development of the forest resources is fundamental to improving the island's economy, not only because of the large area suited to forestry and the rich reserves, but also because of the quick growth of valuable species of trees which is due to favorable climatic conditions.

Forest values need to be measured in relation to conservation of soil and water. Especially in Taiwan, where the rugged surface features, highly erosive soils, and strong typhoons demand a forest cover as protection for its limited agricultural lands, the forests are needed to retard the silting of dams, to reduce the flood damage done by the short, deep-cut rivers, and to give greater permanency to hydroelectric development. Also the daily life of the inhabitants of Taiwan is intimately dependent upon wood. Taiwan needs wood for fuel, for equipment, for her communication and transportation, and as a supply of pulp for her books and papers. The country needs lumber for construction and maintenance of buildings, and huge quantities of wood for military purposes. Thus, perpetuation of Taiwan's forests is inextricably linked not only with the maintenance of its living standards, but also with its economic existence.

Although more than one-half of the land surface of Taiwan is better suited for the growth of trees than for any other purpose, Taiwan finds itself with the necessity of importing wood for her domestic needs. During the Japanese occupation, large quantities of wood had to be imported; and since then, because of insufficient maintenance in wartime and an increase in population, Taiwan's need for wood has risen sharply.

Taiwan has had long experience in forest management and in reforestation, but war and the dislocations following the war have caused the forestry program to degenerate. The demand for land increases each year, erosion is widespread, costly hydroelectric installations are endangered by silting and by falling water storage, agricultural land is obliterated by sand dunes and floods, and destructive agricultural practices and fires steadily degrade the forest soils. Thus, there is an urgent need for a forest program that will obviate Taiwan's present dependence on wood imports, preserve her agricultural soils, protect her storage dams and hydroelectric installations from excessive silting, and give far greater permanence to her systems of irrigation. With the dense population and the limited amount of agricultural land in Taiwan, the conservation of the soil and of water resources has become an urgent necessity. Additional values provided by forests include fixation of sand dunes and windbreaking action of trees. The forests serve a number of public purposes, such as maintenance of scenic and recreational areas and of habitats for wildlife. In Taiwan the heightened pace of industrialization and the increasing population, together with the needs of the military, are creating greater pressures for further forest development.

The forest program should be directed toward a dual goal. In dealing with the timberland, whose chief function is protection, the program's policy should be that, regardless of ownership, the public interest is paramount and that a forest cover must be preserved. In dealing with forests, whose chief function is production, the policy should hold that they be managed as a perpetually-renewable resource. Thus, in addition to assuring a perpetual flow of forest products, the objectives of the program should work toward combating soil erosion, reclaiming idle lands, improving water storage, and promoting water control. The farmers in Taiwan consider farming as the best use of land. Actually, most of the land on the island is best suited for forests; and, when used for agriculture, it can contribute to the already widespread erosion damage. Forest management is a long-term affair and must have continuity of purpose, policy, and administration.

In making a classification separating agricultural from forest land, there is no conflict between the respective needs of forestry and agriculture. The high mountains and steep slopes are clearly forest soils. The level areas and gently sloping lowlands are clearly agricultural. It is in the marginal zone between the two that field examination will be necessary. The destructive forces of wind, erosion, and flood can be combated by keeping forests on the hillsides. Some of the most highly erosive soils in the world are found in Taiwan. In attempts to deal with them, control measures have been confined largely to the lower slopes. Yet it is well established that the place to attack erosion is at the top of the watersheds. In extreme cases, it may be necessary to eliminate agriculture in certain areas and establish tree growth to hold the soil in place. This takes time, and reforestation will involve annual expenditures over a span of at least fifteen years.

Forest types

In order to obtain reliable statistics on Taiwan's forested land areas, timber volume, and current growth, the Chinese-American Joint Commission on Rural Reconstruction launched, in 1954, a forest resource survey which combined the use of aerial photography with ground sampling procedure. The resulting data are invaluable for the formulation of a forest policy that will assure proper management in harvesting indigenous forest products. It was the first time that Taiwan had obtained accurate data on its forestry. The figures of the following section, and *Table 49*, are based on its survey.[7]

Of the total forested land on the island (4,924,000 acres), hardwoods cover 72 per cent (3,568,400 acres), conifers, 19 per cent (932,700 acres), bamboo, 6 per cent (284,800 acres), and mixed stands of conifers and hardwoods, 3 per cent (138,300 acres). Of the forested land, 95 per cent is considered operable and 4 per cent is considered as nonoperable owing to rough surface features, such as slopes of more than 75 degrees. More than half of the operable area includes 3,239,000 acres of land presently inaccessible in terms of transportation.

Forest tree types vary according to elevation. In Taiwan, the conifers predominate at the higher altitude, and hardwood types at the lower. Besides these two major types, there are mixed conifers and hardwoods which occupy limited areas. The conifers can be classified as follows:

CYPRESS.—These are the most valuable trees in Taiwan. Almost all of the area now covered by this type is in well-stocked virgin stands of large trees. Reproduction after logging is not common: grass, brush, and noncommercial bamboo usually take over the site. Only 31 per cent of the cypress is accessible.

HEMLOCK.—This type covers 326,000 acres, but only 17 per cent, or 58,300 acres, is accessible. A considerable amount of hemlock is used for pulp and paper. Very little hemlock wood is used for construction purposes. Owing to the high cost of logging and the low value of the product, not much logging of hemlock has been carried out. As with cypress, brush, grass, and non-commercial bamboo take over the site after logging.

SPRUCE-FIR.—This grows in the highest mountains—above 7500 feet— and, therefore, is the most inaccessible timber in Taiwan. Less than 10 per cent, or 13,300 acres, is accessible. The high cost of logging, transportation, and so forth, has prohibited use of this type of tree.

Table 49. Accessibility of Forested Land (in thousands of acres) by Forest Types*

Forest type	Operable			Non-operable	Total
	accessible	inaccessible	subtotal		
Conifers	279.9	593.2	873.1	59.6	932.7
Cypress	33.5	65.0	98.5	9.0	107.5
Hemlock	58.3	250.0	308.3	24.3	332.6
Spruce-Fir	13.3	129.0	142.3	11.0	153.3
Pine	59.8	106.7	166.5	9.0	175.5
Other conifers	115.0	42.5	157.5	6.3	163.8
Hardwoods	2665.3	781.5	3446.8	121.6	3568.4
Tropical	1451.3	52.0	1503.3	28.8	1532.1
Subtropical	962.5	387.0	1349.5	65.0	1414.5
Temperate	251.5	342.5	594.0	27.8	621.8
Conifers and Hardwoods	66.8	63.0	129.8	8.5	138.3
Bamboo	267.3	15.7	283.0	1.8	284.8
Total	3279.3	1453.4	4732.7	191.5	4924.2

* GEORGE E. DOVERSPIKE, PAUL ZEHNGRAFF, and HSING-CHI YUAN, Forest Resources of Taiwan (Chinese-American Joint Commission on Rural Reconstruction, Taipei, 1956).

PINE.—This type is found at high altitudes—up to 9800 feet—and as low as 2600 feet. The stands are scattered but are the most accessible of the conifer types; they cover 34 per cent, or 59,800 acres, of the accessible land. The use of controlled burning to obtain natural regeneration seems promising and warrants further investigation. Plantations of Luchu pine have been successful at the lower elevations in the northern part of the island. The Luchu pine, a fast-growing species, was introduced from the Ryukyu Islands and will soon provide a readily-accessible wood supply for making pulp and paper.

OTHER CONIFERS.—Other important types of conifers are the Chinese fir and the Japanese fir. Both are exotic species that have been extensively and successfully planted. Japanese fir grows best at an elevation of from 3900 to 6600 feet. Chinese fir has a wider range and grows well at 2600– 5900 feet. Both species grow quite fast.

HARDWOODS.—These occupy three-fourths of the forests of Taiwan. As they occur at the lower elevations, usually less than 6600 feet, they are more accessible than are the coniferous trees. Seventy per cent of the accessible volume is in hardwoods and over 40 per cent of it is in trees less than 16 inches in diameter at chest height. The hardwoods can be classified as follows:

TROPICAL HARDWOOD.—Covering 1,532,100 acres, nearly 30 per cent of the forested land and 44 per cent of the accessible forest land, the tropical hardwood presents a serious land and forest management problem. This type of tree probably has the greatest forest potential, but, with a few exceptions, it is contributing least on a acre basis to Taiwan's national need for timber. The great demand for timber has caused the accessible areas to be heavily overcut and has led to their being badly managed.

Among the commercial species of hardwoods, the acacia trees are the most important, as large areas are in young plantations. They serve a good purpose in producing fuel for the population of the lowlands. The acacia is easily managed through cutting and sprouting.

Camphor trees, the source of camphor and camphor oil, have been planted with considerable success, primarily on the east side of the island.

Teak and mahogany are planted only to a limited extent and only in the southern part of the island. Both species require a deep, porous soil; they are not suited for planting on the shallow mountain soils. Teak plantations previously established were for the most part cut during World War II.

SUBTROPICAL HARDWOOD.—This type covers nearly 1,414,500 acres, of which 962,500 acres is accessible. It has been subjected to the same adverse treatment as the tropical types, but to a lesser extent. It includes some valuable species such as the oaks. Most of the subtropical hardwoods, however, have little commercial value, owing to the short lengths and poor form of the logs. The rate of mortality is high. Past logging practices have removed the trees of the valuable species, leaving the less valuable ones to regenerate.

TEMPERATE HARDWOOD.—Temperate hardwood is the least accessible hardwood type, and its lumber value is low. It covers about 621,800 acres, but only 40 per cent, or 251,500 acres, of it is accessible.

Forest industry

With the wide scope of their use, the variety of their finished products, and their intimate relationship with human life, forest products are ranked with coal and petroleum at the top among industrial raw materials. Wood is used for building material, furniture, railroad ties, telephone poles, boxes, packing paper, newsprint, plywood, artificial board, charcoal, wood alcohol, animal feed, yeast, and artificial fibers (from refined pulp) for clothing.

Forest products are an efficient kind of raw material. Different parts of a tree can be utilized to maintain different industries. For instance, before the tree is felled, the gum, tannin, and bark can be used as raw materials for manufacturing rosin, in leather tanning, and in the cork industry. After felling, a large straight trunk, free of knots, can be used as raw material for the plywood industry; a trunk with a diameter of more than eight inches at the tip can be used by the lumber industry; and branches can be cut into chips for making pulp, paper, and artificial board.

Furthermore, the products of trees of different species may be used together for some purposes; and the waste material produced in one kind of forest industry may be utilized as raw material by another.

Owing to the above conditions, the forest industry has gradually developed into a definite pattern; that is, when a considerable area of forest is available and it is under sustained effective management, there is produced annually a nearly fixed amount of lumber, which can be supplied as raw material to a "manufacturing center." The manufacturing center includes different kinds of factories whose raw materials come from the same forest land. In the United States, such integration of forestry and industry, with perpetual renewal of forest products to maintain a group of related industries, is called "industrial forestry." With a number of factories concentrated in one place, not only can the expenses for transportation of both raw materials and waste materials be minimized, but also the raw material can be used efficiently. Such a pattern of modern forestry management has reached a high point in forest utilization.

The forest industry is an important one in Taiwan. With the warm, wet climate and the mountainous terrain, more than half of Taiwan's total area, or 5.6 million acres, is classified as forest land, with an estimated total timber reserve of about 56 million cords. With these rich forestry resources, the industry has a good reserve of raw material. The importance of the forest industry is reflected in the fact that a considerable part of the island's population—300,000 people, or 3 per cent—earn their living by logging, lumbering, or processing forest products.

Despite Taiwan's rich forest resources, why has the island never produced enough timber in the past years to meet its domestic needs? First, timber resources are located in the mountains which are difficult to reach; this causes high cost of production and transportation. Another reason is that there is a low degree of efficiency in logging operations and poor practices in the cutting of timber, hence importation of certain forest products, such as railroad ties, wood pulp, poles, and even lumber, has been cheaper than use of local products.

A quite large portion of the foreign exchange has been spent on Luan logs from the Philippines, used principally to make plywood sheets. In addition to the direct importation of lumber, a limited amount of the locally-produced, high-quality coniferous timber has been exported to Japan to barter for more Japanese pine, of a lower grade, to meet the local timber shortage.

Since practically all the high-grade coniferous trees are located in the national forests, and since conifers are most profitably logged, government logging is concentrated principally on these species. At present, the Taiwan Forest Administration operates six logging stations, producing timber of which approximately 90 per cent is of coniferous species. Also, many privately-operated sawmills are located in various parts of the island. Hardwood species constituted three-fourths of the public and private timber production.

The process of timber production includes logging, yarding, hauling, storing, and milling. Logging is done by manual labor, owing to the lack of equipment, the steepness of the terrain, and the cheapness and plentitude of labor. Yarding is done with equipment powered by steam, diesel, or gasoline engines. Hauling is carried on by means of successive sections of cableway and railway stretching from the logging site to the foot of the mountain. Milling is done chiefly by sawmills which are operated by the government at each of its six logging stations. On the whole, owing to the roughness of the terrain, hauling presents the most difficult problem; and, of all the steps in the operation, it entails the highest cost.

Transportation difficulties are exemplified in the operation of the Ali Shan logging station, which began operations in 1913. The 40-mile railroad, connecting the logging station with the city of Chiayi, has a grade of 5 per cent with 74 tunnels totaling more than 6 miles in length. It also has bridges totaling nearly 2 miles in length. On the 22-mile journey from the forest to the sawmill, the logs are transferred 7 times over 3 aerial cableways and 4 narrow-gauge logging railways before they are unloaded at the mill. Consequently, transportation constitutes more than half the cost of the station's log production. Because of the natural surface features and the violent nature of the rivers in Taiwan, water transportation of forest products is not possible. Truck logging has been limited in the past; however, 27 miles of high-grade logging road is now under construction to open up a new logging area, Tai-hsueh Shan. It will be the first logging operation on the island in which transportation is carried on completely by truck.

WOOD PRESERVATION.—Not only do the logging and lumbering of the forests in Taiwan present problems; the preservation of timber also has its difficulties. About two-thirds of the total timber reserve and over half of the present timber production in Taiwan is of hardwood, which is more susceptible to decay and termite attack than is wood from coniferous trees. Located in a subtropical zone, Taiwan is a hotbed for the growth of worms. Railroad ties, poles, mine props, bridges, and other timbers are all subject to serious termite and worm attacks. It is necessary to combat decay and worms through wood-preservation treatment. The average life of untreated hardwood railroad ties is only two and one-half years; a creosote-treated tie will last from fifteen to twenty-five years. There are at present two wood-treating companies in Taiwan. Creosoted timber, however, is unsuitable for interior use because of its odor and its oily surface, which cannot be painted. Some preservative chemicals, however, like wolman salt, makenit, and pentachlorophenol are used to combat creosote's disadvantages.

A way to develop the wood-preservation industry, and to encourage timber treatment practices in Taiwan, is to have several small units of treating equipment strategically located at large metropolitan building areas and lumber-production centers in order to reduce the amount of timber transportation and to make full use of the wood-treating units.

PLYWOOD INDUSTRY.—Within the last few years, a plywood industry has been developed on Taiwan; in that industry, more than 78,000 cords of wood were used. However, only about 10 per cent of the logs used are from the local forests. The other 90 per cent are imported Luan logs (Philippine mahogany).

With its cheap labor, Taiwanese manufacturers process the Luan logs into plywood sheets. A portion of the plywood is exported to recover some of the foreign exchange spent on the Luan logs. About 10 per cent of the plywood used locally is used in constructing boxes for export of tea. Although the volume of plywood business is small, the export market includes many parts of the world, including Hong Kong, Okinawa, South Korea, Holland, South Africa, the United States, and South America. Despite Taiwan's cheap labor, the competition with Japan for the world plywood market is keen, as the Japanese plywood mills obtain their logs duty-free. Efforts are being made to improve the quality of the plywood and reduce the cost of manufacture in order to develop the export business. At present, more than 1100 persons are employed in the plywood industry.

CAMPHOR INDUSTRY.—Taiwan is one of the few places in the world that produces natural camphor. While it can be extracted from any of the five varieties of *Cinnamomum camphora*, only two varieties are extensively utilized for their extractions.

Camphor production has been decreasing, owing to an unfavorable foreign market price, which is due to export of huge amounts of camphor from the mainland of China and from Japan. The local demand for camphor is very limited, in fact, about 80 per cent of the amount produced is exported. The industry now employs 2000 workers, 1600 at the nearly 500 stills in operation and 400 in the refinery. Because of its importance as an export item, camphor was established as a government monopoly in 1899 by the Japanese and continued as such until November 1952. Currently, the industry is an enterprise of the Taiwan Provincial Government.

MATCH INDUSTRY.—Besides camphor, Taiwan also has a match industry which is dependent upon the national forests. A total of eleven manufacturing firms on the island produce 21,600 tins of matches annually. Each tin contains 1200 small wooden boxes of matches. In making matches, wood is needed both for the matchsticks and for the boxes. The annual consumption of wood for those purposes amounts to about 1400 cords. This match industry has provided jobs for 1600 persons who have an estimated 8000 dependents.

REFERENCES

[1] T. F. CHANG, "Livestock raising in Taiwan," *Quart., Bank of Taiwan* **5**, 3 (1952). [In Chinese].

[2] F. K. KUO, "Hog raising in Taiwan," *Quart., Bank of Taiwan* **5**, 50 (1952). [In Chinese].

[3] T. F. CHANG, "Cattle raising in Taiwan," *Quart., Bank of Taiwan* **5**, 71 (1952). [In Chinese].

[4] P. N. LEE, "The poultry in Taiwan," *Quart., Bank of Taiwan* **5**, 20 (1952). [In Chinese].

[5] WILLERT RHYNSBURGER, *Area and Resources Survey, Taiwan* (International Cooperation Administration, Mutual Security Mission to China, Taipei, 1956) p. 120.

[6] P. H. YEH, *Fishery Section of the Gazeteer of Taiwan* (The Historical Research Commission of Taiwan Province, Taipei, 1955), p. 4. [In Chinese].

[7] GEORGE E. DOVERSPIKE, PAUL ZEHNGRAFF, and HSING-CHI YUAN, *Forest Resources of Taiwan* (Chinese-American Joint Commission on Rural Reconstruction, Taipei, 1956).

TWENTY-ONE

Industry

CHARACTERISTICS

TAIWAN'S INDUSTRY has four notable characteristics: (1) Most of the industrial projects are publicly controlled; (2) Industrial development is financed from three sources: government, private interests, and United States aid; (3) The most important of the manufacturing industries is food processing; (4) The industries that manufacture domestically-consumed products depend largely on foreign sources of raw materials.

Public industrial projects on the island fall into three categories: those operated by the central government, those controlled jointly by the central and the provincial government,* and those entirely under the provincial government.

The predominance of publicly-controlled industry has been largely a historical by-product. At the time the Chinese Nationalist government took over Taiwan in 1945, private enterprise had neither the funds nor the wish to buy out and operate the projects left by the Japanese. Private owners bought some printing houses, match factories, food-processing factories, and coal mines. The remaining fourteen corporations are operated by three governmental groups, as follows: Central Government—Chinese Petroleum Corporation, Taiwan Aluminum Works, Taiwan Gold and Copper Mining Administration, Chinese Salt Corporation, Hsinchu Coal Mining Administration, Taiwan Steel Works; Central and Provincial Governments— Taiwan Power Company, Taiwan Sugar Corporation, Taiwan Fertilizer Company, Taiwan Alkali Company, Taiwan Shipbuilding Company, Taiwan Machinery Manufacturing Corporation; Provincial Government— Taiwan Tobacco and Wine Monopoly, Taiwan Camphor Bureau.

* Taiwan is a province of China, so it has a provincial government. In 1949 when the Communists controlled the mainland, the Nationalists retreated to Taiwan. The Nationalists moved the capital from Nanking to Taipei, which is now the seat of the central government, while the seat of the provincial government is at Taichung.

The governmental investment sources—central, provincial, and local—are used chiefly for the development of industries producing power, fertilizer, petroleum, and for the transportation industries.

Private financing comes from local, overseas Chinese, and foreign sources. Its major investments are in textiles, chemicals, cement, paper and board, window glass, and electrical appliances.

The United States aid is given directly to both government and private projects, mainly for production of power, fertilizer, chemicals, metals, and paper and pulp, and for development of the food-processing and the transportation industries.

Of the various manufacturing industries, food processing stands out as predominant. The relative value of the products of the manufacturing industries in 1960 may be seen from the following figures: processed food, 27 per cent of total products; textiles (22); chemical products (21); tobacco and wine (13); timber (5); machinery and ship-repairing (3); iron, steel, aluminum, and other metals (3); cement and ceramics (2); and miscellaneous (4).

The industries that contribute the lion's share to exports are, in the main, those devoted to the processing of agricultural resources. In 1954, for example, the value of such products constituted about 75 per cent of the total value of the products exported. Sugar, tea, rice, and bananas combined constituted more than 70 per cent of the processed agricultural products, or accounted for 68 per cent of the total export value. In 1960 their percentage of the total export value was far greater. In that year sugar accounted for more than half, or 58 per cent, of the value of the total exports. In second place (10 per cent) was tea. Next in line was rice (8 per cent), then bananas (4 per cent), canned pineapple (4 per cent), citronella oil (3 per cent), salt (1 per cent), and molasses (1 per cent).

While the major export industries are based mainly on utilization of the island's agricultural resources, the industries (so basic to the people's livelihood) that manufacture goods domestically consumed depend largely on foreign sources for their supply of raw material, especially from the United States aid imports. For example, in recent years cotton occupied 19 per cent of the total imports; crude oil 9 per cent; beans and peas 7 per cent; wheat 5 per cent; and perfumes, wax and fats 4 per cent.

It is clear from the above figures that it is the industries in the textile and chemical categories that depend most heavily upon foreign sources for their supply of raw materials. Thus there is a dangerous element in the island's economy. While the very nature of agricultural products makes them subject to the fluctuations of international prices, the industries producing consumed goods domestically are also influenced in their cost structure by international changes in the prices of raw material. Therefore achievement of proper balance to control these influences represents one of the island's basic problems.

ADVANTAGES

In the Far East Taiwan's industry is second to none but Japan's. The island is benefited by several factors that few regions in southeast Asia enjoy. These factors include the following:[1]

POWER.—With the steep slopes of its surface configuration and its heavy rainfall, Taiwan is endowed with abundant water power. The rate of growth of the Taiwan power industry is the highest in the world. Peak capacity during the Japanese occupation was 321,000 kilowatts. It reached 923,040 kilowatts in 1962—85 per cent hydroelectric and 15 per cent thermoelectric. According to a study made of the available water resources, it will be possible, through full use of such resources, to generate a total of 1,500,000 kilowatts. Power generation for 1962 totalled 4,692,-700,000 kilowatt-hours, or three times that of 1953. Per capita generation is 400 kilowatts, second in Asia only to Japan. Not only is power in Taiwan abundant in supply, but because water power constitutes the main source of electricity, the cost of generating it is extremely low. The average rate is $0.012 per kilowatt-hour—the lowest in the world except in Norway.

COMMUNICATION.—Taiwan is served by a network of railways as well as by highways reaching almost every corner of the island. Most of the major highways are well surfaced, and all the localities that are suitable for the setting up of factories have easy access to railways or highways. In addition Taiwan has two large deep-water ports, Keelung and Kaohsiung, which have modern equipment and which are serviced by railways and highways.

LABOR SUPPLY.—Taiwan has an abundant labor supply. A large reserve of laborers in the rural areas is available for the development of industry. With their capacity for education, their stable living conditions, their intelligence, and their physical fitness, persons from rural areas can be turned into skilled workers after a reasonable period of training. The low cost of living that prevails in the Far East is another favorable factor. Also, on this small island there are as many as 3000 eminent engineers who evacuated from the mainland since 1949. Taiwan has the highest density of engineers in the Far East.

FOUNDATION OF INDUSTRY.—Taiwan's industries reflect credit on the former Japanese rule of the island, and its present industrial structure has been built on the good foundation left by the Japanese.

SOCIAL STABILITY.—Taiwan enjoys a high degree of social stability. Life and property are fully protected. This factor, so vital to the operation of industrial and commercial enterprises, is seldom found in underdeveloped areas.

DISADVANTAGES

Despite the favorable factors mentioned above, Taiwan has experienced certain difficulties in the course of its industrial development. Some of the difficulties are common to all underdeveloped countries, such as the shortage of capital, the lack of entrepreneurs, and the lack of technical know-how. Other difficulties, such as the limited scope of its domestic demand and foreign market and the shortage of industrial raw material, are specifically Taiwan's.

LACK OF CAPITAL.—The major problem encountered in the industrialization of Taiwan is the lack of capital. The national per capita income is only
about $100 each year, which certainly cannot meet the requirements for
industrial development. Therefore, an inflow of capital, either in the form
of foreign investment or foreign aid, is necessary.[2]

Small sums of money are not suitable for production purposes and they
are invested mostly for the purpose of drawing interest. In general, investment in industries is not very attractive to capital. This difficulty has
been alleviated to some extent by the government's policy of granting income tax exemptions and special loan assistance to essential industries.

LIMITED NATURAL RESOURCES.—The natural resources of Taiwan are rather
limited and produce little raw material for industry. Apart from hydraulic
power none of the island's natural resources is of major importance. Coal
is available, but in limited quantities; iron ores are almost nonexistent;
and other mineral deposits are meager. Petroleum is the only prospected
mineral. This limitation of natural resources has put a considerable obstacle in the way of broad industrial development. Rapid industrial progress has been difficult. It is only through careful planning, implemented by
technical proficiency, and through utilization of the abundant manpower
and plentiful electric power supply that any progress has been made, and
that progress shows the worth of tireless human endeavor in the face of a
severe shortage of natural resources.

LOW DOMESTIC DEMAND.—The low domestic demand for industrial products restricts the size of industrial plants, and in some industries it also
prevents the use of cost-saving devices. Products made in these small-
scale plants are usually too costly to compete in the world market. The
difficulties can be overcome only by a gradual increase in production efficiency and an expansion of production capacity.

LACK OF FOREIGN MARKETS.—On the whole, Taiwan's industrial production
has reached its highest possible point. The most urgent problem to be
solved today is the opening up of more foreign markets rather than an increase of production. Industrially-advanced countries are concentrating
their efforts not only on production but on export as well. This makes it
even more difficult for Taiwan to gain a foreign market. In recent years
the United States has tackled this task of export promotion; so has Great
Britain. Postwar Japan has concentrated her efforts on developing foreign
trade, and has increased it by 36 per cent of what it was before World War
II. The most successful country is, perhaps, West Germany, which has
gradually rebuilt her industries out of ruin and rubble; the volume of her
export now exceeds that of prewar time by 30 per cent. In this struggle for
a share of the world market, which seems to be Taiwan's only possible
outlet for industrial products, the island will find it difficult to find a place.

LACK OF COORDINATION OF SUPPLY AND DEMAND.—Another obstacle confronting a majority of industries in Taiwan is the lack of coordination between the market and the supply of raw material. Some enterprises have
more than sufficient raw material and thus overproduce, so that their products pile up and cause a glut in the market (e.g., alkalies, petroleum, and
textiles). Other industries have too little raw material; their supply of

products cannot meet the demand of the market (e.g., the aluminum, paper, and pineapple industries).

LACK OF EXPERT MANAGEMENT.—Another of industrialization's handicaps in Taiwan is the lack of expert management. Any industrial project needs land, labor, and capital. But the three must be put under the direction of a talented, experienced, farsighted manager. Some economists even consider management as the fourth most important factor affecting projection. Industrially-advanced countries in Europe and America attract first-rate talents in industry, but Chinese tradition has established the superior position of scholars and agriculturists. Talented people try for recognition, but few in Taiwan have undertaken to be industrial managers. There are some persons in Taiwan with capital who are aware of the bright future of industry, and who have the land and the labor needed. But they cannot find men on whom to rely for the management of their enterprises, and as a result, their capital remains idle.

OTHER DISADVANTAGES.—Besides the above, there are other factors in the island's difficulties in industrial development, attributable to the following three main points:

First, some hardships have been caused by Taiwan's becoming economically independent. Japan, when she ruled the island, pursued a determined policy to make Taiwan an economic satellite—to develop an agricultural Taiwan to meet the demands of an industrialized Japan. After World War II, when Japan retroceded the island to China, Taiwan was ready to become an integral part of the Chinese economy. It was expected then that Japan's role in Taiwan's trade relations would soon be taken over by China. However, since the Communists occupied the Chinese mainland, Taiwan has become an independent economic unit and constantly faces the need for foreign markets for local products, foreign exchange for imports, and a capital for economic development.

The second factor is the rapid increase of population. The natural growth rate of Taiwan's population is 3.5 per cent a year, the highest in the Far East. In other words, if agriculture and industry increased production only 3.5 per cent, it would be enough to compensate for the increased population.

The third factor is the standard of living. Although a higher standard of living is desirable, it must be accompanied by ever-increasing productivity. Otherwise, it will cause so great a consumption of the island's wealth, that the necessary capital for economic development will not be available.

INDUSTRIAL DEVELOPMENT

During the period of Japanese occupation, Taiwan's economy was that of a colony producing raw materials and semi-finished products to serve the needs of the Japanese Empire. The economy of the island had not been developed in the direction of self-support and independence, and this had an adverse effect on the livelihood of the island's inhabitants. The manufacture of consumer goods and finished products was disregarded.

In 1945, when the island was restored to China, it directed its initial efforts toward establishment of the basic industries that would provide the daily necessities of life or otherwise would have a direct bearing on the welfare of the island's population. Thus top priority was given to the development of the electric-power, fertilizer, and cotton textile industries.[3] The development of industry in Taiwan in recent years can be divided into three periods, 1946–1952, 1952–1957, and 1957–1963.

First period (1946–1952)

In the first period, effort was focused on rehabilitation of the island's industry, which had been seriously crippled, not only by Allied bombing, but also through excessive wear and tear and a virtually complete absence of wartime maintenance. By 1952 substantial reconstruction had been achieved through repairing and replacing basic machinery. Many prewar projects had been completed and a number of new products developed. It was also during this period that United States financial and technical assistance began to play a significant role in the industrialization of Taiwan. A valuable asset was the new availability of technical personnel in Taiwan —most of them coming from mainland China. Almost all the work of rehabilitating the island's industry—repairing, erecting, and operating the plants—was done by Chinese engineers, with a small number of foreign personnel to assist in the more difficult phases.

The principal aim of the first period was to increase industrial production so that the domestic economy would be stabilized and international payments balanced. Remarkable increases were registered in the major industrial products, such as aluminum ingots, cotton yarn, petroleum, paper, wheat flour, fertilizer, cement, and generated power. Though the actual production goal was not reached, the development did help to stabilize the island's economy.

Second period (1952–1957)

In the period 1952–1957 the economy of the island began to move into a new phase of development, characterized by new construction and expansion. As a result of this intensification of industrial development, the need for capital investment was steadily on the rise. In other words, the ratio of capital output to capital investment was considerably enlarged.

The progress of industrial development during this period may be illustrated by the rise in the index of industrial production. The production index of 1956 was more than double that of 1951, and the index of 1957 is estimated to be 6 per cent above that of 1956. In 1957, in per capita annual output of sugar, Taiwan ranked highest among the Asian lands. In power, in coal, in cement, and in paper the island was in second place.[4]

The fertilizer, cement, paper, and petroleum industries have been greatly expanded, as well as the power and transportation facilities. The textile and aluminum industries provide good examples of industrial development during this period.

Although the textile industry was practically non-existent before World War II, it has since become one of the island's fastest growing industries. This has been the result of government encouragement and, primarily, of private efforts. This industry is now capable of supplying all local needs for textile products made of cotton, wool, silk, and ramie. It is also capable of producing surplus for export. In the short span of nine years (1948–1956) textile production achieved a gain of no less than 1000 per cent.

The aluminum industry illustrates the transformation of the island's economy. Prior to the second World War, only aluminum ingots were available, and all that were produced were shipped to Japan for fabrication. Now the island's aluminum industry is producing not only ingots, but also sheets, foil, and a great variety of aluminum ware, thereby providing increased opportunities for employment and new sources of income. Many other manufacturing and processing industries, with products such as footwear, bicycles, and window glass, have also gradually been established, though on a small scale.

In the second period, the main emphasis was on the development of the industries that could make the best use of local advantages in power supply and labor cost. Stress was also laid on the existing capacities and on the modernization of important industries such as sugar refining and machinery manufacturing.

In the scheme of development, priority was given to processing industries that use local materials, preferably the by-products of existing industries—bagasse, molasses, waste gas, chlorine, waste wood, and so forth. High priority was also given to the chemical industry because some of its basic raw materials can be obtained from existing industries (petroleum, caustic soda, coal, salt, and sugar). Thus, in the second plan, projects for the manufacture of urea, acetic acid, benzene, soda ash, formaline, and methyl alcohol were given due consideration. The cement and paper industries expanded under this plan, owing to favorable local conditions, and good exporting prospects.

At the end of 1956, there were more than 20,000 factories in operation in Taiwan, one-third of them established after 1952. Along with the establishment of new factories, the number of industrial workers has increased from 274,000 in 1952 to 340,000 in 1956.

Comparison of different countries with regard to industrial employment and increase in population, as given in the *International Statistical Year Book*, indicates that Taiwan has been rather successful in creating jobs through expansion of its industry, as is shown in *Table 50*.[5]

Top priority was also given during this period to the development of electric power and transportation facilities with a view to achieving economies for the future development of other industries. In the field of mining and manufacturing first emphasis was placed upon the development of the fertilizer industry.

Industrial investment during the second period was distributed among

*Table 50. Industrial Employment Compared to Total Population**

Country	Period	Ratio of industrial employment increment to population increment
Philippines	1918–49	1:1.2
Turkey	1927–50	1:1.6
India	1946–48	1:0.7
Brazil	1940–50	1:5.8
Taiwan	1946–55	1:6.8

* Based on GERALD C. PAN, "The accomplishments of the first Four-Year Plan—an initial analysis," *Industry in Free China* **VIII**, No. 3 (1957).

the various industries in such a way that 52 per cent of the total was for manufacturing, 27 per cent for power, 17 per cent for transportation, and 4 per cent for mining.

Third period (1957–1963)

During the third period the industry developed far ahead. For example, industrial production in 1960 rose by 14 per cent over 1959, the highest since 1953. The output of individual industries with the exception of sugar, whose production was reduced as a result of international quotas, showed significant increase in 1960. Increase in the production of plate glass was more than 100 per cent. Cotton yarn, cotton cloth, electric fans, fluorescent tubes, steel bars, canned pineapples and machinery each showed an increase of more than 20 per cent; power generation, coal, petroleum refined, caustic soda, paper and cement increased more than 10 per cent. Considerable increase was also recorded in the output of fertilizer, cigarettes, and alcoholic beverages, sheet glass, and plywood.[6]

During the third period, from 1957–1963, the main objectives were to raise national income, to enlarge employment opportunities, to expand exports, and to further reduce international payment deficits. Its achievements show increases of 42 per cent in agricultural production, 86 per cent in industrial production, 50 per cent in national income, and 22 per cent per capita income.[7]

In this stage, Taiwan's old industries underwent a continuous expansion and new industries sprung up one after another. There has been a vertical rise in production—an increase of 147 per cent in 1960 over that of 1952. During this period, however, the growth was limited to the industries with a domestic market or to those demanding no great technical skills. So there are only two problems in its industrial development—shortage of capital and of entrepreneurs. The availability of U.S. aid makes the capital shortage not a serious problem and government efforts have solved the shortage of private entrepreneurs, as most of the existing plants are established with government planning, sponsorship, and assistance.[8]

However, during this period the industry in Taiwan is facing two problems. The first is a lack of investment opportunity because of a saturated domestic market. The second is the lack of technical know-how. For the present, industries which the inhabitants in Taiwan can erect and operate have been exhausted. Technical difficulties will be encountered if the country ventures into new industries.

Also during this stage, in spite of the rapid industrial growth, industrial employment increased by 12,000 persons only. Employment rose mostly in the textile, metal, machinery, and chemical industries, against reduction in minor small industries.

What has been significant in all these developments is the fact that many small businessmen and landowners have become increasingly aware of the island's trend toward industrialization and have become more and more inclined either to invest in or switch into industrial and productive enterprise. Other gradual changes have taken place in the size of individual private enterprises and in their form of organization. Though family proprietorship has always been predominant, the corporate organization has gained increasing acceptance.

Another change in the last few years has been the transfer from government to private ownership.

The industries that need large investments, such as those that manufacture cement, artificial fiber, soda ash, and diesel engines, have all been taken over by private investors. The private industries have reached unprecedented dimensions in the scope of their activities and in the size of their investments. ·

INDUSTRIAL TRENDS

Expansion of industrial production tends to promote the diversification of Taiwan's economy. The economy, which is mainly agricultural, is still backward. The implementation of the three stages is ushering in gradual changes. Industry is making headway in the struggle for economic supremacy, while agricultural industry is losing its grip. For instance, in 1952 agriculture (including forestry, fisheries, and animal husbandry) represented 35 per cent of the national income as compared with 19 per cent represented by industry (including manufacturing, mining, and power). In that year the ratio of agriculture to industry was 65 per cent. In 1960 agriculture's contribution receded to 32 per cent while the industrial portion progressed to 21 per cent; the ratio thus narrowing to 63 per cent.[9] Despite this seemingly small margin gained by industry, its growth rate is by no means small from a long-term point of view.

Industries that process raw materials imported from abroad and make them into finished goods for export must have at their disposal an ample power supply, good communications, and abundant labor. Taiwan has these requirements, but her supplies of raw material are somewhat inadequate, as are those of the British and the Japanese textile industries.

As has been shown, the economic future of Taiwan lies in the development of its industries, and its industrial future lies in the exportation of its products. Therefore, any rapid progress in Taiwan's economic development depends exclusively on improvements in its industries' productive technique, organization, and management. To effect these improvements, the government of Taiwan should strengthen industrial education, send large numbers of technical and managerial personnel abroad for specialized training, and invite foreign experts to Taiwan for consultation.[10] In addition, it should encourage investment both by foreign nationals and overseas Chinese, and establish research centers to help industries solve their technical and managerial problems[11].

In view of the above-mentioned difficulties, it seems necessary for Taiwan to use its limited natural resources in the most effective and appropriate way possible. Owing to its small size, Taiwan can hardly be self-sufficient economically. It must produce more exportable goods to provide foreign exchange for imported material.

The industry of Taiwan today depends upon a few processed agricultural products, such as sugar, rice, and pineapples, for its economic well-being. In view of the fact that the prices of these commodities are affected by fluctuations in the world market, a more diversified economy will have to be sought.[12] It is imprudent for Taiwan to depend mainly on a very limited number of exportable goods. If changes take place in the international market or if prices decline drastically, the island's economy will be in a precarious position. Other places, such as Chile and Thailand, have experienced economic crises resulting from a reduction in the price of rice and of fertilizer. Taiwan's internal economic stability is often influenced by external factors. For example, in the past few years the decline in the price of sugar on the foreign market has greatly affected Taiwan's economy.[13] Therefore, in the process of industrialization, the economy must be put on a broader basis through diversification of products so as to increase its flexibility and stability. While the diversification of products will expand foreign trade, the drive to increase production within should maintain a balance between agriculture and industry. Since there is an annual increase of one-third of a million persons in population, there remains the basic need to have an adequate food supply. Accordingly, agricultural production must be increased continually. Nevertheless, industrial development is essential for Taiwan. The island's agriculture and industry are in different stages of development, and they should be treated differently.

In future industrial expansion the development of the more basic industries (other than production of fertilizer, food, textiles, and power) should be emphasized. One of these is steel, which has not participated fully in Taiwan's overall economic growth. This lack has adversely affected the progress of practically all of the important steel-consuming industries, such as metalworking and the manufacture of machinery.[14]

The total annual imports of machinery and tools increased from 5 per cent in 1951 to no less than 12 per cent in 1955, and to 15 per cent in 1956. Imports of metals and metal products, plus some ores, also increased, from 8 per cent in 1951 to 11 per cent in 1955 and 14 per cent in 1956. While these expenditures for imports reflect Taiwan's industrial progress, they also constitute an increasingly heavy drain on the government's foreign exchange.[15]

At present there is a good possibility of establishing a modern steel industry. Although iron ores are not found in abundance on the island, there are enough deposits of coking coal, high-grade limestone, and dolomite for that purpose. Iron ores can be supplied by neighbors, such as the Philippines and Malaysia.

Taiwan is also modernizing the bagasse pulp mills so as to produce pulp. A bagasse hardboard plant (the largest in the Far East) has just been completed. After doing more experimental work on the extraction of alpha cellulose from bagasse for the manufacture of regenerated fiber, Taiwan will be leading the world in the utilization of sugar-cane by-products.

In recent years the government has been working on the development of the forest resources on Tai-hsueh Shan (Big Snow Mountain). This is the first time Taiwan has started a logging station using the truck-logging method on a large scale. The station's work will be coordinated with that of modern sawmills and with the manufacture of artificial wood-board, and other products made of wood.

Norway, a country with 25 per cent of its land in forest, derives as much as 30 per cent of its export revenue from lumber and lumber products. More than 55 per cent of Taiwan's land is in forest, and yet it still must import its lumber. A determined and thoroughly coordinated effort should be made toward development of the forest industry.

313

Turning to the basic industries, efforts in the last few years have been concentrated on the production of fertilizer; calcium cyanide, super-phosphate, and ammonium sulfate are being produced. Such projects now underway will produce ammonium nitrate, nitrophosphate, and urea. Fertilizer has been a major item of import, and it is hoped that in the near future the value of its importation may be reduced by more than 10 million dollars.

Petroleum can now be produced locally, for a modern refinery, capable of handling more than one million tons of crude oil annually, has been modernized. Manufacture of machinery and metalware has also been improved or expanded.

The last group of industries includes those depending on importation of raw materials. Industries producing textiles, flour, edible oil, and rubber products all belong in this category.

As far as Taiwan's economic reconstruction program is concerned, the wisest plan, of course, is to develop electric power and the manufacture of fertilizers. Other products worthy of special encouragement include automobile tires, caustic soda, jute (for spinning and weaving), water pumps and pipes, aluminum sheets, galvanized iron, steel wire and cable, electric motors, telegraphic materials, artificial fiber, pottery and porcelain, pharmaceuticals, synthetic chemicals, dry-distilled coal, paper pulp, canned goods, and small machines.

As the population of the island increases, the demand for manufactured consumer goods can reasonably be expected to increase proportionately. From the point of view of supply and demand, in many such lines there will be distinct advantages in local production. Furthermore, favorable power supplies and cheap labor will undoubtedly give the island local advantages for more production in some sectors of manufacture.

Taiwan is now in a stage that we may call "the period of want between two harvests." Some years later, when the people's purchasing power has been augmented due to the economic development, the consumption of local products will undoubtedly be expanded. Furthermore, if productive techniques can be improved, and the cost of production cut down, foreign markets can be opened up for Taiwan's products.[16]

While it may be true that agriculture and industry in Taiwan should be stressed equally, and that the possibility of close coordination in their development should not be overlooked, the fact remains that agriculture's development is already fairly advanced. Industry offers much greater opportunities because it is still at the stage of initial development, and its youth is basic to the overall development of Taiwan's economy.[17]

In determining which industries should be given priority in their development, three factors must be considered, the feasibility of their development, the importance of the industries, and their advantages to the island.

There must first of all be a possibility of establishing a certain industry—its development must be feasible. The necessary equipment has to be considered—whether or not it can be manufactured locally or must be imported, and whether its cost at foreign exchange can be borne at the moment. Technical knowledge is another item to consider. Does the available staff possess the ability necessary for the operation of the equipment, or will the assistance of foreign technicians have to be called upon? Is a good manager available? Besides the necessary equipment and managerial and technical skill, the availability of raw material, of a market, and of skilled labor have to be considered.[18]

In evaluating the importance of a certain industry, its nature must be examined. Is it a national defense industry, or one for the production of basic daily necessities, or one whose products may be exported for obtaining more foreign exchange or substituted for imported goods in order to reduce the spending of foreign exchange? Is it an industry that can be successfully operated without a large amount of capital?[19]

Comparative advantage is a term used in the study of international trade; it is also an important condition for deciding on the types of industries to be developed.

Further attention should be paid to the resources, power, and transportation required by the industry.[20] Its possible domestic and foreign markets should be thoroughly studied; and in this regard special attention should be paid South East Asia, an area heavily populated with Chinese immigrants and their descendants.

A modern industry needs not only natural endowments but also expert managers, good organization, sufficient capital, and encouraging laws. If any one of these factors is lacking, no industry can prosper. In Taiwan new equipment and technique and scientific organization and management are the two wings of the industrial bird; lack of either would cripple the bird.

GOVERNMENT INDUSTRIAL POLICY

The government of Taiwan has suggested the following considerations for industrial development:

(1) There should be a continued expansion of the service and basic industries, because these are the very foundation of industrial development.

(2) Industries whose raw materials can be supplied locally, and whose products can be substituted for those that are now imported or that can be exported should be developed.

(3) At the present time high priority should be given to the development of medium- and small-sized industries. Large-scale industries should be established with extreme caution. Not until an adequate supply of raw materials and a sufficient demand are assured should the establishment of large-scale enterprises be pursued.

(4) Industries selected for development shall preferably be those that require less investment of capital, but which can bring, within a short time, considerable improvement to the economy. However, industries on too small a scale to be economical should not be established. In this regard, merger of existing small factories and mines is to be encouraged.

(5) Adequate consideration should be given to the development of cottage and handicraft industries, which absorb more labor or can improve the underemployment situation in the rural communities.

(6) Heavy industries that require imported raw materials and need huge capital investments should be given low priority.

(7) Equal emphasis shall be given to the establishment of new industries and to the improvement of those already existing.

(8) Idle plants and equipment are a loss to the economy. Now full utilization of existing facilities is of more importance than expansion.[21]

GEOGRAPHICAL INDUSTRIAL DISTRIBUTION

As with many other parts of the world, the location of Taiwan's various industries is influenced by geographical factors; by availability of raw materials, of labor, and of transportation facilities; and by nearness of markets.

Since two-thirds of Taiwan's land is mountainous, its agriculture, manufacturing, and commerce are concentrated on the remaining land—a fertile coastal plain that extends northeast–southwest the whole length of the island, west of the mountains. The plain includes most of Taiwan's arable land, and most of its population live there (*Figures 68* and *69*).

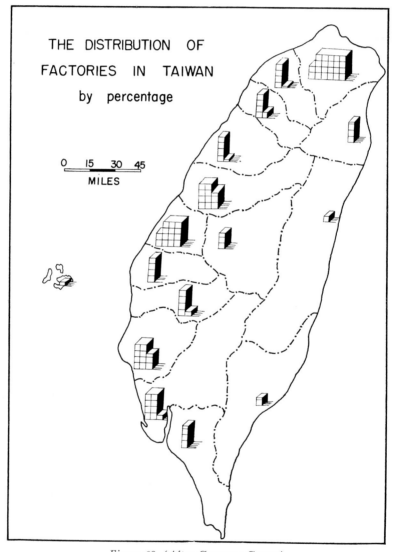

THE DISTRIBUTION OF
FACTORIES IN TAIWAN
by percentage

0 15 30 45
MILES

Figure 68. (*After* CHI-YUN CHANG)

On this plain are located two seaports, Kaohsiung in the south and Keelung in the north. Most of the island's basic or heavy industries are located in Kaohsiung—iron and steel, aluminum, machinery, petroleum, acids and alkalis, and so forth. The light industries, producing consumer goods, are located near the capital, Taipei, which uses the facilities of Keelung Harbor to bring in imported raw materials, such as cotton for the nearby textile mills.

Industries depending on local agricultural products, such as the sugar industry, are concentrated in the southern part of the island.

Some industries, such as the knitting industry, are dependent chiefly on the labor supply and therefore are located in or near cities. Some food industries have been established in cities near agricultural areas, where seasonal laborers are numerous. Among those food industries are: rice hulling; grain milling; manufacture of edible oil, of bean curd, and of condiments.

Processing of marine products, including fish canning, is done on the northeast and southwest coasts. The solar salt industry is located on the southwest coast. That is also the location of the cement industry, which is carried on near the limestone-producing area in the south.

Among the consumer goods produced in the cities are articles made of leather, of wood, and of rubber; soap is also produced there. The printing industry also is carried on in the cities.

The lumber industry is concentrated in and near the forested mountain areas in the central part of the island.

Tea, which is cultivated on the hilly land in the northwest, is processed in cities near the plantation area.

Pineapples, grown in the southern part of the plain, are canned in cities near the fields.

Electric power, usually an influential factor in the location of manufacturing industries, has little to do with the distribution of factories in Taiwan, for all areas are served by the hydraulic power center in the mountains. The place that consumes the greatest amount of electric power is the southwest, where are located the metal and machinery-manufacturing industries, the food industries, and the cement industry, and where irrigation projects are operated. Next in consumption of electric power are the northwestern areas, where coal, gold, and copper are mined and where the fertilizer, textile, and metal industries are located.

The steel industry is essential to the development of all other industries, but Taiwan has only one blast furnace and a few steel mills of moderate size. Development of this industry has been handicapped by the nonexistence of iron ore, the limited supply of coking coal, and the small demand for steel products.

The machinery industry in Taiwan is also on a limited basis. During the Japanese occupation the machinery industry consisted only of repair work for agriculture, mining, and hydrography. Besides several companies sponsored by the government today, there are 700 factories owned by private companies, which are only in small-scale operation; only three of these factories have as many as thirty employees.

A similar situation is seen with regard to the shipping industry. In an island country daily existence depends on the ability to sell and send goods

317

out and to buy and bring in the necessities for life and development. England and Japan have made their islands strong, with merchant fleets that have carried their goods and their flags to the whole world. Important as it is, the shipping industry in Taiwan is still in the stage of preparation.

A brighter picture is presented by the sugar industry, the chemical industry, and the forestry industry, which are well suited to Taiwan's environment.

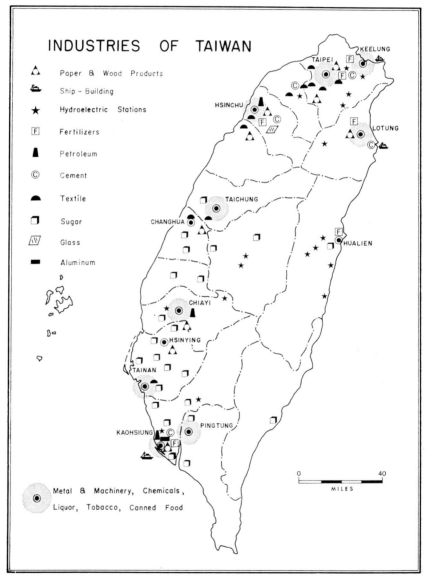

Figure 69

ELECTRICITY

Electrical power in Taiwan is about three-fourths generated by water power. It is cheap and is within reach of practically every part of the island. About 82 per cent of the population is supplied with electricity. The whole island is electrified—a rare condition in the Orient.

The planning of electric power was started in the 19th century, but the island was ceded to Japan before the plan was put into practice. In 1902 the Japanese completed a plant which produced 600 kilowatts of electricity; it supplied the Taipei area only. In 1919, after World War I, the Japanese organized the Taiwan Electric Power Company and started the electrical engineering work at Sun Moon Lake. After the electric power work at Sun Moon Lake was completed, the foundation for electric power for the island was laid. Because of the cheapness of the power, many large-scale industries were gradually established. These included the aluminum, fertilizer, and alkali industries.

Owing to an increase in the demand for electricity the Japanese built a second power station in 1937; thus the western part of the island has been well served by electricity. It was not until 1944 that electricity was provided by the Taiwan Electric Power Company to the eastern part of the island. During World War II Taiwan served Japan as a base in its efforts to conquer southeast Asia, and many military industries were established on the island. For these much electricity was needed. At the end of 1944 the power station was serving 34 localities, with an electricity production of 321,000 kilowatts, of which hydroelectricity amounted to 267,000 kilowatts and thermoelectricity to 54,000. The number of families using electricity at that time was 420,000.

Power facilities suffered heavily from Allied bombings toward the close of World War II. Owing to the repeated bombings and also to severe typhoon and flood damage on the east coast at about the same time, the serviceable capacity for electric power in Taiwan in October 1945 was only 84,000 kilowatts out of a capacity of 321,000 kilowatts. When the Nationalist Chinese government took over the power facilities from the former Japanese company, the rehabilitation of this war-torn system was an enormous task. For the first few months the operation and management were maintained by the original Japanese staff under the supervision of the Chinese government. This lasted until May 1946, when the present Taiwan Power Company was organized. At present 58 per cent of the capital stock of the company is held by the central government, 34 per cent by the provincial government, and the remaining 8 per cent by private individuals. After vigorous efforts by the company's Chinese engineers the power system was completely restored. In 1950 the production surpassed the 177,000 kilowatt record of the Japanese era.

During the Japanese management, Taiwan's power company operated a major system on the western plain and a minor one on the east coast. Completion of a cross-island transmission line in 1952 brought the two systems into one integrated network. The present system has a total capacity of 923,040 kilowatts, provided by 36 power stations.

Water-power resources in Taiwan are bountiful, but great fluctuation of river flow and lack of reservoirs in Taiwan has made it essential to provide adequate thermal stations to firm up the power supply. There are at present ten thermal stations, producing a total of 185,000 kilowatts of electricity. Of these, five are coal-burning; they total 180,000 kilowatts. These stations are located either near the coal mines around Keelung in the north or at the industrial center, Kaohsiung, in the south. The remaining five thermal stations are small diesel outfits with a combined capacity of about 5000 kilowatts, serving places not yet connected with the main power system.

The average annual increase in power sales is more than 18 per cent since 1946. In 1958 the total sales amounted to 2416 million kilowatt-hours, of which 80 per cent went to industries and 20 per cent to residential and commercial customers.

Of the electrical energy used by the industries, the fertilizer industry is the heaviest consumer; as much as 24 per cent of the industrial power consumed on the island goes into fertilizer production. Owing to the government's aim of self-sufficiency in fertilizer manufacture, consumption of electric power by that industry should increase further. The aluminum industry, which consumes 11 per cent of the total, comes second. It is of interest to note that since 1946 power consumption in Taiwan by some industries multiplied many times: for example, manufacture of textiles 78 times, of chemicals 36 times, and of ceramics (including cement), 24 times.

ALUMINUM

In nearly all countries the aluminum industry is the major metal development of this century. It is second only to iron and steel in quantity of production and in fields of application. Its volume production has surpassed the total for copper, lead, and zinc. No other industry has grown so rapidly.

Aluminum is now the only major metal industry in Taiwan. The industry was founded by the Japanese in 1935 and was heavily damaged in World War II. Rehabilitation and restoration work on the aluminum industry has been concentrated in the Kaohsiung area.

The main raw material of aluminum is bauxite. Before the Communists took over mainland China, the island had no bauxite problems; a supply of that ore came from the mainland. But, after that the supply of bauxite had to come from other countries. Fortunately all Taiwan's neighbor countries, such as Malaysia, the Philippines, and Indonesia, produce this ore. The present supply of 20,000–30,000 tons of bauxite per year is mainly obtained from Malaysia. Owing to the smallness of aluminum production in Asia, the amount of bauxite now mined is already much in excess of what is needed, and there is little likelihood that a shortage of the material will occur. The other raw material used in Taiwan for processing aluminum is cryolite (sodium aluminum fluoride). One-half of the cryolite supply is met by a local plant from a by-product of superphosphate. The remaining half is imported from West Germany. The annual amount purchased is 550–770 tons. Since the quantity needed is small, it can be easily procured.

The aluminum industry consumes much electrical power for smelting and fabrication annually—about 26,000 kilowatts.

The main costs of aluminum production are for raw materials, power, and labor, of which the latter two are abundant in Taiwan. The cost picture here is similar to that in West Germany. If the power rates can be adjusted at the American level, Taiwan should become a new aluminum center to compete favorably in the world market.

As far as a market for aluminum is concerned, Taiwan has no problem at the moment. Every year many new factories are built, as well as about 700 bus and truck bodies, more than 500 railway passenger and freight cars, and 50,000 bicycles. Also, aluminum is used extensively in the military field.

If aluminum is used instead of steel for frames and bodies of cars and other machines, not only will their weight be reduced, but the cost of construction will be lower. Also, owing to the durability of aluminum, maintenance and replacement costs will be reduced.

Owing to lack of fabrication equipment, the aluminum industry in Taiwan has hitherto not processed enough aluminum products to meet local demands. At present the retail outlets consist of only seventy-four cooking-utensil shops.

The economic value of the aluminum industry has not been fully developed in the past because there were no adequate facilities for manufacturing the higher-priced products. What has been supplied to the local market includes some ingots for the manufacture of cooking utensils and a moderate quantity of aluminum sheets for use in house building and for miscellaneous purposes. The export has consisted mainly of ingots.

The aluminum industry is one of the few industries that can flourish in Taiwan, because it depends a great deal on power and the island will have available more than one million kilowatts of dependable electric power when its capacity is fully developed. At present the small production of 8800 tons per year for consumption in the local market is profitable since freight and other charges are low. When power rates are lowered, ingots manufactured in Taiwan will be able to compete in the world market.

Another encouraging factor is that the neighboring countries of Taiwan—the Philippines, Thailand, South Vietnam, Malaysia, and Indonesia—import aluminum products, and the Philippines, Malaysia, and Indonesia produce not only bauxite, but rubber, tin, and other raw materials that Taiwan needs. If arrangements are made to exchange Taiwan's aluminum products for these countries' raw materials, the trade will benefit all concerned.

ALKALI

An abundance of salt and cheap supplies of electricity provide the necessary conditions for the development of the alkali industry in Taiwan. Besides the chief producer, the Taiwan Alkali Company, which was organized through consolidation of four former Japanese alkali factories, there are eleven small private companies. The main products are caustic soda, hydrochloric acid, liquid chlorine, bleaching powder, and soda ash.

All the caustic soda produced on the island is made from salt by electrolysis. The factories' capacity for producing caustic soda in a year is 11,700 tons (Taiwan Alkali Company) and 3300 tons (eleven small, privately-owned plants).

The market distribution of caustic soda is as follows: 38 per cent for paper and pulp manufacture, 35 per cent for soap manufacture, 10 per cent for the aluminum industry, 7 per cent for the textile industry, 3 per cent for the food industry, 2 per cent for chemical manufacture, and 5 per cent for other uses.[22]

The most important use of chlorine is in the manufacture of hydrochloric acid. It is used also in the manufacture of liquid chlorine and of bleaching powder; some gaseous chlorine is made into DDT and chlorate.

Soda ash is used in glass manufacture, in food industries, in soap manufacture, in textile industry, and in others.

Before 1950 more than half of the production of caustic soda was shipped to Shanghai, and the closing of this big market caused products to decrease. Since both the Taiwan Pulp and Paper Company and the Taiwan Aluminum Works have now begun to expand their production, the prospects of the alkali industry are improving.

Owing to the fact that caustic soda can be produced from two sources, the price of caustic soda drops immediately after a new soda ash factory opens. For the benefit of future development of the alkali industry in Taiwan, it seems that a factory should be established immediately to supply cheaper soda ash.

TEXTILES

Taiwan had no textile industry while the Japanese ruled the island; they did not develop any industry to provide clothing materials for the island.

Wool

Even though it is situated in the subtropical area, Taiwan has seven woolen and worsted mills, with 8000 spindles and 200 looms. The combined production at present of these mills is about 2,000,000 pounds of woolen and worsted goods.

Silk and rayon

The silk and rayon industry is a recent development in Taiwan. There are 279 silk looms and 300 weaving looms which are capable of producing 400,000–600,000 square yards of silk and rayon materials per month.

Cotton

Among the textiles now manufactured on the island, cotton is the most important. The cotton industry in Taiwan was built up only after the outbreak of World War II, when a shortage of cotton goods was keenly felt. At the close of the war, in 1945, the 300 cotton mills had 30,000 spindles and 1000 looms, of which only fewer than half of the spindles and one-fifth of the looms were serviceable. By 1955 the number of mills in operation had been increased to 200,000 spindles and 12,000 looms, which made it possible to meet the requirements of the Taiwanese population for 85,000,000 square yards of cotton cloth each year.

Besides the cotton yarn and cloth industry, there is a cotton knitting industry, with fifty-five factories. The 500 knitting machines of various types in these mills are capable of producing yearly 2,300,000 dozen sets of underwear. There are also 400 towel looms installed in 32 towel factories, which have a production capacity of 1,600,000 dozens of towels a year.[23]

Since Taiwan does not grow cotton, at present the bulk of its raw cotton is shipped to the island under the American aid program. The question as to whether Taiwan should undertake to raise the material needed by the cotton factories is controversial. Some people hold the view that it is not wise to use American aid funds to promote a textile industry on the island because cotton textile products can be imported from Japan at low cost and also because Taiwan does not produce raw cotton at all.

However, there are conditions favoring the development of the cotton industry. Three possible methods are available to make the textile industry self-sufficient: One is to promote the manufacturing of synthetic fibers; another is to grow cotton; and the third is to exchange raw materials for finished goods. The three methods should be advocated at the same time in order to gain speedy results, but the growing of cotton is the most efficient way and should be emphasized.

Is cotton growing really possible in Taiwan? Success with that crop depends primarily on climate. Cotton, when budding and blossoming, requires a good supply of rainfall. After the cotton bolls appear, the plants need dry weather. Those requirements are admirably met in areas in the southern part of the island.

Cotton growing in Taiwan, however, is not without handicaps. Typhoons and boll weevils are two deterrents to planting that crop.

In Taiwan typhoons occur frequently in August and September, but cotton can be planted in any season of the year and the planting can be so timed that the typhoon season is bypassed.

During the Japanese occupation cotton raising could not be done successfully because of inability to combat the boll weevil. Today, however, there are drugs to prevent the worst damage from that pest.[24]

At present the area of cotton cultivation amounts to 1500 acres scattered in the central part of Taiwan. That crop has been estimated at roughly 1320 bales of cotton, about 1200 pounds per acre. This figure for Taiwan is not discouraging when it is compared with the figures for other cotton-growing places. For example, the average cotton production in the United States is only 6300 pounds per acre; and in Egypt, which is world renowned for cotton production, it is 8100 pounds per acre.

Since Taiwan's arable land is limited, how can there be land for cotton cultivation? Fortunately, cotton can be interplanted with other crops, such as sugar cane, peanuts, and sweet potatoes, without injuring the other crop's production.

The public generally has doubted that cotton can be intercropped with sugar cane in Taiwan without reducing the amount of sugar cane produced. Especially the Taiwan Sugar Corporation opposes the intercropping of cotton with sugar cane. Their opposition is based on the following:

First, about 70 per cent of the sugar cane farms use machines in cultivation of the cane. If sugar cane and cotton were interplanted, mechanized farming would not be possible and farming efficiency would be undermined.

Secondly, conditions for supplying raw material for the sugar industry are totally different from those for the textile industry. Sugar cane must be grown near the sugar factories. If the source is more than 12 miles away the supply will not be effective. For the textile industry, on the other hand, the cotton may come from thousands of miles away with no discernible adverse effects. Therefore, concentrated planting of sugar cane is preferred to interplanting with another crop, and increase in unit area production should be emphasized.

However, intercropping experiments made by Japanese agriculturists took place between 1933 and 1940 at the Taiwan State Agricultural Laboratory. Different strains of cotton and of canes were planted and various methods used to make nearly 40 tests. The conclusions were that there was little difference in the sugar cane whether it had been intercropped or not. The loss in production of cane was only 5–6 per cent more than the loss in normal non-intercropped production. Furthermore, the intercropping of farm products is one of the effective methods of economizing on tillable land, which is urgently needed in mountainous Taiwan. According to recent experiment reports, though intercropping of sweet potatoes and of flax with sugar cane reduced sugar cane production by 20 per cent, intercropping between cotton and sugar cane has no adverse effects on cane production in volume and very slight effect on the average sugar yield per acre.[25]

The Taiwan Sugar Corporation has 99,000 acres of cane fields of its own. If it follows the three-year rotation planting system, about 37,000 acres will be planted in cane each year. If half of the area is intercropped with cotton, the corporation will receive a large additional income.

Taiwan needs 60 million pounds of cotton a year. This would require intercropping in 198,000 acres of sugar-cane fields. This goal, of course, can hardly be achieved in a short time. However, if the advantages of intercropping are fully demonstrated to the sugar-cane growers, they should embrace the idea enthusiastically. This action would contribute greatly to Taiwan's economy.

The cultivation of cotton has many benefits for the farmers. The 1954 experiments showed that one acre of land produced more than 10,700 pounds of cotton seed. It took the farmer only five months to raise the cotton. Even after paying for labor, fertilizer, and pest prevention, the farmer made a profit that could be described as enormous. Farmers therefore are flocking toward cotton planting.

Not only is the cotton fiber valuable, but cotton by-products are also. Cotton seeds are good for extraction of oil, which Taiwan needs badly. Cotton seed oil is one of the best vegetable oils, and it can be refined into a butter substitute. The skin of cotton seed can be put to chemical use. In fact, the economic advantages in raising cotton are manifold.

LEATHER

The importance of leather products in Taiwan is not less than that of the products of the other three leading industries, sugar, paper, and textiles, for leather products are not only necessities of daily life, but also important items for military use.

During the Japanese occupation much attention was paid to the leather industry. In 1938 there were six leather manufacturing factories on the island. When the Sino-Japanese War broke out in 1937, the Japanese immediately put the leather industry in Taiwan under government control, more so than any other industry. About 80 per cent of the leather products were supplied for military use; thus they became luxuries to civilians.

After the restoration of Taiwan to China in 1945, the production of leather goods in Taiwan began to rise as a result of industrial development and improvement of living standards. There are at present 74 tanneries, with a total capacity for producing 180,000 sheets of cowhide per year.[26]

The local production of cowhide is very small—only 30,000 sheets per year. About 80 per cent of the hide for the leather industry, the dyes, and most of the tanning materials such as sodium dichromate are imported; this drains the foreign exchange of large amounts each year. The policy of Taiwan's leather industry is to reduce gradually the importation of leather for shoes but to import more hides as raw material for that type of leather. This will result in some saving of foreign exchange, and in more employment in local tanneries. At present buffalo hides in Taiwan are used for making sole leather. For uppers, Taiwan's potential raw material could be hogskin, as the island annually slaughters about two million hogs.

The most needed leather product is shoes—both for civilians and for military personnel. The annual demand for civilian shoes is 1,500,000 pairs, and for military shoes, 600,000 pairs. The shoe industry can well be developed with the potential supply of hogskin, coupled with the highly-developed rubber, plastic, and textile products as auxiliary materials. There is considerable scope for increased production and consumption of leather goods, mostly because the tanning and shoe industries do not require extensive capital investment.

CHEMICALS

In Taiwan the natural resources are inadequate, and the rapid growth of population causes an increased demand for such goods as rubber, metals, and fats and oils. All these needs can be met by developing the chemical industries and conditions for building up those industries are favorable.[27]

First, Taiwan has abundant supply of water power, which is a basic requirement in developing the chemical industries.

Second, the island has some industries that will help in the development of chemical industries. Sugar refining, paper manufacturing, fertilizer manufacturing, salt electrolysis, petroleum refining, and camphor distilling all have a fairly good foundation, laid by the Japanese, and the Taiwanese have gained considerable experience in carrying on those industries.

Third, there is a steady supply of some basic chemical raw materials, such as natural gas, petroleum, salt, limestone, and coal, as well as a good water supply. From natural gas, together with hydrogen, the aliphatic hydrocarbons such as acetylene and ethylene can be made. From petroleum or coal tar, the aromatic hydrocarbons, such as benzene, toluene, and naphthalene, can be obtained. Limestone and coke may combine to produce calcium carbide, which in turn yields acetylene. As for salt, it can be the source of caustic soda and chlorine. Bagasse, a by-product in sugar manufacturing, can be used as raw material for making cellulose, and molasses is widely used in making alcohol. Again, from the gas exhaust in petroleum refining, certain chemical materials can be extracted, such as ethylene, propane, and butane. If the proper techniques of chemical synthesis are applied to these basic raw materials, there should not be much difficulty in solving the problem of manufacturing enough of certain consumer goods to meet the daily needs of Taiwan's millions of residents.

Taiwan does not have a strong basis for developing heavy industry, nor can some other industries develop without limitation. But the chemical industries stand out as having a favorable environment. Emphasis at present should be put on the three key industries, salt electrolysis, petroleum refining, and fertilizer manufacturing, by-products of which can be used to make synthetic chemicals. Those three industries have a firm foundation in Taiwan. Their equipment is available for immediate operation; and no problem will be encountered concerning technical know-how or marketing. There is an extremely abundant supply of raw material for salt electrolysis. In the case of petroleum, though the local output of crude oil at present is not plentiful, a great possibility of development exists. Moreover, the petroleum-refining industry has a great capacity, which insures its successful operation as long as crude oil can be brought from abroad.

For Taiwan's overall industrial development, especially for the chemical industries, two things should be emphasized:

First, research work should be intensified. Chemical industries are industries that aim to "transform what is worthless into wonders," and are the key to such transformation through research work. For example, a new term, "sucrochemical," has been coined by an American chemist; it suggests that from granulated sugar and its by-products various clothing materials, foodstuffs, and other daily necessities can be fabricated. In view of the abundance of sugar produced in Taiwan, that concept certainly gives the island much inspiration.

Second, because of the interdependence among chemical industries, it is highly desirable to have them integrated in operation. In the small-scale factories it is usually difficult to have operating efficiency or to reduce the cost of production. In a chemical industry the integration in operation is the only way to avoid being uneconomical, wasteful, and incapable of competing against a modernized industry.

PAPER

Manufacturing paper and pulp is one of Taiwan's prosperous industries. There are at present fifty mills of various sizes in operation, ranging in capacity from 5000 to 6000 tons per year, manufacturing paper, paperboard, and pulp.[28] A marked upward trend in paper output in Taiwan has been occurring on a yearly basis.

The rate of paper consumption is a reliable yardstick for the culture and living standard of a country. In this connection it is interesting to note that the paper consumption rate of Taiwan has been steadily increasing during recent years. In 1951 the per capita consumption rate of paper in Taiwan was 7 pounds per year. In 1952, it was 9.5 pounds; in 1953, 10.5; in 1954 and in 1955, 14.

The rapid development of the paper industry in Taiwan in recent years is partly due to the fact that the raw material is in easy reach. Paper and pulp are made mainly from plant fibers that consist principally of cellulose. Favored by the subtropical climate, with abundant rainfall, Taiwan is very rich in cellulose resources. Four available plant materials can profitably be utilized to be transformed into paper and pulp: wood; bamboo; rice straw; and bagasse. Wood is by far the most-used cellulosic raw material for making paper and pulp. Of all the trees that grow on Taiwan, a species of hemlock has been found best suited for converting into pulp; and pine, in spite of its high resinous content, has been found most satisfactory for groundwood.

Bamboo can be utilized profitably for manufacturing paper and pulp, provided transportation does not present a problem. Because of the requirements of irrigation and flood control, Taiwan cannot afford to use up all the available pulpwood, but bamboo can be used freely.

Taiwan produces much rice, and the enormous quantity of rice straw resulting from each harvest is valuable as raw material for the island's pulp and paper industry. Rice straw is particularly useful in the production of yellow strawboard. Taiwan produces 1,980,000 tons of rice straw per year. If a quarter of this amount is used as cellulosic raw material for paper and pulp, one can expect production of 137,500 tons of paper and pulp per year from rice straw alone.

As long as Taiwan produces its present amount of sugar, the pulp and paper industry need not worry about the depletion of bagasse as a valuable and dependable cellulosic raw material. For each ton of sugar produced, more than two tons of bagasse are left, with 40 per cent moisture content. Taiwan produces as much as 660,000 tons of sugar per year, and therefore some 1,200,000 tons of bagasse. If a third of this amount of bagasse is used as raw material for pulp and paper, one can expect the production of more than 100,000 tons of those products per year from sugar cane alone.

It is clear that Taiwan has no raw material problem in its paper industry. The inexhaustible supply of bagasse provides an opportunity for future expansion of the industry.[29] However, with the overproduction of paper during recent years, an outlet must be found for the surplus, and the best outlet is, of course, the foreign market. In fact, ever since the overproduction was first noted, about five years ago, manufacturers have worked to put the surplus paper on the foreign market. Their strenuous efforts were rewarded when they found customers in Korea, Ryukyu, Thailand, and South Vietnam. Also Taiwan's paper products are generally welcomed in southeast Asia. With the advantage of the foreign market, the paper industry's overproduction problem will sooner or later be solved.

JUTE

Jute is in demand in Taiwan, for it is the raw material for gunny bags, which are used for packaging sugar and rice and also other commodities.

If Taiwan did not produce jute, and had to import it for manufacturing gunny bags, the foreign exchange required for the nearly 20,000 tons of jute used in a year would be several million dollars. If the 13 million needed gunny bags were imported, the foreign exchange needed would be another several million dollars (a calculation made according to the prices in India and Pakistan, where government policy makes the cost of gunny bags lower than that of jute). Production of jute in Taiwan, therefore, saves much foreign exchange.

The planting of jute in Taiwan dates back to the Japanese period. At that time the acreage was always more than 24,000 acres, and the unit area production was more than 940 pounds per acre. During the Japanese rule the year of peak production of jute was 1943, when the area planted in jute amounted to more than 27,000 acres, the harvest to more than 15 million pounds, and the production per acre to 963 pounds. By the end of World War II a shortage of fertilizer, as well as other factors, had forced a general lowering in unit area production, as well as in acreage and in total production. In 1945 the area planted in jute amounted to only about 12,000 acres; the harvest to less than 4.5 million pounds; and the production per acre to 291 pounds. Since 1952 the island's jute production each year has exceeded the Japanese occupation peak. In 1955, for example, the area planted in jute amounted to nearly 37,000 acres, the harvest to more than 41 million pounds, and the production per acre to about 1158 pounds.

The type of gunny bags most needed are sugar bags, which make up over 60 per cent of the total demand and which need to be ready between November and April of each year. This seasonal demand for sugar bags presents a problem for some gunny-bag producers, who are unable to meet the demand in time. At present there are four jute processing factories in Taiwan, with a total production of 14 million bags, which meets the island's requirements. But if the sugar and rice production continues to increase, or if other needs arise, the supply of jute will be strained. Thus, improvement in methods for production of jute per unit area should be considered.

SUGAR

The sugar industry is the mainstay of Taiwan's economy. Sugar export accounts for more than half of the island's total export value. During the Japanese occupation period, there were 42 sugar factories on the island, operated by four companies. In 1945, when the Chinese Nationalist government took over the industry, only eight out of the 42 factories had not been destroyed or damaged by bombings during World War II. The four companies were then merged to become the Taiwan Sugar Corporation, and the 42 factories were consolidated to form 36. The Taiwan Sugar Corporation is now jointly owned by the Ministry of Economic Affairs of the central government and the Taiwan provincial government, with about 3 per cent of the stock held by private interests. The corporation owns 235,000 acres of sugar cane land. It cultivates 124,000 and leases the rest to local cane farmers.[30]

The Taiwan Sugar Corporation has more than 18,000 regular employees and leases land to 200,000 families. Taking dependents into account, it is no exaggeration to say that the corporation provides the means of livelihood to more than a million islanders. As a source of revenue for the government, the corporation contributes half of the total value of its production.

The corporation also spends large sums on transportation and harbor facilities annually, and buys large amounts of fertilizer and also large numbers of jute bags locally produced. Furthermore, the sugar industry has provided 60 per cent of Taiwan's total foreign exchange funds.

The Taiwan Sugar Corporation is believed to be the largest single corporation in the world making sugar directly from cane. The average annual yield during the Japanese occupation period was 3.7 tons of sugar per acre. In 1950, the average yield of a Taiwan Sugar Corporation farm was 2.5 tons of sugar per acre. In 1953 it exceeded 4 tons and in 1955 it was 4.3 tons.[31] This success is attributable to the following factors:

(1) The introduction of a new variety of sugar cane, "N:Co 31." It is a foreign variety, which was released in 1952 for commercial planting in Taiwan. It not only has a heavy yield of cane and a high sucrose content, but it is adapted to all types of soils. Since the new variety has a slender stalk in contrast to the thick stalk of the old varieties, many more stalks of the new variety are grown in one acre. Moreover, the new variety ratoons successfully; that is, it sprouts from the root of the previous year's plant. Since ratooning enables the farmer to grow new cane from the left-over roots of the previous crops after harvesting, instead of making a second planting, the new variety has the advantage of saving seedlings for planting and of shortening the growing season from the usual 18 months to about 12 months. The yield of ratooned sugar cane is about 80 per cent that of the non-ratooned planted cane.

(2) Next to the introduction of N:Co 31, mechanization has brought about the most striking progress. In the sugar-cane farms of the Corporation nearly 500 tractors are operated, performing steps such as plowing, harrowing, making rows, and cultivation. Use of the tractors not only increases the average yield of the corporation's farms, but also reduces the operating cost. It also helps the farmers to keep up with the crop season so that each field operation is done at the most suitable time. Aiming at mechanization, the sugar corporation purchased 19 sets of automatic sugar sowing and weighing machines and also 50 new locomotives to replace the 60 that were more than 45 years old. The new locomotives run on alcohol produced by the corporation's own alcohol distillers. Also, to reduce costs, the corporation applied a locally-produced, higher concentration nitrogen-solution fertilizer in place of the solid ammonium sulfate previously used.

(3) The third factor responsible for the significant achievements of the Taiwan sugar industry is the effort to utilize the by-products of sugar manufacturing. Sugar cane can be produced at a very low cost by the application of science and technology and it is one of the cheapest agricultural products on earth. However, more than 90 per cent of Taiwan's sugar production has to be exported, with severe competition; and in order to reduce the cost of production development of by-products is needed. Through chemical and biochemical synthesis, hundreds of pharmaceuticals and other chemicals can be synthesized from sugar cane. The main by-products of sugar in Taiwan are yeast and bagasse.

Yeast

In January 1957, with United States aid, the Taiwan Sugar Corporation completed the world's biggest yeast plant, producing 44 tons a day.

Yeast contains a very concentrated form of protein, together with a large amount of vitamins. Both are of special importance to underdeveloped countries like Taiwan, where carbohydrates are abundant but proteins and other important nutritional materials are in short supply. According to the nutrition experts' calculation, 44 tons of yeast could supply the daily requirement of protein for almost a quarter of a million people.

During World War II the Germans manufactured a kind of yeast as a substitute for animal protein; it was known as "artificial meat." When Germany was faced with acute shortage of proteins for food and fodder, interest in large-scale production of yeast made from molasses developed, and the yeast was consumed extensively by the military and by civilians.[32]

Most of the yeast produced in Taiwan is used in feeding hogs, as a substitute for imported soy-bean cake. At present the Taiwan Sugar Corporation owns 40,000 hogs, which are fed on this yeast. The hog manure, which is of immense value to the land, is applied to the sugar-cane fields. It has been estimated that a 20 per cent increase in sugar production in Taiwan will be obtained on areas fertilized by hog manure. It will save for Taiwan a considerable amount in foreign exchange. A better-fed hog means more income for the farmers, more food for the people, and precious fertilizer for the cane field.

Bagasse

Bagasse is another important by-product of sugar cane. It is the fibrous residue of sugar cane after the juice has been extracted. In Taiwan if 7,700,000 tons of cane are ground in a crop year, the sugar produced would amount to 1,694,000 tons (about 22 per cent of the total cane ground), and the bagasse would amount to slightly more than 110,000 tons.[33] Utilization of bagasse has been attempted with vigor in Taiwan for a long time, and Taiwan was one of the first countries to convert bagasse into paper pulp. Most processes for making paper pulp use wood as the raw material, but in Taiwan wood has always been costly and difficult to transport. The cost of bagasse is only one-third that of wood, and it presents no transportation problem. Bagasse contains 40–50 per cent moisture and 40 per cent sugar. Besides being a source of pulp and paper, bagasse can be made into insulating boards for building. Manufacture of building materials from bagasse on a large scale is a rare practice in the world, and in that field Taiwan has the leading position. In other parts of the world only Cuba is setting up a plant for that purpose.

The establishment of a bagasse factory in 1957 was the beginning of an important by-product of sugar manufacture. It was a project of Sino-American cooperation. With a total annual capacity to make 50 million square feet of insulation board and hardboard, the bagasse factory in Taiwan is the biggest and newest of its kind in the Far East, and it will undoubtedly make an important contribution to the supply of housing materials, of which there is a shortage. The factory can also relieve Taiwan's unfavorable balance of trade in two ways: first, by providing a domestic substitute for the plywood now made from imported logs, and second, by creating a salable export commodity. It is estimated that in these two ways this single factory can save considerable foreign exchange for the island.

Sugar beets

The beginning of successful cultivation of sugar beets in Taiwan is also of importance for the sugar industry of the world. It is generally understood that the growing of sugar cane is limited to tropical and subtropical regions, and the growing of sugar beets to the temperate. Trials of planting sugar beets in Taiwan have shown that the yield of sugar beets on the island compares very favorably with that of the yield in other places, both in Europe and America, and that production of beet sugar in Taiwan amounts to about 2.2 tons per acre.

The experiments in intercropping sugar beets with sugar cane and paddy rice, were carried out by the Corporation. Because of the acute shortage of arable land in Taiwan, the intercropping of sugar beet with sugar cane and with paddy rice would be a great contribution to the agricultural economy. Furthermore, cultivation of beet sugar side by side with cane sugar would lower the production costs of both. At the same time, the increasing need for animal and poultry feeds in Taiwan would be partially met.

EXPANSION OF THE SUGAR INDUSTRY

Consumption of sugar in Taiwan amounts to only about 55,000 tons annually; each year there is a substantial surplus available for export. Although the loss of the mainland market was a blow to the sugar industry, it has been offset by the expansion of sales to foreign countries.

Through the introduction of the new species of cane, the mechanization of cane farming, the extension of ratooning, and the utilization of by-products, together with other improvements in farming methods and in water conservation, much progress has been made in Taiwan's sugar production. The unit area production has been increased while the cost has been slashed. The unit production in recent years has been 4.6 tons per acre, which is far beyond the peak record attained during the Japanese occupation period. The growth period for sugar cane has also been reduced from 18 months to 12 months.

Besides the sugar industry itself, a few additional industries now depend on the utilization of sugar. Parallel with the petrochemical industry, for example, a sugar-chemical industry has been rising, using sugar in the manufacture of various products. It has succeeded in producing pyroxylin lacquer made of sugar. In fact the sugar industry in Taiwan has passed the stage of mere subsistence and has embarked on a multi-purpose program that will continue to increase its impact on Taiwan's economy.

At present the sugar industry in Taiwan is facing two problems: how to increase production and how to expand the foreign market.

Expansion of production

Because of the limited amount of arable land on the island and the rapid increase of population, sugar cane planting on Taiwan should not be permitted to exceed a certain limit, if adverse effects on the production of other necessities are to be avoided.

In recent years a shortage of sugar cane has closed down the factories in a number of locations. As a result the sugar cane plantation area has

331

dwindled. Even though the sugar cane growing period has been shortened and will be shortened further when ratooning and mudseeding are extended, the following steps are indispensable in order that the present sugar production of the island may be maintained.

The first is to expand the sugar plantation area to the mountain land of central Taiwan. If the new mechanical methods can be applied to the mountain land, the sugar mills will be willing to trade their plain fields for the mountain land, and thus their raw material shortage can be abolished.

The second step is to improve an area in the southwest part of the island where there are between 74,000 and 99,000 acres of dry stony land. If the intercropping method and mudseeding are applied there, the stony soil of the area can be converted into good sugar cane fields in from three to five years.

The third step is to expand the sugar acreage by means of conversion to usable farm land of the slaty land along the seashore in western Taiwan.

International Sugar Conference

When Taiwan joined the world sugar agreement in 1953 the action was not only a turning point for the sugar industry of Taiwan, but also for the whole economy of the island. Thus the agreement has been surveyed in detail by Huang.[34]

The first International Sugar Conference was held in London in 1953, with fifty countries participating. The main purpose of the conference was to stabilize the price of sugar on the world market through the balancing of supply and demand. Before the agreement took effect an oversupply had been lowering the sugar price. Through regulation of the supply so that it would just about meet the demand of the world market, the countries realized that the price of sugar would be more stable. Therefore a quota system was set up, and each exporting country was assigned a basic export tonnage. The export quota for Taiwan, as specified in the agreement, was limited to 660,000 tons a year; the quota became effective in January 1954.

The second International Sugar Conference, held in Geneva in 1956, revised the 1953 agreement and increased Taiwan's export quota to 720,500 tons. Taiwan's quota is second to Cuba's quota of 2,656,500 tons. Both Cuba and Taiwan are important sugar exporters; but the importance of sugar to Taiwan and to Cuba is not comparable. Taiwan is self-sufficient in rice as a staple food; Cuba depends on importation of food.

In 1953 the amount of sugar exported from Taiwan was more than 990,000 tons. In 1954, after Taiwan joined in the International Sugar Agreement, it amounted to only 561,000 tons—nearly 430,000 tons less than the 1953 amount, a decline of 45 per cent. This meant that the foreign exchange earned from the sugar export decreased by 40 per cent. Thus, for the cause of international cooperation, Taiwan made a great sacrifice of her sugar export potential, even though stabilization of the price of sugar in the world market will in the future protect Taiwan's sugar production.

Most of the sugar exported from Taiwan goes to Japan, for Japan needs more than one million tons of sugar a year and produces less than

33,000 tons herself. The question has arisen as to whether the International Sugar Agreement would affect the Taiwan–Japan sugar trade. The answer is no. Taiwan will lose its Japanese market to some other exporters, for example to Cuba, which has plenty of sugar waiting for export. But that has not worried Taiwan. For Taiwan enjoys a freight differential over Cuba, owing to its proximity to Japan. Furthermore, an open account has been set up between Taiwan and Japan, which permits bartering of goods between the two. In past years Taiwan exported from 330,000 to 440,000 tons of sugar a year to Japan and was never anxious to export more. The main reason for this is that Japan wanted to pay for the sugar through bartering and Taiwan could not use up all the credit, for many import materials needed by Taiwan are not available in Japan. Taiwan would prefer to export sugar to countries farther away and at a lower price—to sell its sugar for United States dollars and to use the money to buy products that cannot be obtained in Japan.

Also, Japan prefers to diversify its source of sugar import. Japan is a country whose economy depends on foreign trade; she can use sugar purchases to enhance trade relationships and to promote the export of Japanese manufactured goods. If Japan had her way, she would import sugar from Cuba to the extent of more than half a million tons a year through bartering, as with Taiwan. However, Cuba does not need much in the line of Japanese products. The other places from which Japan can obtain sugar through barter are Brazil and Indonesia, but they can barter only to a limited extent. In short, Japan does not wish to buy all of Taiwan's sugar nor does Taiwan care to sell all its sugar to Japan. Therefore the international agreement has no effect on Taiwan's sugar export to Japan.

Aside from Japan, Taiwan's important export markets are in southeast Asia and the Middle East, where Indonesia is the only keen competitor, enjoying the same nearness to those markets and supplying the same kind of sugar. Would Indonesia threaten Taiwan's sugar sales by not participating in the International Sugar Agreement? The answer is again negative. It is true that 1,650,000 tons of sugar a year will be needed in the Far Eastern and Middle Eastern countries, aside from their local production. Also it is true that Japan wants very much to take Indonesia's sugar, and Japan has oversold her products without being able to get the bills paid or to obtain goods in return. But low production limits Indonesia in its sugar exports to an estimated 165,000 tons a year.

The major sugar exporting countries in the Far East are Taiwan and Indonesia, which together can supply not more than some 880,000 tons. This figure is far below the areas need. Therefore, if Indonesia increased sugar production and exported more, this would only serve to crowd other suppliers, such as Cuba, out of the Asian market. So Indonesia's refusal to ratify the agreement was due more to pride than to any advantage she could gain by non-participation in the agreement.

In short, the International Sugar Agreement, when conscientiously followed by participating countries, will definitely have the effect of stabilizing world sugar prices, thus enabling sugar producers to operate at a reasonable profit. Taiwan may have sacrificed her sugar export potential, but she has played an important role in stabilizing the international sugar price.

PINEAPPLES

Pineapples could become a banner of foreign exchange for the island of Taiwan, but in marked contrast to the sugar industry, which has achieved much progress in recent years, the pineapple industry has not gained much in the island. Unlike the acreage and yield of sugar cane, the acreage planted in pineapples has reached only about half that of the Japanese record year and the yield of pineapples has not increased much. The yield per unit area has recently matched the Japanese record, but the amount of canned pineapple amounted to only 60 per cent of the Japanese record.

K. T. Li observes the following interesting facts.[35] First, in the five years from 1951 to 1955 there was practically no increase in the area planted in pineapples. Second, the average harvested area during those five years represents only 60 per cent of the 1938 area, the year of Japanese peak production of canned pineapples. Third, except in 1955, the production of pineapples per acre did not exceed the Japanese record of 5.4 tons set in the peak year. Even in 1955, the increase was too small to be of any significance. Fourth, although the production of canned pineapple was much higher in 1954 and 1955, it still represented only 43 per cent of the Japanese peak record.

With the current yield every acre of pineapples harvested in Taiwan could earn 30 per cent more foreign exchange than every acre of sugar cane. This percentage might be multiplied several times if pineapples were planted on the marginal dry land on hills, which is well adapted to the cultivation of pineapples but not of sugar cane. Taiwan's pineapples not only could be at least as good an earner of foreign exchange as is Taiwan's sugar, but they also have the potential of becoming more than three times as good an earner as is sugar.

How does Taiwan's pineapple industry compare with that of Hawaii? In the slightly more than fifty years since Hawaii's first pineapple company was organized, the pineapple industry has enjoyed a spectacular growth and is the source of as much as 70 per cent of the total world production of canned pineapple. The annual canned-pineapple production per unit area cultivated in Hawaii in 1955 was more than four times that in Taiwan, without counting the additional production of juice.

The difficulty in Taiwan's pineapple industry is lack of an all-out effort toward production, processing, and foreign trade. There are more than 60 pineapple-canning factories in Taiwan. Except for six owned and operated by the Taiwan Pineapple Company, all the rest are small factories. The pineapple farmers total 16,000; they are engaged in pineapple cultivation on 17,300 acres. This means that the average farmer cultivates only a little more than an acre. This figure is painfully small and does not suggest good management and use of technological improvements.

In contrast to the situation in Hawaii and in Malaysia, there is not in Taiwan a central organization of the pineapple industry to coordinate its three essential phases, production, processing, and marketing. As a result, each farmer, packer, and trader has been very much on his own, without consideration for the overall interests of the industry. In fact, lack of coordination may be the most important single factor that has caused the slow progress of this and some other industries in Taiwan.

For better production, attention should be paid (a) to the increase in the yield per unit area through such measures as seedling improvement, more effective fertilization, better control of insects and plant diseases, adoption of closer planting, and upgrading of fruits; (b) to the expansion of the planted area through fuller utilization of hilly land; and (c) to better organization of independent small farmers.

For more efficient processing, by-products should be utilized fully and the procurement of tin plate for cans and the manufacture of cans centralized.

For improved marketing, emphasis should be placed on joint sales promotion; on closer cooperation among farmers, packers, and traders; and upon the centralization of handling and processing fruit for the purpose of export.

HANDICRAFT

In an economically underdeveloped area such as Taiwan, where capital and equipment are lacking but human labor is abundant and cheap, the handicraft industry needs to be developed and should be a natural occupation of the people. In order to succeed in the foreign market, the handicraft industry in Taiwan must not cling to old, primitive, inefficient methods, but should be able—in order to be competitive—to create new designs, shapes, textures, and patterns.

In the Western world, machines can produce goods at very low cost, and most of the articles needed by the average Western consumer are machine-made. No matter how low wages are in Taiwan, its hand-made products can hardly compete in price with machine-made ones. However, the Western consumer sometimes prefers hand-made products because of designs and styles. Handicraft products will never be able to invade the market already conquered by machine-made products, which emphasize utility; but they can go into the luxury market, emphasizing art and originality. Countries that excel in making hand-made products have even created a new profession—industrial artists—to supply designs; and they have large numbers of industrial schools. In competing with other places in handicraft production, Taiwan's handicraft industry should mix machine exactness with human art, combining the advantages of the machine made and the purely hand made.

Among Taiwan's handicraft products are hats, bamboo articles, seagrass mats, and carved wooden articles. Their market lies in the United States, but they have strong competitors in southeastern Asian countries. For example, the bamboo products are threatened by those made in Japan, and the mats by those made of hemp in the Philippines, as well as by Chinese-style clothing made in Hong Kong.

HATS.—Taiwan's hand-made hat industry started in 1897, using the rushes growing in the Tachia River as the only material. Later on, Lintou rushes, Hincki fiber, Manila hemp, ramie, coconut leaves, palm leaves, and pineapple leaves, were also used as raw materials, The hatmaking industry was a family line, handed down from one generation to another. It was distributed along the western coastal plain.

335

The year 1934 was the golden age of the industry when 150,000 female workers turned out 15,000,000 grass hats—about 15 per cent of the world's grass hat production. It is estimated that between 1912 and 1941 the average annual export was 5,300,000 hats. They were sold via Japan to the United States, Australia, Africa, Southeast Asia, and the Chinese mainland.

After Taiwan was returned to China in 1945, the number of female hat workers was reduced to a little more than 20,000, as a result of low wages.

BAMBOO PRODUCTS.—Bamboo forests occupy an area of 114,000 acres in Taiwan, and the annual production is more than 40 million poles. Bamboo trees in Taiwan mature rapidly and can be cut for use every three years. Since the retrocession of Taiwan to China, poles and fishing rods are the only bamboo items that have been exported in numbers. In previous years the bamboo items exported also included bamboo chips, twigs, and baskets. The chips and twigs were exported to Hong Kong where they are processed into dining-room screens for export.

In the last few years the international market has shown an unprecedented interest in bamboo production, with the United States, Australia, and European countries as the most important purchasers; they want bamboo items for picnic wares, for travel, and for summer restaurant equipment.

Japan and Hong Kong are Taiwan's principal competitors for bamboo export, and they enjoy certain advantages over Taiwan. It costs more than twice as much to ship a ton of bamboo goods from Taiwan to the west coast of the United States as it does from Japan to the same place. Hong Kong exports to Great Britain are tax free, provided that 25 per cent of the raw materials used comes from either Hong Kong or other British Commonwealth areas. Thus 80 per cent of the bamboo goods exported to the United States is manufactured in Japan, and 90 per cent of that exported to the Commonwealth areas is manufactured in Hong Kong.

Since the growing of bamboo is rare in the Western Hemisphere, there is always a good market for it there. In quality, the bamboo grown in Taiwan is far better than that in Japan; the poles are longer and have fewer knots. If Taiwan improves its bamboo products, they will be one of its important handicraft commodities. In 1953 Taiwan exported 200,000 bamboo screens, and in 1954, 500,000.

RICE PAPER.—At the peak of rice-paper production, which took place during the Japanese period, more than 30 factories were in operation, employing 2500 workers and exporting 5000 cases of rice paper. At present there are only 17 factories, employing 400 workers; and less is exported— half of the peak production. The majority of the factories lack working capital and depend on orders from exporters.

SEA-GRASS MATS.—Sea grass, of which mats are woven by hand, grows in abundance in marshlands in the southern part of the island. Most of the workers in this industry are women. Since no equipment is needed, the technique is simple and the industry is growing. The mats are exported to the United States. However, in recent years, the Manila hemp mats of the Philippines have become a keen competitor.

CARVED WOODEN ARTICLES.—Because of their dignified richness, ornateness, and uniqueness, the Chinese hand-carved wooden articles have enjoyed a peerless international fame for many years. The craft dates back to early Chinese history in Taiwan; however, it was not until 1950 that the first wood-carving factory was established on the island. Today, there are three such factories, employing 360 workers. The kinds of wood principally used are camphor and cedar.

DRAWN HAND-WORK.—The drawn hand-work industry is a relatively new one; it was started in 1951, when a factory was established by refugees from the Chinese mainland. The main drawn hand-work items of export are handkerchiefs. Irish linen is considered the best material for them, with Swiss and American linens second. Besides handkerchiefs, the drawn hand-work products also include tablecloths, bed sheets, and other items. Taiwan exports 5 million dozen handkerchiefs a year, most go to the United States.

TOURISM

The tourist industry is an effective means of obtaining foreign currency, and it is well known that since the turn of the century the development of that industry is constantly taking rapid strides forward. As with Europe, where Switzerland, France, and Italy have long been renowned for their efforts to promote tourism, post-war Japan and America's new Hawaii are progressing in that field. It is reported that in 1955 Hawaii had 110,000 visitors, who spent a total of $55,000,000. Tourism ranked third in Hawaii's sources of revenue, next to the export trade of sugar and pineapples.[36] In 1955 Japan received 100,000 visitors who spent $45,000,000 in that country.

Taiwan has many favorable conditions for the tourist industry: (a) situated midway between Japan and Hong Kong, Taiwan enjoys a locational advantage; (b) even more significant is the beauty of Taiwan's scenery, with flowers blooming abundantly in its warm climate all year round; (c) since it is difficult to obtain a visa to visit mainland China, Taiwan is now the only place to find Chinese culture—the Chinese cuisine, opera, dress, and books; Hong Kong has too much Cantonese flavor, and not much Mandarin style; and (d) the island has convenient transportation facilities, including airlines, railroads, and highways.

However, in order that the island may develop its tourist industry and become known as a "paradise in the Pacific," hotels, restaurants, and roads should be modernized.

REFERENCES

[1] T. C. PAN, "An appraisal of Taiwan's economy," *Industry in Free China* **III,** No. 3, 13 (1955).
[2] C. C. CHEN, "Taiwan's industries as I see them," *Industry in Free China* **I,** No. 2, 17 (1954).
[3] ROBERT CHIEN, "Post-war industrial development in Taiwan," *Industry in Free China* **X,** No. 5, 13 (1958).
[4] JACOBUS SHIH, "New look of Taiwan's industrialization," *Industry in Free China* **IX,** No. 4, 2 (1958).
[5] GERALD C. PAN, "The accomplishments of the first Four-Year Plan—an initial analysis," *Industry in Free China* **VII,** No. 3, 4 (1957).
[6] P. Y. HSU, "A brief review of the current economic situation in the Republic of China," *Industry in Free China* **XIII,** No. 4, 1 (1960).
[7] C. T. YANG, "Economic and social development in the Republic of China during the past decade," *Industry in Free China* **XIII,** No. 4, 7 (1960).
[8] K. G. YIN, "Current economic situation of Taiwan," *Industry in Free China* **XV,** No. 3, 2 (1961).

[9] K. T. Li, "The growth of private industry," *Industry in Free China* **XIV**, No. 2, 32 (1961).

[10] T. Y. Wang, "The trend of economic development in Taiwan," *Industry in Free China* **IV**, No. 1, 6 (1955).

[11] K. T. Li, "The effect of industrialization in Taiwan on the welfare of the people," *Industry in Free China* **IV**, No. 2, 3 (1955).

[12] Fong Hui, "Some important factors in the economic development of Taiwan," *Industry in Free China* **IV**, No. 5, 20 (1955).

[13] K. T. Li, "A review of the economic situation in Taiwan in 1958," *Industry in Free China* **XI**, No. 3, 11 (1959).

[14] ——, "Characteristics and trends of industrial development in Taiwan," *Industry in Free China* **VII**, No. 6, 8 (1957).

[15] ——, "How industrialization could help improve Taiwan's balance of payments," *Industry in Free China* **VII**, No. 2, 8 (1957).

[16] P. Kiang, "The current economic situation of Taiwan," *Industry in Free China* **VI**, No. 4, 3 (1956).

[17] Shih-cheng Liu, "On the development of Taiwan's industry," *Industry in Free China* **I**, No. 5, 16 (1954).

[18] K. Y. Yin, "A discussion on industrial policy for Taiwan," *Industry in Free China* **I**, No. 2, 5 (1954).

[19] W. P. Li, "Pushing toward industrialization," *Industry in Free China* **VII**, No. 5, 15 (1957).

[20] Chang Fong, "An intermediate course between free enterprise and government control," *Industry in Free China* **I**, No. 5, 13 (1954).

[21] T. C. Pan, "Industrial development planning in the Republic of China," *Industry in Free China* **X**, No. 4, 7 (1958).

[22] Y. C. Yen, "Alkali industry of Taiwan—present status, trend and policy," *Industry in Free China* **XIII**, No. 4, 12 (1961).

[23] K. Y. Lin, "The development of the textile industry in Taiwan," *Industry in Free China* **I**, No. 1, 16 (1954).

[24] T. H. Chien, "Can Taiwan support itself in its cultivation of cotton?," *Industry in Free China* **IV**, No. 3, 1 (1955). [In Chinese].

[25] Sun Feng-chi and Shih Wen-piao, "Intercropping and its various effects on the growth and production of early crop sugar cane," *Taiwan Sugar Institute Research Report*, No. 7 (1951).

[26] C. Chu, "Leather industry in China," *Industry in Free China* **V**, No. 2, 8 (1956).

[27] K. Y. Yin, "Prospects of chemical industries in Taiwan," *Industry in Free China* **III**, No. 6, 4 (1955).

[28] K. H. Yu, "The pulp and paper industry of Taiwan," *Industry in Free China* **V**, No. 6, 1 (1956).

[29] Y. C. Yen, "Developing paper industry," *Industry in Free China* **IV**, No. 3, 9 (1955).

[30] Han lih-wu, *Taiwan Today* (Hwa Kuo Publishing Company, Taipei, 1956) p. 106.

[31] C. T. Yang, "Sugar industry in Taiwan," *China Today*, No. 1, 30 (1953).

[32] H. C. Chin, "Yeast used for food," *Industry in Free China* **III**, No. 3, 4 (1955).

[33] T. Y. Chow, "By-products of sugar industry," *Industry in Free China* **I**, No. 6, 49 (1954).

[34] J. C. Huang, "Effects of the International Sugar Agreement on the Taiwan sugar industry," *Industry in Free China* **I**, No. 3, 1 (1954).

[35] K. T. Li, "Taiwan pineapple as a big banner of foreign exchange," *Industry in Free China* **III**, No. 2, 22 (1955).

[36] Ho Ying-ching, "Some ways and means for tourism development in Taiwan," *China Today* **III**, No. 5, 1 (1960).

TWENTY-TWO	Prospect and World Contact

PROSPECTS

WHAT ARE THE PROSPECTS for the island of Taiwan? They depend upon many factors, such as the world political situation, Communist military strategy, and the economic development in Taiwan. The first two topics lie outside the scope of the present study. The evidence which has been collected and examined here relates above all to the economic conditions in Taiwan, and in this field it is possible to make some summary judgments.

The critical problem of Taiwan is the relation of population growth to land productivity and to the growth of manufacturing. In order better to understand the island's prospects, this problem may be analyzed from the geographical point of view.

POPULATION

Taiwan is one of the most densely populated regions in the world; its density is exceeded only by that of the Netherlands and of Belgium. Owing to the island's surface configuration, the distribution of its population is by no means even. About 66 per cent of the total population is concentrated in the western coastal plains, which constitute only 22 per cent of the total area of the island of Taiwan. The birth rate has been more than 40 per thousand inhabitants in each year, and there is little reason to believe that the rate will decline significantly in the near future.

The most striking feature of the population situation is the rate of increase. From 1905 to 1960 the population of the island more than tripled. Except for the increase due to the two major Chinese immigrations—one in

1661 and the other in 1949, Taiwan's rises in population have been due to the natural increase among the Taiwan-born Chinese. Perhaps the most remarkable aspect of the vital statistics picture in Taiwan is the rapid fall in the death rate, as contrasted with the relatively stable birth rate. The death rate declined from 30 deaths per thousand population in 1910 to 20 per thousand in 1930 and to 10 per thousand in 1950. The rate of population growth in that period has been 3.8 per cent per year, compared with 1.2 per cent in Asia and 0.8 per cent in western Europe. The increase of population due to immigration may be a temporary rise, but the natural increase of population does not appear likely to stop. At present the annual natural increase of population—380,000—is larger than the number of people living in Kaohsiung, the island's second largest city. The increase over the next ten–twenty years will probably continue at about the present rate. Assuming that the rate of increase will continue the same, the population will double in twenty years.

The present density of population on the island is extremely high for an agricultural economy. The birth rate is one of the highest in the world. The death rate is lower than that in many European countries and only slightly above that in the United States.

The land area of Taiwan totals about 13,884 square miles. The number of persons per square mile is 840, compared to 659 in Japan, 248 in the Philippines, 293 in the Chinese mainland, and 51 in the United States. Taiwan is more densely populated than are some highly-industrialized countries such as the United Kingdom and Germany.

As for population density per unit of cultivated land, when Taiwan's density is compared with that of Japan, the lesser dependence of Japan on soil resources must be taken into account. Relevant in this connection is the fact that about 23 per cent of Japan's population is engaged in full-time agriculture, compared with about 57 per cent of Taiwan's population. The number of persons per square mile of cultivated land in Taiwan is 26 per cent greater than that in Belgium, which has a highly industrialized economy.

The population density per square mile of land is 4.6 times as great as in the Philippines. This is significant inasmuch as the economies of the two areas are somewhat similar. Taiwan's population density per square mile of cultivated land is extremely high for an economy largely dependent on production and processing of agricultural commodities. If the rate of population increase does not exceed the rate of increase in agricultural production, the population expansion will do no harm since the expansion can be supported by the increase in the means of subsistence.

LAND USE

Even though only one-quarter of Taiwan's total land area is under cultivation, three-quarters of the gainfully-employed Taiwanese are engaged in farming, and farm produce represents 80 per cent of the value of the island's total production. Rice, sugar cane, and sweet potatoes are the leading crops, with rice in undisputed first place. Generally two rice crops are harvested from a plot each year. Under Japanese rule about half of Taiwan's annual rice production was exported, whereas now seven-eighths of it is consumed at home. Taiwan ranks as one of the world's largest producers of sugar and sugar is its chief export. About four-fifths of the total produced is exported, chiefly to Japan and southeast Asia.

Although production of tea has fallen off in recent years, it is the island's fourth most valuable export, ranking after sugar, rice, and bananas. Before World War II, 95 per cent of the tea crop went to Japan. Four-fifths of it is now exported, mainly to the United States and southeast Asia.

Before the war Taiwan was the third largest producer of canned pineapple in the world (after Hawaii and British Malaya). At that time the entire crop went to Japan. As a result of the loss of that market after Japan's defeat in 1945, many farmers have shifted to cassava.

In spite of the constantly-increasing size of the agricultural population of Taiwan and the limited amount of cultivated land, Taiwan's farmers not only are able to provide themselves with the basic foodstuffs, but also they are able to export a surplus of rice, sugar, tea, fruit, and other products. The high crop yields of the farms in Taiwan are the result of the diligence of the farmers as well as of the intelligent use of such agricultural practices as irrigation, fertilization, rotation of crops, and the introduction of new crops.

Land use in Taiwan not only is intensive, but changes rapidly. The land has changed from brushland to dry farming land, from grassland to plantations producing bananas, tea, and cassavas, from subtropical hardwood forests to bamboo groves, and from sand flats or sea beaches to fish ponds and salt fields or as the result of population pressure to farmland for sweet potatoes and peanuts. Generally, the acreage for food crops has increased in comparison with that of the years before World War I, while the acreage of cash crops such as tea and fruits has decreased.

Agricultural production may be expanded by (a) increasing the cultivated acreage; and (b) increasing the intensity of cultivation. Fortunately, however, up to the present, the growth of the island's total population as well as of its farm population has been accompanied by the expansion of farm land.

In order to obtain as much production as possible from small farms intensity of cultivation is necessary. The plan of cultivation in Taiwan is to get the greatest return per acre rather than the greatest return per unit of labor because farm labor is cheap but farm land is expensive. The way to increase cultivation is (a) increase the number of crop acres or the multiple-crop index; (b) select crops such as rice and vegetables, that produce a greater amount of food value per unit area than other crops, even though they consume a large amount of labor; and (c) plant hybrid seeds and use such measures as scientific fertilization and pest control.

Of the various kinds of cultivated land, the double-crop paddy fields are the most efficient. Such fields occupy about 38 per cent of the total area of cultivated land and their multiple-crop index is the highest among all agricultural lands. The multiple-crop index of these fields is usually more than 200 per cent.

Almost all kinds of farm land in Taiwan are used for the production of food. Among the food crops, rice is by far the most important. Rice can supply a greater amount of food energy per acre (in terms of calories) than can most other crops. Thus it can support the high density of population. However, rice requires a large number of laborers for its cultivation.

341

The most important crop next to rice is sugar cane, which is cultivated in the central and southern parts of the island. Sugar is the most important export commodity.

Other important farm crops are sweet potatoes, bananas, tea, pineapples, peanuts, and citrus fruits.

As already mentioned, in Taiwan the increase of population has been keeping pace with the increase of farm land. But the expansion of farm land must be limited, or the limitation will come later by natural conditions. Although the increase of Taiwan's population due to immigration may be a temporary situation, the growth of population as a result of high birth rates and low death rates in Taiwan continues without limitation.

Increased productivity

However, the prospects for Taiwan's economy are not unpropitious because there are favorable factors for increasing the amount of agricultural products.

Taiwan's agriculture is rather intensive already, but it can become more intensive, as it is in Japan. For example; the application of nitrogenous fertilizer to rice land in Taiwan averages 306 pounds per acre per crop, while in Japan the comparable figure averages 508 pounds. The number of labor days used per acre in Taiwan was 257, that in Japan was 521, nearly twice as great as that in Taiwan. The average yield per acre in Japan is also much higher than that in Taiwan. If the intensity of cultivation in Taiwan is pushed to the same degree as it is in Japan, the population pressure on agricultural products will be eased. This may be accomplished by using a greater amount of fertilizer, expanding irrigation facilities, and improving cultivation methods by the use of a deep plowing technique. Great intensity of cultivation brings about a high yield of products per unit area. Thus the amount of farm products raised can be increased at a rate corresponding with that of the present increase in population.

Only 25 per cent of this mountainous island area can be cultivated; and as the growth of the population has been rapid, the cultivatable land has been intensely used. There is little future for expansion of production horizontally. For the future Taiwan should look either up to the mountains or down to the sea. "Up to the mountains" indicates development of the forest resources in which Taiwan abounds, and "down to the sea" means development of its fisheries.

An estimate has already been made that the number of trees per unit area may be increased from two to ten times the present number. Chemical industries using forest products as raw materials may be greatly extended.

Taiwan has received more than 7 million United States dollars to develop the fisheries from the International Bank for Reconstruction and Development and the future of fisheries is bright.

A demographic factor in Taiwan is also favorable to potentialities for increased production. Taiwan's population is young compared with that of most western countries. Only 10 per cent of the island's people are 50 years of age or older, while about 50 per cent of the total population fall within the 15–49 year age group. This indicates, of course, that the labor force includes a larger proportion of the total population than in most western countries, and the old and inactive people a smaller proportion. The small proportion of people more than fifty years old is, however, offset somewhat by the large proportion of children of fourteen years of age and below (41 per cent), who produce little in the way of goods and services.

Development of resources and increase in production are also affected by the state of health of the people. Taiwan's relatively favorable present and prospective health conditions indicate that, given a minimum of other essential productive resources, labor productivity should increase more rapidly than in most countries of the Far East.

Another factor in Taiwan's ability to increase production is a rise in literacy. Taiwan compares favorably in this respect with other areas in the Far East. In 1962, the number of students reached 2,740,000, about 23.8 per cent of Taiwan's total population. On the elementary level, Taiwan had about 2000 schools and 2,087,000 pupils. The percentage of school-age children attending was 97. Elementary education is free and compulsory. Through increase in literacy an improvement of technical ability may be more easily achieved, and the workers can increase production more effectively.

GROWTH OF MANUFACTURING

Taiwan's industry is second to none in the Far East except Japan's. The favorable factors for the development of its industry include cheap power, excellent transportation, abundant labor supply, good foundation of industry, and social stability. But as with all underdeveloped countries, Taiwan suffers a shortage of capital, a lack of entrepreneurs, and a lack of technical know-how. Also its mineral resources are rather limited, especially those most useful to Taiwan's industry, such as iron ore and bauxite.

Owing to its small size, Taiwan can hardly become self-sufficient economically. The industry of Taiwan today depends on a few processed agricultural products, such as sugar, rice, and pineapples, and largely on imported materials. The island must produce more exportable goods to provide foreign exchange for the imported raw materials. Both the raw materials and the processed agricultural products are affected by fluctuations in the world market. To avoid depending mainly on a limited number of exportable goods and to cope with the fluctuations in the price of the imported raw materials, Taiwan will have to seek a broader basis of economy through diversification of products.

In future industrial expansion, development of basic industries besides those producing fertilizer, food, textiles, and power, should be emphasized.

Taiwan does not have a strong basis for developing heavy industry, nor can some other industries develop without limitation. But the chemical industries stand out as having favorable conditions—an abundant supply of power; a steady supply of some basic materials such as natural gas, petroleum, salt, limestone, and coal; and some experience with industries such as sugar refining, paper manufacturing, fertilizer manufacturing, salt-electrolysis, petroleum refining, and camphor distilling.

An industry that Taiwan needs to develop, and that should be a national occupation of the people, is handicrafts. In an area such as Taiwan, where capital and equipment are short, but human labor is abundant and cheap, the products of handicraft should have a bright future.

The tourist industry should bring some foreign currency to the island. Its good location between Japan and Hong Kong, its beautiful scenery, its excellent transportation facilities, and the fact that it is now the only remaining home in the free world of Chinese cultural traditions should be favorable factors in developing the tourist industry.

WORLD CONTACT

Being an independent island and no longer a colony, Taiwan realizes that world contact is essential for its existence. World contact is of two kinds: material contact, which means foreign trade, and cultural contact, which includes technical exchange of personnel, membership in international conferences, and exhibition of paintings, art, and books.

Material contact

Foreign trade is important in Taiwan's economic development. As is exemplified by Britain and Japan, any island country has to emphasize foreign trade as a main center of economic policy. At present Taiwan is endeavoring to penetrate the world market, starting with the southeastern Asiatic countries and gradually expanding to Africa and South America. The success of industry in Taiwan hinges on exporting its products. For example, the molasses production of the sugar industry of the island has developed very well, simply because it has a good foreign market.

TRADE WITH JAPAN.—Trade between Taiwan and Japan amounts to only about 3 per cent of Japan's total import and export, but it is one of the most important factors in Taiwan's total. Taiwan–Japan barter began early in 1950. In the first year of barter the value of Taiwan's exports to Japan was twice as great as the value of its imports from that country. Between 1951 and 1955 the amount of Taiwan's foreign-exchange settlement doubled, and the import settlement rose by 50 per cent. The main items of barter from Taiwan to Japan are sugar and rice, and from Japan to Taiwan, fertilizer and electrical equipment. Because of Japan's nearness, Taiwan saves both time and money by importing goods from Japan.

Since Taiwan's industry was founded by the Japanese during their occupation, Taiwanese factories and public utilities still welcome supplies of Japanese equipment, and most Taiwanese technicians can converse easily with their Japanese counterparts.

TRADE WITH KOREA AND THE RYUKYUS.—During the Korean War the Koreans did not like to trade with Japan, and so Taiwan's exports to Korea suddenly increased. Then came the armistice, and American good will helped to soften Korean-Japanese animosity. Large amounts of Japanese goods, instead of Taiwanese products, began to be sold to Korea.

Taiwan has been enjoying a steady gain in the Korean trade because few Korean products are wanted in Taiwan. In the period 1952–1956 the value of Taiwan's import from Korea was only one-twentieth of the value of its export to that country. Exports from Korea to Taiwan consist mostly of agricultural, sea, and mining products, with very little industrial goods.

Since Korea is industrially backward and needs to buy from overseas, Taiwanese industrial products find a good market in Korea.

344

The Ryukyu Islands urgently need rice, glass, industrial products, sugar, building materials, salt, and steel pellets. In the past Ryukyus depended to a great extent on Japanese supplies, but they now find some Japanese quotations too high. Thus the Ryukyus are turning toward other areas for procurements, but Japan still holds the edge as there is regular shipping service between the two island groups. Navigation is the key to trade promotion with the Ryukyus. In 1956 the Ryukyus imported more than $7 million worth of rice. Since Japan is trying to curtail its Taiwan rice purchases the Ryukyus should soon become a customer of Taiwan for rice. Taiwan is able to supply the Ryukyus with meat, farm products, eggs, fish, rice, flour, tea, fruits (especially canned pineapple), onions and other vegetables, salt, soap, paper products, bicycles, sewing machines, cement, shoes, and other products. The Ryukyus' exports to Taiwan consist mainly of scrap iron and non-ferrous metals.

TRADE WITH SOUTHEASTERN ASIATIC STATES.—Thailand, Viet Nam, Laos, and Cambodia have a great need for textile products and may well be a good market for Taiwan textiles and other industrial products.

Although Thailand, like Taiwan, produces rice, her other products are entirely different from Taiwan's. Thus a barter agreement is not just a remote possibility. Exports to Thailand could be greatly increased in the future, especially sugar, tea, textiles, sewing machines, and bicycles.

Industry in Communist-threatened Viet Nam is not well developed because of shortages in power, fuel, and raw materials, and the lack of skilled workers. Viet Nam depends almost entirely on imports for her daily necessities, and her exports are quite limited. Viet Nam, therefore, should serve as a first-rate market for Taiwan's industrial products. However, the rigid foreign exchange controls exercised by the Saigon government have been choking imports. The favorable factor is the economic influence of the overseas Chinese which when put to good use, will greatly enhance expansion of Taiwan–Vietnamese trade. The overseas Chinese, who are multitudinous in number and patriotic in sentiments, prefer to use Chinese products and should help greatly in Taiwan's export program. Taiwan's exports to Viet Nam include aluminum ingots and sheets, cotton goods, sewing machines, plywood, camphor, and other products.

As for Taiwan's trade with Singapore and Malaysia, the volume was once large, but has shown a tendency to taper off in recent years. Singapore and Malaysia have rubber, cocoanut oil, and metals to export to Taiwan, accepting sugar and tea in return. But trade prospects for textiles, aluminum sheets, and other products catering to overseas Chinese taste are also bright. Southeastern Asia is a good market for Taiwan's industrial products. To win those markets the quality and packaging of Taiwan's industrial products should be improved, the cooperation of the overseas Chinese should be won, publicity stepped up, more ships sent into regular runs, and the cost of production lowered. The printing and dyeing of Taiwan's synthetic cotton fabric are so advanced that the product may easily win a market in Southeastern Asia.

TRADE WITH THE PHILIPPINES.—Trading with the Republic of the Philippines has not been easy for Taiwan, as that Republic exerts rigid control on foreign exchange and trade and is overly dependent on trade with the

United States. Taiwanese products sold to the Philippines include citronella, oil, salt, camphor, tea, aluminum ingots, and scores of other goods. In the future there also will be rice and cotton products. Exports from the Philippines to Taiwan are limited to Tuan wood, ores, manila sisal, rope, and tobacco. The volume of Taiwan–Philippine trade is only 4 or 5 per cent of the total Philippine trade volume and only 2 per cent of the total Taiwan trade. The factors holding back Taiwan–Philippine trade expansion are (a) similarity of the Philippines' and Taiwan's products because of almost identical weather conditions, (b) over-dependence of the Philippines on the United States, (c) lack of navigational means in spite of geographical propinquity, and (d) preferential customs duties in favor of American imports (one-fourth of that levied on goods from other countries).

TRADE WITH HONG KONG.—Taiwan and Hong Kong are close to each other—a favorable condition in international trade. Also, Hong Kong is the most outstanding trans-shipment port in the Far East and serves well as a springboard for the export of Taiwanese products. Taiwan exports sugar, tea, and coal to Hong Kong plus cotton cloth, citronella oil, ramie, camphor, pineapples, bananas and other products. Hong Kong sends to Taiwan machinery and parts, tools, metals, and chemical and industrial raw materials.The high quality and low cost of Taiwan's industrial and farm products have led Hong Kong business interests to buy from Taiwan for selling or for trans-shipping at a profit.

Among the reasons for Hong Kong's desirability as a trading post are the following: (a) Hong Kong is a free port, and transportation of commodities to it is not restricted; (b) world businesses converge in Hong Kong and it is therefore well provided with trade information; (c) Hong Kong's light taxes facilitate the exchange of goods; and (d) Hong Kong has good communication with many areas in southeast Asia, especially by sea.

Cultural contact

Taiwan participates in much cultural contact. Since the Communists took control of the mainland of China, people from non-communist nations have found it extremely difficult to obtain permission to make visits to this country. Thus Taiwan is the only place in the world where Mandarin culture is preserved. Not only have the Chinese customs, dress, dialects, and cuisine been transplanted to Taiwan, but the island has also become the storehouse for Chinese philosophy, Chinese painting, and other fine arts. As a result the National Palace Museum and the National Central Museum in Taichung and the Central National Library in Taipei are crowded with foreign visitors, and some American universities have set up a Chinese Study Center in Taiwan.

At the present moment 63 countries maintain diplomatic relations with Taiwan. Thirteen of these countries are in Asia, 9 in Europe, 22 in the Americas, and 19 in Africa. In recent years more than 2000 dignitaries have made state visits to Taiwan. Among these dignitaries were Kings, Presidents, Premiers, and Secretaries of State. Since 1949 the Nationalist Government in Taiwan has signed 14 cultural treaties with other nations.

In recent years many American engineers, professors, and technicians have come to Taiwan to teach in the institutions and to promote industrial development, and several American universities are carrying on programs in cooperation with the universities in Taiwan—Purdue University with Chen Kung University in engineering, the University of Michigan with Provincial Normal University in journalism, the University of Missouri with the National Political Science Institute in industrial education, and Duke University and the National Taiwan University in medical research.

Taiwan has also been active in international conferences. Not only does the government send delegates to various meetings, but also some international conferences have been held in Taiwan, such as the Asia International Rice-Cultivation Conferences and the recent Asia Historical Conference.

Taiwan not only brings in cultural "imports," but also sends out "exports." The exhibition of China's art treasures in four large American cities—Washington D.C., New York, Chicago, and San Francisco—in the years 1961 and 1962 was the largest of its kind ever held in a foreign country. Exhibits were selected from the rich collections of Taiwan's National Palace Museum and National Central Museum. These consisted of ancient paintings and sculptures; and items of pottery, embroidery, bronze, lacquer, jade, and enamel. In the last three years the government has sent out on a world-wide basis more than 30 cultural exhibits.

The most important cultural "export" from Taiwan is experienced agriculturalists. These men go to help farmers in underdeveloped countries in Africa, South America, and southeast Asia. In those areas the most important agricultural technique needed is not large-scale, mechanical assistance, but scientific technology. The assistance given by Western countries to these underdeveloped areas is sometimes not welcome in an underdeveloped society because of their high living standards and their colonial history. The only white persons welcomed in these areas would be people from the Scandinavian countries; this is because of the noncolonial background of those countries. However, those countries are located in northern latitudes and are not experienced in subtropical agriculture. With low living standards, knowledge of advanced agricultural technology, especially with rice, and the ability to endure hardship, Chinese agriculturalists from Taiwan are welcomed to Africa, South America, and southeast Asia and are reported to attain good results. In the meantime many African agriculturalists have been sent by their governments to Taiwan for a short period of training.

Many Chinese engineers in Taiwan have been sent to southeast Asia— and also to Pakistan, Siam, and South Viet Nam. There are many overseas Chinese and the common blood, language similarity, and traditional linkages with the Chinese engineers from Taiwan make it easy for the people of the countries in southeast Asia to accept their advice.

Bibliography

WIRTH ALBRECHT, "The Aborigines of Formosa and the Lin-Kin Island," *Amer. Anthrop.* **10**, No. 11 (1897).

J. W. BALLANTINE, "I Lived on Formosa," *Nat. geogr. Mag.* **10**, No. 1 (1945).

Bamboo Forest and Bamboo Material in Taiwan (Provincial Bank of Taiwan, Research Series, Taipei, 1951) No. 11. [In Chinese.]

Banana in Taiwan (Monograph of Taiwan's Special Products, Provincial Bank of Taiwan, Taipei, 1949) No. 4. [In Chinese.]

GEORGE W. BARCLAY, *A Report on Taiwan's Population* (Princeton University Press, Princeton, 1954).

——, *A Report on Taiwan's Population to the Joint Commission on Rural Reconstruction* (Office of Population Research, Princeton University, Princeton, 1954).

H. MacCLEAR BATE, *Report from Formosa* (E. P. Dutton, New York, 1952).

E. DE BUNSEN, "Formosa," *Geogr. J.* **70** (1927).

EUGENIA CAGE, "Industrial Development in Formosa." *Econ. Geogr.* **26**, No. 3 (1950).

W. CAMPBELL, *Sketches from Formosa* (Marshall, London, 1915).

——, *Formosa Under the Dutch* (Marshall, London, 1915).

——, "Formosa Under the Japanese," *Scot. geogr. Mag.* **18** (1902).

Camphor in Taiwan (Monograph of Taiwan's Special Products, Provincial Bank of Taiwan, Taipei, 1952) No. 6. [In Chinese.]

C. S. CHANG, "The 'Sansa Overthrust' and the related Geologic Structure," *Bull. geol. Surv. Taiwan* No. 10 (1951). [In Chinese.]

——, "Petroleum in Taiwan," *Quart. J.*, Provincial Bank of Taiwan. **3**, No. 2 (1950). [In Chinese.]

CHI-YUN CHANG, (Editor) *National Atlas of China*, Vol. 1, *Taiwan* (National War College in cooperation with the Chinese Geographical Institute, Taipei, 1959).

——, "Taiwan, China's Lost Province," *Asia and Americas* (1945).

CHI-LU CHEN, *Woodcarving of the Paiwan Group of Taiwan and its Affinities*. Proceedings, Second Biennial Conference, International Association of Historians of Asia (Taipei, 1962).

——, *Woodcarving of the Paiwan Group of Taiwan* (Taipei, 1961). [In Chinese.]

——, "A Cultural Configuration of the Island of Formosa," *Bull. Ethnol. Soc. China* **II** (1958).

——, "Basketry of the Budai Rukai," (Bulletin of the Department of Archaeology and Anthropology, Taipei, 1958). No. 11.

——, "The Agricultural Methods and Rituals of the Budai Rukai," *Studia Taiwanica* No. 1 (1956).

——, "Aborigines," *A Scientific Review of Taiwan* (Education and Cultural Association, Taipei, 1956).

——, "Family and Marriage of the Budai Rukai of Pintung, Taiwan," *Bull. Ethnol. Soc. China* **I** (1955). [In Chinese with English summary.]

K. C. CHEN, *Underground Water in Taiwan* (Provincial Bank of Taiwan, Research Series, 1952) No. 7. [In Chinese.]

PING-FAN CHEN, "Mineral Resources," *A Scientific Review of Taiwan* (Education and Cultural Association, Taipei, 1956).

P. Y. CHEN, "Heavy Mineral Deposits of Western Taiwan," *Bull. geol. Surv. Taiwan* No. 4 (1953).

SHAO-HSING CHEN, "Population Change in Taiwan," (Bulletin of the Department of Archaeology and Anthropology, National Taiwan University, Taipei, 1955) No. 6.

——, "Population Growth and Social Change in Taiwan," (Bulletin of the Department of Archeology and Anthropology, National Taiwan University, Taipei, 1955) No. 5.

S. M. CHEN, "Taiwan's Pineapple," *Fruit in Taiwan* (Monograph of Taiwan's Special Products, Provincial Bank of Taiwan, Taipei, 1955) No. 12. [In Chinese.]

S. S. CHENG, "The Passenger Traffic in Taiwan's Railroad," *Quart. J.* Provincial Bank of Taiwan **9** (1957). [In Chinese.]

HSIEN-TSIU CHANG, *Natural Environment and Crop Distribution in Taiwan* (Chinese-American Joint Commission on Rural Reconstruction, Plant Industry Series, Taipei, 1956) No. 13.

——, "Agricultural Regions," *A Scientific Review of Taiwan* (Education and Cultural Association, Taipei, 1956).

H. Y. CHANG, "The Changes of Taiwan's Economy During the Japanese Rule," *Quart. J.* Provincial Bank of Taiwan **9** (1951). [In Chinese.]

JEN-HU CHANG, *Agricultural Geography of Taiwan* (China Cultural Service, Taipei, 1953).

KWANG-CHIH CHANG, "A Brief Survey of the Archaeology of Formosa," *Sthwest. J. Anthrop.* **12** (1956).

K. C. CHANG, "Hydrography," *Taiwan Hsin-chih* (China Cultural Publication Committee, Taipei, 1954). [In Chinese.]

L. S. CHANG, "Petroleum of Taiwan," *Quart. J.* Provincial Bank of Taiwan **3**, No. 2 (1950). [In Chinese.]

——, "Limestone Groups in Taiwan and Their Characteristics," *Bull. geol. Surv. Taiwan* No. 2 (1949).

——, "Discussion on the Stratigraphy of Taiwan," *Ti chih lun Ping* **13**, Nos. 3–6 (1948). [In Chinese.]

N. C. CHANG, "Taiwan's Tea," *Tea in Taiwan* (Monograph of Taiwan's Special Products, Provincial Bank of Taiwan, Taipei, 1949) No. 3. [In Chinese.]

S. C. CHANG, *A General Study on the Soil Fertility of Taiwan* (Taiwan Fertilizer Corporation, Taipei, 1951). [In Chinese with English abstract.]

S. S. CHANG, "Six Years of Hydraulic Construction in Taiwan," *Free China Rev.* **1**, No. 6 (1951).

T. F. CHANG, "Livestock Raising in Taiwan," *Quart. J.* Provincial Bank of Taiwan **5** (1952). [In Chinese.]

TE-TSUI CHANG, "Land Utilization in Taiwan," *Far east. Econ. Rev.* **10**, No. 19 (1951).

C. C. CHEN, "Taiwan's Industries as I see Them," *Industry in Free China* **1**, No. 17 (1954).

CHENG-SIANG CHEN, *A Geography of Taiwan*, Vols. 1–3 (Fu-min Geographical Institute of Economic Development, Taipei, 1959). [In Chinese.]

——, "The Growth of Taipei," *China Today* No. 7.

——, "The Fertility and Mortality of Taiwan's Population," *Quart. J.* Provincial Bank of Taiwan **7**, (1955). [In Chinese.]

——, *The Gazetteer of Keelung* (Historical Research Commission, Taipei, 1954). [In Chinese.]

——, "Climate," *Taiwan Hsin-chih* (China Cultural Publication Committee, Taipei, 1954). [In Chinese.]

——, "Land Utilization in Formosa," *Geogr. Rev.* **16** (1951).

——, *Atlas of Land Utilization in Taiwan* (National Taiwan University, Taipei, 1951). [In Chinese.]

——, and CHI-HSIEN TUAN, *Population of Taiwan* (Institute of Agricultural Geography, National Taiwan University, Taipei, 1951). [In Chinese.]

——, *Land Utilization in Taiwan* (National Taiwan University, Taipei, 1950). [In Chinese.]

ROBERT CHIEN, "Post-War Industrial Development in Taiwan," *Industry in Free China* **10**, No. 13 (1958).

T. H. CHIEN, "Can Taiwan Support Itself in its Cultivation of Cotton?" *Industry in Free China* **4**, No. 1 (1955). [In Chinese.]

H. C. CHIN, "Yeast Used for Food," *Industry in Free China* **3**, 14 (1955).

C. Y. CHOW, "Soils," *A Scientific Review of Taiwan* (Education and Cultural Association, Taipei, 1956).

S. W. CHOW, *The Economic History of Taiwan During the Japanese Rule*, Vol. 1 (Provincial Bank of Taiwan, Taipei, 1958). [In Chinese.]

——, "The Robber Economy in Taiwan During the Dutch Period," *Taiwan's Economic History*, Vol. 4 (Provincial Bank of Taiwan, Taipei, 1956).

——, "A General Economic History of Taiwan," *Taiwan's Economic History*, Vol. 2 (Provincial Bank of Taiwan, Taipei, 1955). [In Chinese.]

T. Y. CHOW, "By-Products of the Sugar Industry," *Industry in Free China* **1**, No. 6 (1954).

C. CHU, "Leather Industry in China," *Industry in Free China* **5**, No. 8 (1956).

Civil Affairs Handbook (Office of the Chief of Naval Operations, United States Department of Navy, 1944).

Coal in Taiwan (Monograph of Taiwan's Special Products, Provincial Bank of Taiwan, Taipei, 1950) No. 5. [In Chinese.]

"Colonial Demography—Formosa", *Population Index*, Vol. 10 (Princeton, 1944).

BIBLIOGRAPHY

ARCHIBALD R. COLQUHOUN, "The Physical Geography and Trade of Formosa," *Scot. geogr. Mag.* (1887).
E. CONVERSE, "Formosa: Private Citadel," *Far east. Surv.* **18**, No. 12 (1949).
ALDEN CURSHALL, "Taiwan: Japan's Southern Base," *J. Geogr.* **43**, No. 7 (1944).
J. W. DAVIDSON, *The Island of Formosa, Past and Present* (Macmillan, London, 1903).
Definite Plan Report on the Shihmen Reservoir Project (Shihmen Planning Commission, Taipei, 1955).
Y. DEGUCHI, "The Mercury Deposit of Taiwan," *J. geol. Soc. Japan* **20**, No. 236 (1913). [In Japanese.]
Directions for the Treatment of Geographical Names in Taiwan (Formosa) (United States Department of Interior, Board on Geographical Names, Washington, 1944).
Directory of Taiwan (China News and Publication Service, Ltd., Taipei, 1951).
GEORGE E. DOVERSPIKE, PAUL ZEHNGRAFF, and HSING-CHI YUAN, *Forest Resources of Taiwan* (Chinese-American Joint Commission on Rural Reconstruction, Forest Series, Taipei, 1956) No. 3.
Economic Geography of Taiwan (Provincial Bank of Taiwan, Research Series, Taipei, 1950) No. 2. [In Chinese.]
Economic Insects in Taiwan (Provincial Bank of Taiwan, Research Series, Taipei, 1951) No. 12. [In Chinese.]
Economic Progress in Formosa, Vol. 1, No. 2 (United States Mutual Security Agency Mission to China, Chinese-American Economic Cooperation, Taipei, 1952).
ISE EIKTCHI, "Summary of the Studies on the Correlation Phenomena among the Characters of Rice Plants and its Application in Practice," *Bull. Taiwan agric. Res. Inst.* **1**, No. 20 (1946).
Electricity Problems in Taiwan (Provincial Bank of Taiwan, Research Series, Taipei, 1952) No. 16. [In Chinese.]
W. F. FEI, "Transportation Development in Taiwan", *Industry of Free China* **9** (1958).
Fertilizer Problems in Taiwan (Provincial Bank of Taiwan, Research Series, 1950) No. 5. [In Chinese.]
Fiber Resources in Taiwan (Provincial Bank of Taiwan, Research Series, 1950). No. 1. [In Chinese]
R. H. FIFIELD, "Formosa Acquires Strategic Value in China Crisis," *Foreign Policy Bull.* **28** (1949).
Fifty-one Years of Statistical Abstracts of Taiwan (Taiwan Governor General's Office, Taipei, 1946). [In Chinese.]
P. FLEMMING, "Role of Formosa," *Spectator* **183** (1949).
CHANG FONG, "An Intermediate Course Between Free Enterprise and Government Control," *Industry in Free China* **1**, No. 5 (1954).
"Formosa in Transition," *World Today* **4** (1948).
Fuel Resources in Taiwan (Provincial Bank of Taiwan, Research Series, Taipei, 1951) No. 11. [In Chinese.]
SOICHI FUNAKOSHI, "The Topography of the Eastern Coastal Range in Taiwan," *Globe* **21**, No. 6 (1934). [In Japanese.]
——, "Observation of New Volcano in Northern Taiwan," *Globe* **21**, No. 3, (1934). [In Japanese.]
NORTON S. GINSBURG, *Economic Resources and Development of Formosa* (Institute of Pacific Relations, New York. 1953).
Gold in Taiwan (Monograph of Taiwan's Special Products, Provincial Bank of Taiwan, Taipei, 1950) No. 6. [In Chinese.]
ANDREW J. GRAJDANZEV, *Formosa Today—An Analysis of the Economic Development and Strategic Importance of Japan's Tropical Colony* (Institute of Pacific Relations, New York, 1942).
——, "Formosa (Taiwan) Under Japanese Rule", *Pacif. Affairs* **15**, No. 3 (1942).
ROBERT Y. GRANT, *Mineral Resources Potential in Taiwan*, Vol. 1, No. 4 (United States Mutual Security Agency Mission to China, Chinese-American Economic Cooperation, Taipei, 1952).
LIH-WU HAN, *Taiwan Today* (Hwa Kuo Publishing Co., Taipei, 1956).
YU-SHAN HAN, "Formosa Under Three Rules," *Pacif. Historical Rev.* **19**, No. 4 (1950).
SHIGEJI HANAI, "The Active Faulting of the Taoyuan Tableland in Taiwan," *Geogr. Rev. Jap.* **6**, No. 7 (1930). [In Japanese.]
SYOHSPIROH HANZAWA, "Notes on the Raised Coral Reefs in Taiwan," *Geogr. Rev. Jap.* **7**, No. 2 (1931). [In Japanese.]
——, "Notes on the Stratum and Topography of the Ryukyuan Limestone in Taiwan," *Geogr. Rev. Jap.* **7**, No. 3 (1931). [In Japanese.]
——, "Notes on the Raised Coral Reefs and Their Equivalent Deposits in Taiwan (Formosa) and Adjacent Islets," *Rec. oceanogr. Wks. Jap.* **3**, No. 2 (1931).
ICHIRO HAYASAKA, "An Outline and Some Problems of the Stratigraphy of Taiwan," *Acta geol. taiwan* **2**, No. 1 (1948).

——, "An Outline of the Geology and Geography of Taiwan," *Hsueh I*, **18**, No. 6 (1947). [In Japanese.]

——, "The Recent Physiographic History of Taiwan as Observed from Geology and Geomorphology," *Bull. Ass. Mus. Taiwan* **19**, No. 101 (1943). [In Japanese.]

——, "Terraces in Taiwan—A Preliminary Note," *C. R. Cong. int. Geog.* **2**, Trans. B (1938).

——, "Contribution to the Post-Tertiary Physiographic Development of Taiwan (Formosa)," *Proc. Pacif. Sci. Congr.* **3** (1934).

——, "On the Tableland Gravel of Taiwan," *J. geol. Soc. Tokyo* **41**, No. 494 (1934). [In Japanese.]

——, "Observations in the Intermontane Basin Region of Central Taiwan. A Preliminary Note," *Taiwan Tigaku Kizi*, Vol. 1 (1930). [In Japanese.]

C. S. Ho, *Mineral Resources of Taiwan* (Shinchu Research Institute, Chinese Petroleum Corp., Taipei, 1953).

——, and W. P. KENG, "Geology and Mineral Deposits of the Area Between Peipu, Hsinchu, and Nanchuang, and Miao," *Bull. geol. Surv. Taiwan* No. 4 (1953).

——, "Ground-Water of Taiwan and its Utilization," *Taiwan Reconstruction Monthly* No. 7 (1951). [In Chinese.]

——, and T. L. Hsu, "Geology of the Chialo Coal Field, Hsinchu, Taiwan," *Bull. geol. Surv. Taiwan* No. 3 (1951).

——, "Geological Studies in Taiwan Within the Last Fifty Years," *Ti Chih Lun Ping* **12**, Nos. 5–6 (1947). [In Chinese.]

YING-CHING HO, "Some Ways and Means for Tourism Development in Taiwan," *China Today* **3**, No. 1 (1960).

I. HONDA, "Geomorphological Analysis of Taiwan," *Geog. Rev. Jap.* **15**, No. 1 (1937). [In Japanese.]

L. T. HSI, *Key to the Soil of Taiwan* (Taiwan Fertilizer Company Bulletin, Taipei, 1950). [In Chinese.]

——, "Soils," *Taiwan Hsin-Chih* (China Cultural Publication Committee, Taipei, 1954). [In Chinese.]

E. C. HSIA, *Land Use Conditions in Taiwan* (Chinese-American Joint Commission on Rural Reconstruction, Forest Series, Taipei, 1957) No. 5.

CHIAO-MIN HSIEH, and JEAN KAN HSIEH, *Typhoons on the Southeastern Coast of China and Taiwan* (Chinese Geographical Institute, Taipei, 1962).

——, *The Coast of Southeastern China—Submergent or Emergent?* (Chinese Geographical Institute, Taipei, 1962).

——, "Typhoons and Rice Cultivation in Taiwan," *Proceedings of the International Geographical Union Regional Conference in Japan* (Tokyo, 1959), pp. 326–331.

——, and ALICE TAYLOR, "Formosa," *Focus, N. Y.* **V**, No. 8 (1955).

——, "Sequent Occupance of Formosa," *Proceedings of the International Geographical Congress*, Vol. XVII (Washington, 1952), pp. 481–485.

——, "Formosa—A Rich Island of the Far East," *J. Geogr.* **51**, No. 54 (1952).

P. Y. Hsu, "A Brief Review of the Current Economic Situation in the Republic of China," *Industry in Free China* **13**, No. 1 (1960).

S. T. Hsu, "Hydrography of Taiwan," *Gazetteer of Taiwan* (Provincial Commission of Historical Research, Taipei, 1951). [In Chinese.]

T. L. Hsu, and PEI-YUAN CHEN, "On the River Capture of Hualien Chi," *Bull. geol. Surv. Taiwan* No. 3 (1951). [In Chinese with English summary.]

CHI-HSUN HSUEH, "Climatic Environment," *A Scientific Review of Taiwan* (Educational and Cultural Association, Taipei, 1956).

LEE-TANG HSUEH, "Hydrology," *A Scientific Review of Taiwan* (Educational and Cultural Association, Taipei, 1956).

C. K. HUANG, "Asbestos of Taiwan," *Quart. J.* Provincial Bank of Taiwan **3**, No. 2 (1950). [In Chinese.]

——, "Mica of Taiwan," *Quart. J.* Provincial Bank of Taiwan **3**, No. 2 (1950). [In Chinese.]

J. C. HUANG, "Effects of the International Sugar Agreement on the Taiwan Sugar Industry," *Industry in Free China* **1**, No. 3 (1954).

FONG HUI, "Some Important Factors in the Economic Development of Taiwan," *Industry in Free China* **4**, No. 5 (1955).

ALBERT HYMA, *The Dutch in the Far East* (George Wahr Publishers, Ann Arbor, 1942).

TAKASHI ICHIMURA, "Gold-Bearing Quartz Veins in Mt. Morrison," *J. Min.* **17**, No. 4 (1940). [In Japanese.]

——, "Bedded Cupriferous Pyritic Deposits in the Crystalline Schist Region of Taiwan," *Taiwan Tigaku Kizi* **19**, No. 2 (1939). [In Japanese.]

——, "Gold Mines in the Tatun Volcanic Group," *J. Min.* **16**, No. 6 (1939). [In Japanese.]

——, "The Geological Observation of Mt. Niitaka," *Taiwan Tigaku Kizi* **8**, No. 3 (1937). [In Japanese.]

——, "On Gravel Beds and Associated Lateritic Soils of the Hori Tableland, Taityu Prefecture," *Taiwan Tiguku Kizi* **8**, No. 3 (1937). [In Japanese.]

——, "The Topography of the Badland as Observed in Taitung District," *Bull. Soc. nat. Hist., Taiwan* **32**, No. 224 (1937). [In Japanese.]

——, "Notes on the Rocks and Minerals of Taiwan," *Taiwan Tigaku Kizi* **3**, Nos. 7–8 (1932). [In Japanese.]

YUICH ICHIKAWA, "Notes on the Conglomerate Formation at Taoyuan Tableland in Taiwan," *J. Geogr.* **41**, No. 485 (1929). [In Japanese.]

——, "Notes on the Coral Limestone of Taiwan," *J. Geogr.* **39** (1927). [In Japanese.]

TSUNENAKA IKI, "Notes on the Tectonic of Taiwan (Formosa)," *Proc. 4th Pacif. Sci. Congr.* **IIB**, pp. 813–818 (1929).

Y. ISHII, "General Remarks on the Geological Structure of Japan, Including that of Taiwan," *J. Geol. Soc. Tokyo* **6** (1898). [In Japanese.]

VEI-CHOW JUAN, "Topography," *A Scientific Review of Taiwan* (Educational and Cultural Association, Taipei, 1956).

——, "Geology," *A Scientific Review of Taiwan* (Educational and Cultural Association, Taipei, 1956).

——, *Physiography and Geology of Taiwan* (China Culture Publishing Foundation, Taipei, 1954).

——, "Landforms," *Taiwan Hsin-chih* (China Cultural Publication Committee, Taipei, 1954). [In Chinese.]

RYOZO KANEHIRA, *Formosa Trees Indigenous to the Island* (Government Research Institute, Taipei, 1936). [In Japanese.]

TADAO KANO, *Zoogeographical Studies of the Tsugitaka Mountains of Formosa* (Shibusawa Institute for Ethnological Researches, Tokyo, 1940). [In Japanese.]

——, "An Investigation of the Distribution of Population and Altitude of Habitation of the Formosa Aborigines," *Geogr. Rev. Japan* **14**, Nos. 8–9 (1938). [In Japanese with English summary.]

——, "Contribution to the Glacial Topography of the Tugitake Mts., Formosa," *Geogr. Rev. Japan* **10**, No. 7 (1934). [In Japanese with English summary.]

——, "Some Topographical Observations About the Mountainland of Formosa," *Geogr. Rev. Japan* **8**, No. 3 (1932). [In Japanese with English summary.]

——, "On the Remains of Megalithic Culture of the East Coast of Formosa," *J. anthrop. Soc. Tokyo* **19** (1930). [In Japanese.]

H. KAO, "Taiwan Fishery Rehabilitation Administration," *Free China Review*, **1**, No. 8 (1951).

SAHURO KAWADA, "Land Utilization in Taiwan," *Geogr. Rev. Japan* **19**, No. 6 (1943). [In Japanese.]

——, "Some Records on the Topography in Taiwan," *Geogr. Rev. Japan* **19**, No. 2 (1943). [In Japanese.]

——, "River Terraces Along the River Takkiri, Formosa," *Geogr. Rev. Japan* **17**, No. 8 (1941). [In Japanese with English summary.]

G. W. KEETON, "The Problem of Formosa", *World Affairs* (1951).

W. P. KENG, "The Asbestos Deposit in Chinyuehtsun and Crystalline Schist Region of Taiwan", *Taiwan Tigaku Kizi* **10**, No. 2 (1939). [In Japanese.]

GEORGE KERR, "Formosa: Island Frontier," *Far east. Surv.* **14**, No. 7 (1945).

——, "Formosa: Colonial Laboratory," *Far east. Surv.* **11**, No. 4 (1942).

P. KIANG, "The Current Economic Situation of Taiwan," *Industry in Free China* **6**, No. 3 (1956).

A. B. KIRJASSIFF, "Formosa the Beautiful," *Nat. geogr. Mag.* **37**, No. 3 (1920).

WILLIAM KIRK, "Social Change in Formosa," *Social. and Social Res.* **26** (1941).

——, "Social Organization Among the Primitives of Formosa," *Sociol. and Social Res.* **25** (1941).

B. KOTO, "Geological Structure of Riukiu Curve," *J. geol. Soc. Tokyo* **5**, No. 1 (1897). [In Japanese.]

F. K. KUO, "Hog Raising in Taiwan," *Quart. J.* Provincial Bank of Taiwan **5** (1952). [In Chinese.]

WOLF I. LADEJINSKY, "Land Reform in Formosa," *Foreign Agric.* **4**, No. 6 (1950).

Land Resources in Taiwan (Provincial Bank of Taiwan, Research Series, Taipei, 1951). No. 10. [In Chinese.]

BING LEE, "Aborigines of Formosa," *Far east. Econ. Rev.* **12**, No. 19 (1952).

P. N. LEE. "Poultry in Taiwan," *Quart. J.* Provincial Bank of Taiwan **5** (1952). [In Chinese.]

K. T. LI, "The Growth of Private Industry," *Industry in Free China* **14**, No. 2 (1961).

——, "A Review of the Economic Situation in Taiwan in 1958," *Industry in Free China* **11**, No. 11 (1959).

——, "Characteristics and Trends of Industrial Development in Taiwan," *Industry in Free China* **7**, No. 8 (1957).

——, "How Industrialization Could Help Improve Taiwan's Balance of Payments," *Industry in Free China* **7**, No. 2 (1957).

——, "The Effects of Industrialization in Taiwan on the Welfare of the People," *Industry in Free China* **4**, No. 3 (1955).

——, "Taiwan Pineapple as a Big Banner of Foreign Exchange," *Industry in Free China* **3**, No. 2 (1955).

P. N. Li, and H. Y. King, "The Manufacture of Tea in Taiwan," *Quart. J.* Provincial Bank of Taiwan **9** (1957). [In Chinese.]

——, "Taiwan's Vegetables," *Vegetables in Taiwan* (Monograph of Taiwan's Special Products, Provincial Bank of Taiwan, 1955) No. 13. [In Chinese.]

W. P. Li, "Pushing Toward Industrialization," *Industry in Free China* **7**, No. 5 (1957).

Joshua W. K. Liao, "Formosa and its Early Inhabitants," *Far east. Econ. Rev.* **10**, No. 6 (1951).

——, "Formosa Under the Dutch," *Far east. Econ. Rev.* **10**, No. 7 (1951).

C. C. Lin, "Mineral Resources," *Taiwan Hsin-chih* (China Cultural Publication Committee, Taipei, 1954). [In Chinese.]

——, "Geology," *Taiwan Hsin-chih* (China Cultural Publication Committee, Taipei, 1954). [In Chinese.]

——, "Quatenary Geohistory of Hualien District," *Formosan sci.* **5**, Nos. 3–4 (1951). [In Chinese.]

——, "Some Problems on the Hsinchu and Miaoli Oil Fields," *Formosan Min. Industry* **3**, Nos. 3–4 (1951). [In Chinese.]

——, "Gold of Taiwan," *Quart. J.* Provincial Bank of Taiwan **3**, No. 2 (1950). [In Chinese.]

——, "Geology and Ore Deposits of the Juifang Mine," *Formosan Min. Industry* **1**, Nos. 1–2 (1949). [In Chinese.]

Hui-siang Lin, *The Primitive Aborigines of Formosa* (Monograph of the Institute of Social Science, Academia Sinica, Shanghai, 1930) No. 3. [In Chinese.]

K. Y. Lin, "The Development of the Textile Industry in Taiwan," *Industry in Free China* **1**, No. 1 (1954).

N. S. Lin, "The Preliminary Report of the Investigation of Black Iron Sulphide Ore Deposit at Chinshan Mine," *Formosan Min. Industry* **3**, Nos. 1–2 (1951). [In Chinese.]

Wei-fang Lin, "Forestry," *A Scientific Review of Taiwan* (Education and Cultural Association, Taipei, 1956).

Shun-sheng Ling, "Ancient Temple and Earth Altar Among the Formosa Aborigines," (Bulletin of the Institute of Ethnology, Academia Sinica, Taipei, 1958) Vol. 6. [In Chinese with English summary.]

——, "Ancient Min-yueh people in South China and the Formosan Aborigines," *Acad. Quart.* **1** (1952). [In Chinese.]

Literature on Rice Cultivation in Taiwan (Provincial Bank of Taiwan, Research Series, Taipei, 1950). No. 6 [In Chinese.]

Shih-cheng Liu, "On the Development of Taiwan's Industry," *Industry in Free China* **1**, No. 5 (1954).

Tang-shiu Liu, *Illustrations of Native and Introduced Ligneous Plants of Taiwan* (National Taiwan University, Taipei, 1962). [In Chinese.]

C. L. Lo, and H. C. Wang, and colleagues, "Investigation and Exploration of the Nickel Deposit in Kuanshan," *Taiwan Reconstruct. Monthly*, No. 8 (1951). [In Chinese.]

C. L. Lo, "Pyrite Deposit of Tsaoshan, Tsochen, Tainan," *Formosan Min. Industry* **2**, Nos. 3–4 (1950). [In Chinese.]

Alan Logan, *The Role of Sugar in the Taiwan Economy* (United States Mutual Security Agency Mission to China, Chinese-American Economic Cooperation, Taipei, 1952) Vol. 1, No. 1.

S. K. Lu, "Taiwan's Sugar and its Research," *Sugar in Taiwan* (Monograph of Taiwan's Special Products, Provincial Bank of Taiwan, Taipei, 1949) No. 1. [In Chinese.]

Chi-lin Luh, *Recent Improvement On Pineapple and Citrus Production in Taiwan* (Chinese-American Joint Commission on Rural Reconstruction, Plant Industry Series, Taipei, 1958) No. 8.

Fengchow C. Ma, *On the Agricultural Mechanization in Taiwan* (Chinese-American Joint Commission on Rural Reconstruction, Plant Industry Series, Taipei, 1958) No. 14.

Ting-ying H. Ma, "Submarine Valleys Around the Southern Part of Taiwan, and Their Geological Significance," *Bull. oceanogr. Inst. Taiwan*, No. 2 (1947).

Tsichi Mabuchi, "The Social Organization of the Central Tribes of Formosa," *J. E. Asiatic Stud.* (1951).

BIBLIOGRAPHY

——, "Rituals and Picture Calendar of the Bunen," *Jap. J. Ethnol.* **2,** No. 3 (1936). [In Japanese.]

GEORGE L. MACKAY, *From Far Formosa* (Fleming H. Revell Co., London, 1898).

TSURUHIKO MAKIYAMA, "The Deluvial Formation in Northern Taiwan," *J. Geol.* **40,** No. 477 (1933). [In Japanese.]

Marine Resources in Taiwan (Provincial Bank of Taiwan, Research Series, 1951) No. 13. [In Chinese.]

S. C. MAO, "Fire-Clay Deposits in Shihpafen and the Refractory Industry In Peitou," *Formosan Min. Industry* No. 8 (1951). [In Chinese.]

G. MASAMUNE, "On the Alpine Vegetation of Formosa and its Origin," *Geogr. Rev. Japan* **14,** No. 7 (1938). [In Japanese with English summary.]

FANG-HAI MAURUS, "A Toponomical Study of Viangten, a Village Near Taipei," *Wen Hsien* (Report of the Historico-geographical Studies of Taiwan, 1950) Vol. 1, No. 4. [In Chinese.]

J. B. M. McGOVERN, *Among the Head-Hunters of Formosa* (Unwin Ltd., London, 1922).

AUSTIN F. MENZIES, *The Climate of Taiwan* (United States Mutual Security Agency Mission to China, Chinese-American Economic Cooperation, Taipei, 1952) Vol. 1, No. 1.

TADANORI MIURA, "A Geographical Study of Taiwan," *Stud. Geogr.,* Nos. 1–2, 5–10 (1953). [In Japanese.]

NAOMI MIYABE, *Crustal Deformations in Central Taiwan* (Tokyo Imperial University, Earthquake Research Institute, Tokyo) Bulletin Pt. 2, Vol. 16. [In English with Japanese summary.]

N. B. MONDIOLA, "Rice Culture in Taiwan," *Philipp. J. Agric.* **14,** No. 1 (1945).

RAYMOND T. MOYER, "Agriculture and Foodstuffs in Taiwan," *Foreign Agric.* **9,** No. 11 (1945).

TEIZO MURATA, and SABURO KAWATA, "The Valley Shape of Tatsukiri Creek in Taiwan," *Geogr. Rev. Japan* **17** (1941). [In Japanese.]

G. W. NUNN, "Forestry and Forest Resources of Formosa (Taiwan)," *Aust. For.* **12,** No. 2 (1948).

M. OGASAWARA, "Cupriferous Pyritic Deposits and Manganese Deposit in the Neighborhood of Tungao, Suao, Taipei," *Reports on Mineral Deposits of Taiwan* (Government-General of Taiwan, 1939) No. 1. [In Japanese.]

——, "Report on the Investigation of Sulphur Deposits," *Report on Minerals and Geology* (Government-General of Taiwan, 1935) No. 2. [In Japanese.]

YANOSUKE OTSUKA, "The Topography of the Valley of Siukuluan River and the Coastal Mountain Chain," *Geogr. Rev. Japan* **4,** No. 2 (1928). [In Japanese.]

GERALD C. PAN, "The Accomplishments of the First Four-Plan—An Initial Analysis," *Industry in Free China* **7,** No. 4 (1957).

T. C. PAN, "Industrial Development Planning in the Republic of China," *Industry in Free China* **10,** No. 7 (1958).

——, "An Appraisal of Taiwan's Economy," *Industry in Free China* **3,** No. 13 (1955).

Paper-Making Industry in Taiwan (Provincial Bank of Taiwan, Research Series, Taipei, 1951) No. 7. [In Chinese.]

H. PASSIN, "Notes on Japanese Research in Formosa," *Amer. Anthrop.* **49** (1947).

Pineapple in Taiwan, (Monograph of Taiwan's Special Products, Provincial Bank of Taiwan, Taipei, 1951) No. 9. [In Chinese.]

Population in Taiwan, (Provincial Bank of Taiwan, Research Series, Taipei, 1951) No. 9. [In Chinese.]

W. E. PRIESTLY, "Formosa, Isle of Camphor," *Asia* **33** (1933).

F. A. RAGER, "Japanese Emigration and Japan's Population Pressure," *Pacif. Affrs.* **14** (1941).

ARTHUR RAPER, and colleagues, *Urban and Industrial Taiwan—Crowded and Resourceful* (Foreign Operations Administration, Mutual Security Mission to China, and National Taiwan University, Taipei, 1954).

ALBERT RAVENHOLT, "Formosa Today," *Foreign Affrs.* **30,** No. 4 (1952).

Republic of China Today (Overseas Chinese Affairs Commission, Taipei, 1963).

WILLERT RHYNSBURGER, *Area and Resources Survey, Taiwan* (International Cooperation Administration, United States Mutual Security Mission to China, Taipei, 1956).

"Rice Culture in Taiwan," *Philipp. J. Agric.* **14** (1949).

Rice in Taiwan (Monograph of Taiwan's Special Products, Provincial Bank of Taiwan, Taipei, 1949) No. 2. [In Chinese.]

FRED W. RIGGS, *Formosa Under Chinese Nationalist Rule* (American Institute of Pacific Relations, Macmillan, New York, 1952).

——, "Chinese Administration in Formosa," *Far east. Surv.* **20,** No. 21 (1951).

E. H. DE RUNSEN, "Formosa," *Geogr. J.* **70,** No. 3 (1927).

OWEN RUTTER, "The Awakening of Formosa," *Scot. geogr. Mag.* (1925).
——, *Through Formosa—An Account of Japan's Island Colony* (Fisher Unwin, London, 1923).
HITOSHI SAITO, "Notes on the Topography and the Development of Communication in Taiwan," *Stud. Geogr.*, Nos. 5–6 (1934). [In Japanese.]
——, "Note on Taipei Basin," *Stud. Geogr.*, Nos. 10–11 (1933). [In Japanese.]
——, "The Harbors and Marine Transportation in Taiwan," *Educ. Geogr.* **10**, Nos. 1–3 (1932). [In Japanese.]
M. SAITO, "Gold-Copper Deposits in Chinkuashih, Taiwan," *J. Geogr.* **48**, Nos. 566–568 (1936). [In Japanese.]
ELLEN MARY SANDERS, "The Climate of Japan and Formosa," *Mon. Weath. Rev.*, No. 48 (1920).
YASUO SASA, "Glacial Topography in the Niitaka Massif, Taiwan," *Proc. imp. Acad. Japan* **12** (1936).
——, "Geomorphology of High Mountains in Formosa," *Proc. imp. Acad. Japan* **12** (1936).
——, "The Topography of the Glacial Erosion in Mt. Niitaka," *J. Geol.* **42**, No. 501 (1935). [In Japanese.]
K. C. SHEN, "Taiwan's Fruit," *Fruit in Taiwan* (Monograph of Taiwan's Special Products, Provincial Bank of Taiwan, Taipei, 1955) No. 12. [In Chinese.]
T. H. SHEN, "Land to Tiller in Free China," *Ann. Acad. Sinica Taipei*, No. 2 (1955).
——, *Rural Economic Conditions in Taiwan* (United States Mutual Security Agency Mission to China, Chinese-American Economic Cooperation, Taipei, 1952) Vol. 1, No. 4.
——, "Food Production and Administration in Taiwan," *Sci. Mon.* **74** (1952).
C. L. SHENG, "Taiwan Power Company in Progress," *Free China Rev.* **1**, No. 9 (1951).
KISABURO SHIBUYA, "Investigations on Alkali Soils of Formosa," *Foreign Agric.* **9**, No. 1 (1912).
JACOBUS SHIH, "New Look of Taiwan's Industrialization," *Industry in Free China* **9**, No. 2 (1958).
Y. H. SHIH, "Typhoons Which Have Raided China Within 51 Years," *Hseuh I Tsai Chih* **17**, No. 8 (1945). [In Chinese with English abstract.]
HISATAKA SHOJI, "The Sand Dune in Hsinchu," *Taiwan Tigaku Kizi* **8** (1937). [In Japanese.]
ARTHUR A. SIMPSON, "Postwar Economy of Taiwan, a Crucial Area of East Asia," *Foreign Commerce Wkly.* **37**, No. 11 (1949).
J. T. SOONG, *A Geography of Taiwan* (Ching Chung Book Co., Chungking, 1946). [In Chinese.]
LEO W. STACH, "Subsurface Exploration and Geology of the Coastal Plain Region of Western Taiwan," (Proceedings of the Geological Society of China, Taipei, 1958).
Starch Resources in Taiwan (Provincial Bank of Taiwan, Research Series, Taipei, 1951) No. 8. [In Chinese.]
Statistical Atlas of Taiwan (Governor General's Office of Taiwan, Taipei, 1947). [In Chinese.]
J. B. STEERE, "The Aborigines of Formosa," *J. Amer. geogr. Soc.*, **6** (1874). "Strategic Importance of Formosa," *World Today* **5** (1950).
FENG-CHI SUN, and SHIH WEN-PIAO, "Intercropping and its Various Effects on the Growth and Production of Early Crop Sugar Cane," (Taiwan Sugar Institute Research Report, 1951) No. 7.
T. C. SUN, "Taiwan's Sugar," *Sugar in Taiwan* (Monograph of Taiwan's Special Products, Provincial Bank of Taiwan, Taipei, 1949) No. 1. [In Chinese.]
T. T. SUN, "A Preliminary Study of the Chianen Irrigation System in Taiwan," *Quart. J. Provincial Bank of Taiwan* **8** (1956). [In Chinese.]
Taiwan Agriculture Yearbook (Dept. of Agriculture and Forestry, Taiwan Provincial Government, Taipei, 1950). [In Chinese.]
Ibid., (1951). [In Chinese and English.]
Taiwan (Formosa)—A Geographical Appreciation (Dept. of Mines and Technical Surveys, Geographical Branch, Ottawa, Canada, 1952).
Taiwan's Economic Statistics (Committee on American Aid, Executive Yuan, Taipei, 1960). [In Chinese.]
YOSABURO TAKEKOSHI, *Japanese Rule in Formosa* (Green, London, 1907).
KEINOSUKE TAN, "Geological Investigation of Taipei Basin," *Collection of Essays in Commemoration of the Sixty-First Anniversary of the Birth of Prof. Yabe*, Vol. 1 (1939). [In Japanese.]
——, "The Development of Erosional Surface in Tatun Volcanic Area," *Rep. Jap. Res. Council* **10**, No. 1 (1935). [In Japanese.]
——, "Old Records and Topographic Change in Taiwan," *Educ. Geogr.* **15**, No. 2 (1932).

BIBLIOGRAPHY

——, "The Terraces in Kannonzan," *Taiwan Tiga Kizi* **1** (1930).

K. Tanaka, "Glaciated Topography Traced in Taiwan (Formosa)," *C. R. Cong. Int. Geog.* **2**, Trans. II A (1938).

——, *The Mountains and Aborigines of Formosa* (Ganjin Co., Tokyo, 1937). [In Japanese.]

——, "Type of Land Utilization of the Taiyal Tribe in Taiwan," *Geogr. Rev. Japan* **13**, No. 2 (1937). [In Japanese.]

——, "A Study of Glaciation of Tzekuo Shan in Taiwan," *Geogr. Rev. Japan* **10**, Nos. 7–11. [In Japanese.]

——, "Geomorphological Observation of the Central Mountains in Taiwan," *Geogr. Rev. Japan* **8**, Nos. 3–6 (1932). [In Japanese.]

Hui-sun Tang, *Land Reform in Free China* (Chinese-American Joint Commission on Rural Reconstruction, Taipei, 1954).

Mei-chun Tang, "A Comparative Study of Bows and Arrows of the Formosa Aborigines," *Bull. Ethnol. Soc. China* **1** (1955). [In Chinese with English summary.]

Tea in Taiwan, (Monograph of Taiwan's Special Products, Provincial Bank of Taiwan, Taipei, 1949) No. 3. [In Chinese.]

Yosiro Tomita, "Characteristic Features of the Formosa Settlements in Taiwan, Japan," *C. R. Int. Geog.*, extract (1938), pp. 172–175.

——, "On the Geomorphological Classification of Fans in Taiwan," *J. Geogr.* **60**, No. 1 (1959). [In Japanese.]

——, "Physiographic Development of the Hori (Puli) Basin Group of Central Taiwan (Formosa)," *Tohoku Geographical Report* (Sendai, 1952).

——, "Some Geomorphological Consideration to the Chao Chou Fault in South Taiwan (Formosa)," *Sci. Rep. Tohôku Univ.* No. 4 (1945).

——, "The Recent Geomorphological Development in Taiwan," *J. Geogr.* **9**, No. 6 (1941). [In Japanese.]

——, "On the Topography of River Valleys in Taiwan," *Collection of Essays in Commemoration of the Sixty-First Anniversary of the Birth of Prof. Yabe* (1940). [In Japanese.]

——, "Topographical Observation of the River Valleys in Taiwan, A Preliminary Report," *Geological Institute of Taiwan* (Tohoku Imperial University, Taiwan, 1940).

——, "On the Terrace in Taiwan," *Sci. Taiwan* **8**, No. 30 (1940). [In Japanese.]

——, "On the Geomorphological Features in Taiwan," *Proc. 8th Pacif. Sci. Congr.* **2** (1956).

——, "On the Correlation of Erosional Surface in Taiwan," *Rep. Jap. Res. Council* **14**, No. 3 (1939). [In Japanese.]

——, "Observation on the Topography of the Rivers of Chihonetsu and Shinsuieietsu in Southern Taiwan," *Taiwan Tigaku Kizi* **10**, (1939). [In Japanese.]

——, "On the Alluvial Fans Developed in the Valleys of Taiwan (Formosa)," *Geogr. Rev. Japan* **14**, No. 10 (1938). [In Japanese.]

——, "Notes on the Erosional Surface in the Valley of the Upper Stream of Tamshui," *Taiwan Tigaku Kizi* **9** (1938). [In Japanese.]

——, "Physiographical Development of Homoclinal Ridges: An Example in Taiwan," *Mem. Fac. Sci. Agric. Taihoku* **13**, No. 4 (1935).

——, "On the Rural Settlement Forms in Formosa," *Proc. 5th Pacif. Sci. Congr.* **2** (1934).

——, "The Landscape of Taiwan," *Stud. Geogr.* No. 1 (1934). [In Japanese.]

——, "A Geomorphological Investigation of the Mountains in Eastern Taiwan," *Collection of Essays in Commemoration of the Sixty-First Anniversary of the Birth of Mr. Uchida* (1940).

Transportation in Taiwan (Provincial Bank of Taiwan, Research Series, Taipei, 1958). [In Chinese.]

T. C. Tsai, "Zircon in Northwestern Taiwan," *Formosan Min. Industry* **3**, Nos. 1–4 (1951). [In Chinese.]

Hsi-lin Tschang, "Potholes in the River Beds of Northern Taiwan," *Erdkunde* **11** (1957).

C. J. Tseng, "The Climate of Taiwan," *Acta Geogr. Sinica* **20**, No. 2 (1954).

P. J. Tsiang, *The Climate of Taiwan* (Provincial Bank of Taiwan, Research Series, Taipei, 1954) No. 26. [In Chinese.]

——, *Etude Sur la Direction du Vent a Taipei, Taiwan*, (La Faculte Agronomique de L'Universite National de Taiwan, Taipei, 1952).

Young-chi Tsui, *A Study of Wheat in Taiwan* (Chinese-American Joint Commission on Rural Reconstruction, Economic Digest Series, 1957) No. 4.

Underground Resources in Taiwan (Provincial Bank of Taiwan, Research Series, Taipei, 1950) No. 3. [In Chinese.]

N. Utsushikawa, N. Miyanioto, and T. Mabuchi, "Genealogical and Classificatory Studies on the Formosa Aborigines," (Institute of Ethnology, Taihoku Imperial University, Taipei, 1935), Vol. 1. [In Japanese.]

Frederick G. Vosburgh, "Poor Little Rich Land—Formosa," *Nat. geogr. Mag.* **97**, No. 2 (1950).

M. H. Walker, "Formosa," *Foreign Commerce Wkly.* **14**, No. 1 (1944).

Richard L. Walker, "Taiwan's Development as Free China," *Ann. Amer. Acad. Pol. Soc. Sci.* **321** (1959).

W. Walton, "Some Notes on Formosa," *Alp. J.* **XIXI**, No. 249 (1934).

———, "Among the Mountains and Headhunters of Formosa," *Geogr. J.* **81**, No. 3 (1933).

Sheng-tsu Wang, "The Agricultural Regions of Taiwan," *Sci. Rep. nat. Tsing Hua Univ.* **1**, No. 3 (1948).

T. Y. Wang, "The Trend of Economic Development in Taiwan," *Industry in Free China* **4**, No. 6 (1955).

Water Conservation Problems in Taiwan (Provincial Bank of Taiwan, Research Series, Taipei, 1950) No. 4. [In Chinese.]

Hisao Watanabe, "On the Origin of the Tableland of Chungli," *Coll. Geogr. Pap.* **8** (1936). [In Japanese.]

———, "A Geographical Investigation of the Water Supply in Taiwan (Formosa)," *Educ. Geogr.* No. 4 (1934). [In Japanese.]

———, "A Geomorphological Investigation of the Alluvial Fans in Taiwan," *Taiwan Tigaku Kizi* **3** (1932). [In Japanese.]

Hwei-lin Wei, "Lineage System Among the Formosa Tribes," *Bulletin of the Institute of Ethnology* (Academia Sinica, Taipei, 1958) No. 5. [In Chinese with English summary.]

———, "Dual Organization Among the Formosa Tribes," *Bulletin of the Institute of Ethnology* (Academia Sinica, Taipei, 1956) No. 2. [In Chinese with English summary.]

———, "Tribal Organization and Dual Chieftanship Among the Formosa Aborigines," *Bull. ethnol. Soc. China* **1** (1955). [In Chinese with English summary.]

B. Willis, "Geological Observations in the Philippine Archipelago," *Nat. Res. Coun.* No. 13 (1937).

Wood Materials in Taiwan (Monograph of Taiwan's Special Products, Provincial Bank of Taiwan, Taipei, 1950) No. 7. [In Chinese.]

C. T. Wu, *Geography of Taiwan* (Commercial Press, Peking, 1959). [In Chinese.]

Norman Wycoff, "Demographic Conditions and Prospects of Taiwan," *Far east. Econ. Rev.* **8**, No. 9 (1952).

Hisakastu Yabe, "A Cartographical Study of the Submarine Relief of the Strait of Formosa," *Rec. oceanogr. Wks Jap.* **1**, No. 3 (1929).

———, and Risaburo Tayama, "On Some Remarkable Examples of Drowned Valleys Found Around the Japanese Islands," *Rec. oceanogr. Wks Jap.* **II**, No. 1 (1929).

———, and S. Hanzawa, "Our Present Knowledge on the Tertiary Foraminiferous Rocks of Taiwan," *Proc. 4th Pacif. Sci. Congr.* (1929).

Naokata Yamazaki, and Denzo Sato, *The General Geography of Japan, Ryukyu and Taiwan*, Vol. 9 (1915).

———, "Unsere Geographischen Kenntnisse von der Inseln Taiwan (Formosa)," *Petermanns geogr. Mit.* **46** (1900).

C. T. Yang, "Economic and Social Development in the Republic of China During the Past Decade," *Industry in Free China* **13**, No. 7 (1960).

———, "Sugar Industry in Taiwan," *China Today* No. 1 (1953).

Hsi-fu Yang, and colleagues, *Taiwan Hsin-chih* (China Cultural Publication Committee, Taipei, 1954). [In Chinese.]

———, "Gazetteer Geography of Taiwan," *Wen Hsien, Rep. hist. geogr. Stud. Taiwan* **1** (1950). [In Chinese.]

J. Y. Yang, "Tea of China and Formosa," *Far east. Econ. Rev.* **14**, No. 14 (1952).

P. H. Yeh, *Fishery Section of the Gazette of Taiwan* (Provincial Historical Research Committee of Taiwan, Taipei, 1955). [In Chinese.]

T. P. Yen, "Sulphur of Taiwan," *Quart. J.* Provincial Bank of Taiwan **3**, No. 2 (1950). [In Chinese.]

———, "Coal of Taiwan," *Quart. J.* Provincial Bank of Taiwan **3**, No. 2 (1950). [In Chinese.]

———, "Copper of Taiwan," *Quart. J.* Provincial Bank of Taiwan **3**, No. 2 (1950). [In Chinese.]

———, "Mercury, Magnetite sand, Manganese, Nickel, Zircon, Phosphate, Graphite, Alunite, and Glauconite of Taiwan," *Quart. J.* Provincial Bank of Taiwan **3**, No. 2 (1950). [In Chinese.]

BIBLIOGRAPHY

——, "The Properties of Taiwan's Coals," *Formosan Min. Industry* **2,** No. 3 (1950). [In Chinese.]

——, "Keelung Volcano Group and its Mineral Deposits," *Formosan Min. Industry* **2,** Nos. 3–4 (1950). [In Chinese.]

——, "The High-Terrace Gold Placers of Taiwan," (Monograph of Taiwan's Special Products, Provincial Bank of Taiwan, Taipei, 1950) No. 6. [In Chinese.]

——, "Mineral Resources of Taiwan," *Formosan sci.* No. 1 (1949). [In Chinese.]

——, and C. S. Ho, "The Magnesium-Bearing Minerals and Rocks Containing such Minerals in Taiwan," *Bull. geol. Surv. Taiwan* No. 1 (1947).

Y. C. YEN, "Alkali Industry—Present Status, Trend, and Policy," *Industry in Free China* **13,** No. 12 (1961).

——, "Developing Paper Industry," *Industry in Free China* **4,** No. 9 (1955).

K. G. YIN, "Current Economic Situation of Taiwan," *Industry in Free China* **15,** No. 2 (1961).

K. Y. YIN, "Prospects of Chemical Industries in Taiwan," *Industry in Free China* **3,** No. 4 (1955).

——, "A Discussion on Industrial Policy in Taiwan," *Industry in Free China* **1,** No. 5 (1954).

——, *Present and Future of Taiwan's Production* (United States Mutual Security Agency Mission to China, Chinese-American Economic Cooperation, Taipei, 1952) Vol. 1, No. 2.

JING-RANG YU, "Vegetation," *Taiwan Hsin-Chih* (China Cultural Publication Committee, Taipei, 1954). [In Chinese.]

——, "Rice Culture in Taiwan," *Rice in Taiwan* (Monograph of Taiwan's Special Products, Provincial Bank of Taiwan, Taipei, 1949). No. 2. [In Chinese.]

L. H. YU, "The Pulp and Paper Industry of Taiwan," *Industry in Free China* **5,** No. 1 (1956).

W. ZELINSKY, "Formosa's Population," *Geogr. Rev.* **45** (1955).

Index